PERSPECTIVES

ON

INTERPROFESSIONAL

EDUCATION

AND PRACTICE

EDITED BY CARMEN MORANO

NASW PRESS

National Association of Social Workers
Washington, DC

Darrell P. Wheeler, PhD, MPH, ACSW, *President*
Angelo McClain, PhD, LICSW, *Chief Executive Officer*

Cheryl Y. Bradley, *Publisher*
Stella Donovan, *Acquisitions Editor*
Julie Gutin, *Project Manager*
Julie Palmer-Hoffman, *Copyeditor*
Jeff Hume-Pratuch, *Proofreader*
Lori J. Holtzinger, Zinger Indexing, *Indexer*

Cover by Britt Engen, Metadog Design Group
Interior design, composition, and eBook conversions by Xcel Graphic Services
Printed and bound by P. A. Hutchison

First impression: February 2017

Library of Congress Cataloging-in-Publication Data

Names: Morano, Carmen L., editor.
Title: Perspectives on interprofessional education and practice / edited by
  Carmen Morano.
Description: Washington, DC : NASW Press, [2017] | Includes bibliographical
  references and index.
Identifiers: LCCN 2016052812 (print) | LCCN 2017005214 (eBook) | ISBN
  978-0-87101-508-2 (pbk.) | ISBN 978-0-87101-510-5 (eBook)
Subjects: LCSH: Social work education. | Social service—Practice.
Classification: LCC HV11 .P4785 2017 (print) | LCC HV11 (ebook) | DDC
  362.1071—dc23
LC record available at https://lccn.loc.gov/2016052812

This text is dedicated first to Barbara Morano, my inspiration, mentor, business partner, and, most important, my spouse and life partner. She emphasized an interprofessional approach to geriatric social work practice long before it became in vogue. Barbara continues to be a source of inspiration and motivation throughout my entire career. Second, this text is dedicated to all those colleagues who have given so willingly of their knowledge and wisdom from their respective disciplines.

TABLE OF CONTENTS

ABOUT THE EDITOR

Carmen Morano, PhD, is a professor at the Silberman School of Social Work and director of Silberman Aging: A Hartford Center of Excellence in Diverse Aging. Morano is a John A. Hartford Faculty Scholar and the former codirector of the Geriatric Social Work Pre-Dissertation Initiative. He is cochair of the Aging Field of Practice and past chair and member of the Health Resources and Services Administration's Advisory Committee on Interdisciplinary Community-Based Linkages. Morano has done extensive lecturing and training in interprofessional practice and was lead social work faculty on the Interdisciplinary Training and Education course at Cornell–Hunter. His research includes developing competency-based curriculum for gerontological social work and in the area of person-centered, participant-directed services. His most recent research has focused on establishing enduring linkages between medical and social systems of care.

ABOUT THE CONTRIBUTORS

Gallane Dabela Abraham, MD, is an assistant professor of emergency medicine and the associate director of the Geriatric Emergency Department at the Icahn School of Medicine at Mount Sinai in New York City. She also serves as a neurotrauma consultant for the National Football League and NFL Players Association. She received a bachelor of arts degree in political science with a concentration in economics from Barnard College of Columbia University, completed the Health Careers Program at Harvard University, and obtained her medical doctorate from Rutgers/University of Medicine and Dentistry of New Jersey–New Jersey School of Medicine. In addition, she completed a fellowship in health services and health disparities research and received a master's in clinical research at the Icahn School of Medicine at Mount Sinai. Abraham is board certified in emergency medicine.

James A. Ballard, EdD, has been the associate director of the University of Kentucky (UK) Center for Interprofessional Health Education since its inception in 2010. Until 2015, he served as an educationist in the UK Department of Family and Community Medicine. Prior to 2010, he held positions as the associate director of the UK Area Health Education Center, manager of the Community Faculty Program, and director of the Medical Professions Placement Service. Nationally, he is a past steering committee member of the Generalists in Medical Education, cochair of the National Area Health Education Center Education Committee, and member of the Research in Medical Education Committee within the American Academy of Medical Colleges Southern Group on Educational Affairs.

Kenya V. Beard, EdD, GNP-BC, NP-C, ACNP-BC, CNE, ANEF, is the associate vice president for curriculum and instruction at Jersey College, and a 2012 Josiah Macy Faculty Scholar. She is the founding director of the Center for Multicultural Education and Health Disparities, an educational initiative that seeks to disseminate research and best practices that focus on increasing workforce diversity. She recently served as the director of Hunter College's Being Excellent Scholars in Transition to Nursing, a program that is federally funded by a workforce diversity grant and seeks to broaden the recruitment, retention, and graduation of underrepresented minority nursing students. She was recently inducted into the Academy of Nursing Education, is a fellow in the New York Academy of Medicine, and serves on the editorial board for the *American Journal of Nursing* and the New York State Board for Nursing.

Robin P. Bonifas, PhD, is an associate professor at the Arizona State University School of Social Work. She has over 15 years of experience working with elders and their families in both long-term care and inpatient psychiatric settings. Robin is a John A. Hartford Faculty Scholar in Geriatric Social Work and earned her doctorate from the University of Washington in Seattle in 2007. She serves on the board of directors for the Association of Gerontology Education in Social Work and is a consulting editor for *Health & Social Work* and the *Journal of Gerontological Social Work*.

Thomas V. Caprio, MD, MPH, MSHPE, CMD, HMDC, FACP, is an associate professor of medicine, clinical nursing, and public health sciences at the University of Rochester Medical Center in Rochester, New York. He serves as director of the geriatric medicine fellowship program, director of the University of Rochester geriatric assessment clinic, and director of the Finger Lakes Geriatric Education Center. He currently oversees the Finger Lakes Geriatric Workforce Enhancement Program and is past president for the National Association of Geriatric Education Centers and the National Association for Geriatric Education.

Louisa Daratsos, PhD, MSW, is the psychosocial coordinator for oncology/palliative care at the U.S. Department of Veterans Affairs New York Harbor Healthcare System, Brooklyn Campus. A longtime employee of her medical center, Daratsos has worked during the various configurations of treatment teams and has participated formally and informally in training medical professionals, particularly in oncology and palliative care.

Diane E. Elze, PhD, is an associate professor at the University at Buffalo School of Social Work, where she also directs the MSW program. She serves on the editorial boards of the *Journal of Youth and Adolescence, Journal of Gay and Lesbian Social Services, Adolescent Research Review,* and the *Journal of the Society of Social Work and Research.* She is a former member of the Council on Social Work Education's Board of Directors, Commission on Professional Development, Commission on Sexual Orientation and Gender Expression, and Commission for Diversity and Social and Economic Justice. She has been a member of the University at Buffalo's Interprofessional Education Leadership Team since 2012.

Judith L. Howe, PhD, is professor at the Brookdale Department of Geriatrics and Palliative Medicine, Icahn School of Medicine at Mount Sinai; associate director of education and evaluation and deputy director at the Bronx VA Medical Center Geriatric

Research Education and Clinical Center; and director of the Consortium of New York Geriatric Centers. She is also director of the VA Interprofessional Palliative Care Fellowship based at the Bronx VA Medical Center. Howe is the editor-in-chief of *Gerontology and Geriatrics Education*, has served as an elected member of the Association for Gerontology in Higher Education, was the president of the State Society on Aging of New York, and is past president of the National Association for Geriatric Education Centers. She is a fellow of the New York Academy of Medicine, Association for Gerontology in Higher Education, and the Gerontological Society of America.

Teri Kennedy, PhD, MSW, LCSW, ACSW, FNAP, is director, Office of Gerontological and Interprofessional Initiatives with the School of Social Work, College of Public Service and Community Solutions, Arizona State University (ASU); research associate, University of Arizona Center on Aging; and faculty affiliate, ASU Center for the Advancement of Interprofessional Education, Practice and Research. She is also ASU site director for the Arizona Geriatric Workforce Enhancement Program; and interprofessional coach with the Interprofessional Primary Care Curriculum Implementation and Evaluation Project with the ASU College of Nursing and Health Innovation.

Kelley Macmillan, PhD, is associate director, Community and Social Services, Sanford Center for Aging; and faculty of the University of Nevada, Reno. In his current position at the Sanford Center, he is assisting with the development of a comprehensive geriatric assessment team, teaching in the School of Social Work, and providing administrative support for three managers of community service programs. His academic career includes teaching MSW individual practice courses, policy courses in aging and behavioral health, and the interprofessional course described in chapter 8.

Kathleen M. Nokes, PhD, RN, FAAN, is professor emerita from Hunter College and Graduate Center, City University of New York. She has almost 50 years of experience as a registered nurse and was involved in the first wave of interprofessional education in the late 1970s. When the HIV/AIDS epidemic emerged in the 1980s, it was clear that only committed members of the interprofessional team would be able to control this raging, evolving, mysterious illness that was taking the lives of so many young, talented people. When the second wave of recognition of the need for interprofessional collaboration was tied to patient safety, Nokes welcomed the opportunity to participate on an academic team that included social work, public health, medicine, and nursing. Nokes has had in-depth global work in South Africa and Japan especially through Fulbright awards and now is on the Review Committee for the Fulbright Specialist award.

James C. Norton, PhD, is the director of the University of Kentucky Center for Interprofessional Health Education. He holds a joint appointment as professor in the Departments of Psychiatry and Neurology at the University of Kentucky, is past president of the Kentucky Rural Health Association, and received the Dan Martin Award from that organization in 2014 for his contributions to rural health in Kentucky. He served as the chair of the Research and Education Constituency Group of the National Rural Health

Association and was a member of its board of directors. He has served as the AAMC Group on Educational Affairs (GEA) Liaison to the Group on Resident Affairs and was the chair of the Graduate Medical Education section of the GEA.

Patricia J. Ohtake, PhD, PT, is an associate professor in the Department of Rehabilitation Science, School of Public Health and Health Professions, at the University at Buffalo. Ohtake is a physical therapist with experience in acute care and intensive care unit clinical practice, and she teaches the clinical management of patients with cardiopulmonary dysfunction and interprofessional collaborative practice in the entry-level doctor of physical therapy program. Her research interests are the management of individuals with critical illness, the role of simulation in enhancing learning outcomes for health professions students, and interprofessional education and collaborative practice. Ohtake serves as an editorial board member for *Physical Therapy*, the American Physical Therapy Association's official journal. Ohtake has served in leadership roles on the University at Buffalo's Interprofessional Education Leadership Team and its Simulation Center Steering Committee since 2010.

Kanako Okuda, MSW, BA, is a licensed clinical social worker and a social work educator and is currently the director of field education at the Silberman School of Social Work. Prior to joining Silberman, Okuda specialized in pediatric oncology at a major teaching hospital in New York City, and she has held lectures and workshops addressing multicultural practice in the United States. In her early career, Okuda worked with multistressed families in the child welfare system in New York City, as well as Japanese-speaking children and their families through the New York City Department of Education to address cultural and language barriers. Her work also extends to East Africa, particularly Kenya, working with a community of tea farmers for sustainable economic empowerment.

Deborah Rejent, PhD, MSSW, MA, is an associate professor and founding director of the MSW Program, Department of Social Work, School of Health Sciences, at Quinnipiac University. Her academic career includes teaching at the MSW level, completing extensive postgraduate clinical training in psychotherapy, psychoanalysis, and mindfulness-based interventions, and practice experience in clinical treatment, supervision, and administration in a wide range of programs, such as a hospital outpatient psychiatric unit, a medical adult day program, a residential treatment center for children, and a university counseling center.

Martine Sanon, MD, is an assistant professor in the Brookdale Department of Geriatrics and Palliative Medicine and Department of Medicine, Division of Hospital Medicine, at the Icahn School of Medicine at Mount Sinai. She is a graduate of the SUNY Downstate College of Medicine and completed her residency in internal medicine at the same institution and fellowship in geriatrics at the Mount Sinai School of Medicine. Currently, Sanon serves as the director of the Inpatient Geriatric Medicine Clinical Services and as the geriatric liaison to the Department of Emergency Medicine.

Paul T. Wietig, EdD, is the assistant vice president for interprofessional education within the University at Buffalo's Academic Health Center. He previously served as the core curriculum coordinator for the School of Public Health and Health Professions and, most recently, was the interim director of the Teaching and Learning Center of the University at Buffalo. Wietig also serves as adjunct professor in the Department of Rehabilitation Services.

INTRODUCTION

Carmen Morano

A recent Internet search using the term *interprofessional education* yielded over 600,000 entries; a similar search for *interdisciplinary education* generated almost 1,000,000 results. Although it can be said that a rose by any other name would smell as sweet, word choice does matter in this context (Choi & Pak, 2008). This text distinguishes *interprofessional* (from different professions) individuals engaged in practice from *interdisciplinary* (when speaking about the various disciplines) and *multidisciplinary* individuals (who draw on different disciplines but remain within the boundaries) (Choi & Pak, 2008). Although the idea of interprofessional teams in health care has existed for more than a century (Freeth, Hammick, Reeves, Koppel, & Barr, 2005), the uptake of interprofessional and interdisciplinary education (IPE) in the United States has been relatively slow, especially when compared with the growth of IPE internationally.

The process of integrating IPE and interprofessional practice (IPP) in the United States has been complicated by the division of the health and social care systems, the growth of medical specialties, and the fragmented systems of health education (Hall & Weaver, 2001; Institute of Medicine [IOM], 2003, 2008; Wagner et al., 2001). There is a clear imperative to better prepare students and the current workforce. Policy initiatives such as the Patient Protection and Affordable Care Act of 2010 (ACA), which calls for better care, better health, and smarter spending, require a systemic integrated approach to removing the financial, structural, and institutional barriers to IPE and IPP. There are signs that some of the structural and historic barriers are slowly coming down. In the past five years, the number of IPE programs has grown. Is it possible, as Freeth and colleagues (2005) suggested, that IPE is here to stay, even in the United States?

Current indications are that IPE is gaining significant momentum, but sustaining the commitment of institutional resources to support IPE will require evidence that it is worth the investment. There is little doubt that IPE has the potential to improve student knowledge, attitudes, values, and skills, but how this translates to achieving the goals of the ACA is not yet fully established. The IOM (2015) concluded that the current evidence is lacking, and developing this evidence is a complex process that will require a purposeful integration of a multitude of systems and a long-term commitment.

THE IMPORTANCE OF IPE AND IPP

There are a number of factors that influenced the development and organization of this text. During my 20 years of social work practice, the majority of which were spent providing geriatric care management services to older adults and their family systems, I have had the opportunity to participate in countless numbers of interprofessional teams. The collective knowledge and skills of the team translated into significantly better outcomes and, in some cases, unanticipated positive outcomes. One such example is the case of Mr. S.

Case Study: Mr. S

Mr. S was residing in a nursing home, having maxed out his skilled care coverage under Medicare. When admitted to the nursing home, it was thought that he would never be able to return home. When I first met Mr. S, he still had significant left-side weakness that left him with limited movement in his left arm and with no control of his left leg, so that he was unable to stand. At the last case conference, Mr. S and his family were informed by the attending physician at the nursing facility that his care needs were greater than could be reasonably met at home and that they should be planning for his long-term placement in a nursing home.

All Mr. S wanted was to get out of the nursing home and return to his home. Most important, he stated that all he wanted out of life now was to live long enough to attend his daughter's wedding, which was scheduled to take place in 10 months. After the doctors told him that it was unlikely he would be able to go home, he was ready to, as he put it, "just give up." Our office was called to provide mental health services to treat Mr. S's apparent depression.

The interdisciplinary team that began working with Mr. S and his family at the nursing home included a community-based geriatric care manager, a mental health professional, and a physical therapist who was paid privately by the family. The team eventually grew to include an architect for home modification, an aqua therapist (Mrs. S indicated that her husband had been a lifelong swimmer), and a personal companion who was a contemporary that shared similar interests. This team collaborated with the patient and his family to develop a comprehensive interdisciplinary plan. The care manager assumed responsibility for facilitating constant communication about progress and setbacks with all the members of the team.

After nine months of rigorous physical and occupational therapy supplemented with weekly aqua therapy, not only did Mr. S attend the wedding, but he was able to walk his daughter down the aisle. It was experiences like this and others that motivated me to enter academia. Although Mr. S and his family had the resources to pay for services that are not available to everyone,

---

the cost for implementing the plan of care was significantly less than the cost of long-term institutional care and also improved the quality of life for both Mr. S and his family.

Interprofessional Perspectives in Education and Practice was also motivated by my 15 years developing graduate and continuing education curriculum. This text attempts to address a gap in the current body of literature by focusing on successful programs and practices in the United States that administer health and social care in a unique context.

The experiences of participating in interprofessional teams throughout my practice career and then becoming a social work professor, at which time I became a trainer and advocate for IPE and IPP, provided further motivation for this text. It was my social work education and training that gave me the opportunity to develop curriculum designed to train workers from various disciplines to work on interprofessional teams in a timely and practical way. So, too, was the experience of joining an interprofessional team of academics that developed the ITEACH program presented in chapter 11. This experience solidified my resolve to make certain that the social work frameworks of social justice, oppression, and person in environment would be critical contributions that from my perspective were frequently overlooked in other IPE programs. If health care is to become person centered or, as my colleagues say, patient centered, this content must be a foundation on which to build effective interprofessional learning opportunities for students and the workforce.

The role of the social worker on the interprofessional team as a patient advocate is complex and frequently not fully understood. And although I do agree with Freeth and colleagues (2005) that the interprofessional team is a unique type of team, the theoretical foundations and practical knowledge of group dynamics included in most, if not all, social work curricula could be used to expand the social work role that should be recognized as a valuable asset to any interprofessional team.

ORIENTATION TO THE TEXT

As an editor and contributor to this text, I had to decide how to best balance the competing demands of a common voice while honoring the perspectives and voice of different professionals. Although I provided some guidance regarding the content of each section and chapter, I did not edit the contributors' preferred terminology. For example, although "person-centered care" is the preferred vernacular in social work, "patient-centered care" remains the preferred and dominant vernacular in most health care professions.

This book is divided into four sections, each with a different focus. Part 1 establishes a context to better understand the history and development of competence-based education, IPE, and its evaluation. Part 2 provides a review of the four core competencies of interdisciplinary education. Part 3 comprises five chapters from academic programs in the United States. Part 4 provides a perspective on IPP in a variety of different areas. The authors were encouraged to use case illustrations as needed.

REFERENCES

Choi, B.C.K., & Pak, A.W.P. (2008). Multidisciplinarity, interdisciplinarity, and trans-disciplinarity in health research, services, education and policy: 3. Discipline, inter-discipline distance, and selection of discipline. *Clinical and Investigative Medicine, 31,* E41–E48.

Freeth, D., Hammick, M., Reeves, S., Koppel, I., & Barr, H. (2005). *Effective interprofessional education.* Oxford, United Kingdom: Wiley-Blackwell.

Hall, P., & Weaver, L. (2001). Interdisciplinary teamwork: A long winding road. *Medical Education, 35,* 867–875.

Institute of Medicine. (2015). *Measuring the impact of interprofessional education on collaborative practice and patient outcomes.* Washington, DC: National Academies Press.

Institute of Medicine, Committee on the Future Health Care Workforce for Older Americans. (2008). *Retooling for an aging America: Building the health care workforce.* Washington, DC: National Academies Press.

Institute of Medicine, Committee on the Health Professions Education Summit. (2003). *Health professions education: A bridge to quality.* Retrieved from http://iom.edu/Reports/2003/Health-Professions-Education-A-Bridge-toQuality.aspx

Wagner E. H., Austin, B. T., Davis, C., Hindmarsh, M., Schaefer, J., & Bonomi, A. (2001). Improving chronic illness care: Translating evidence into action. *Health Affairs, 20,* 64–78.

Part 1

BACKGROUND AND HISTORY OF INTERPROFESSIONAL EDUCATION

1

COMPETENCY-BASED EDUCATION

Carmen Morano

DEVELOPMENT OF COMPETENCY-BASED EDUCATION

Scholars have been writing about competency-based education (CBE) for more than three decades (Frank et al., 2010). A recent search on EBSCOhost Academic Premier restricted to peer-reviewed manuscripts on competency-based education returned no fewer than 1,500 articles published between 2000 and 2015. Although this was not a rigorous search, it illustrates how competency-based education is an educational priority. Social work (Berkman, 2011; Council on Social Work Education [CSWE], 2008, 2015; Damron-Rodriguez, 2008), medicine (Frank et al., 2010; Iglar, Whithead, & Takahashi, 2012), nursing (Leung, Trevena, & Waters, 2016), psychology (Rudin et al., 2007), and public health (Bennett & Watson, 2015) have all adopted a competency-based approach to learning. Although the operationalization of CBE does vary, there is a consensus that CBE should provide a pedagogy that integrates what the student needs to know with what the student is able to do (Rudin et al., 2007). Demonstrating knowledge transfer to the performance of skills is the goal of all CBE; however, moving from knowledge of theory to practice competence is easier said than done and perhaps even more difficult to evaluate.

To state that there is great variation in the number and content of the competency statements for each health discipline would be an understatement. For example, the 2008 Educational Policies and Standards contained 10 core competencies for foundation and advanced master's practice (CSWE, 2008). More recently, the 2015 Social Work Competencies listed nine competency domains that provide greater clarity of expectations through 31 subcompetencies. The Accreditation Council for Graduate

Medical Education (ACGM) identified the following six areas of competence that are operationalized using 36 subdomains: patient care, medical knowledge, interpersonal skills, communication skills, professionalism, and systems-based practice (Educational Commission for Foreign Medical Graduates, 2012). Last, the American Nurses Association's 2013 statement lists six broad competency domains with 20 competency standards. Given the multiple permutations of competency statements, a detailed description of each is well beyond the scope of this text. This chapter provides a brief review of competency-based education in social work and in the larger arena of CBE in health care by focusing on the work by Englander and colleagues (2013).

CBE IN SOCIAL WORK

The CSWE Educational Policies and Standards (EPAS) describe competency-based education as follows: "Competency-based education rests upon a shared view of the nature of competence in professional practice. Social work competence is the ability to integrate and apply social work knowledge, values, and skills to practice situations in a purposeful, intentional, and professional manner to promote human and community well-being" (CSWE, 2015, p. 6). CSWE mandates that EPAS is to be reviewed and updated every seven years. The 2015 EPAS represents the results of a five-year process to update the original standards established in the 2008 EPAS report. Similar to competency statements in nursing, social work competencies recognize the importance of competencies that address competencies at both the undergraduate and graduate level. Terminology such as "practice behaviors" clearly indicates the importance of demonstrating competence that is grounded in practice and not just demonstrated by mastery of knowledge that is evaluated by an exam. Social work programs are allowed to add to the stated competencies and are encouraged to use an integrated design that is consistent with the mission and goals of the program, the explicit curriculum, the implicit curriculum, and assessment.

The nine CSWE competency domains presented in Table 1.1 are operationalized further by 31 subcompetencies that speak to knowledge, values, skills, and cognitive processes that comprise competency at the generalist level of practice (CSWE, 2015). CSWE accreditation policies and standards provide further guidance distinguishing the expectations for the generalist and specialist levels of education, as well as for the implicit and explicit curriculum, field practicums, and assessment. Guidelines for evaluating CBE emphasize the importance of integrating classroom learning with field practicum. This is most clearly articulated in the Educational Policies section of EPAS, which recognizes field practicum as the signature pedagogy of social work education. As CSWE explains, "Signature pedagogies are elements of instruction and of socialization that teach future practitioners the fundamental dimensions of professional work in their discipline to think, to perform, and to act ethically and with identity" (2015, p. 11). Of relevance to this text, Competency 8, Intervene with Individuals, Families, Groups, Organizations, and Communities, encourages social workers to "use inter-professional collaboration as appropriate to achieve beneficial practice outcomes" and to "facilitate effective transitions and endings that advance mutually agreed-on goals" (CSWE, 2015, p. 9) through person-centered practice.

Table 1.1: Comparison of Core Competencies

CSWE EPAS	IOM	Nursing	ACGME	Englander
Ethical & professional behavior	Patient centered	Assessment	Patient care	Patient care
Engage diversity & difference in practice	Interdisciplinary practice	Diagnosis	Medical knowledge	Knowledge for practice
Advance human rights & social, economic, and environmental justice	Evidence-based practice	Outcome identification	Interpersonal and communication skills	Practice-based learning and improvement
Engage in practice-informed research and research-informed practice	Quality improvement	Planning	Professionalism	Interprofessional communication
Engage in policy practice	Informatics	Implementation	Practice-based learning and improvement	Professionalism
Engage with individuals, families, groups, organizations, and communities		Evaluation	Systems-based practice	Interprofessional collaboration
Assess individuals families, groups, organizations, and communities				Personal and professional
Intervene with individuals, families, groups, organizations, and communities				
Evaluate practice with individuals, families, groups, organizations, and communities				

Notes: CSWE = Council on Social Work Education; EPAS = Educational Policies and Standards; IOM = Institute of Medicine; ACGME = Accreditation Council for Graduate Medical Education; Englander = Englander et al. (2013).

CBE IN THE HEALTH PROFESSIONS

Commentary on the role of CBE in the health professions can be found dating back more than four decades. In 1978, the World Health Organization (WHO) stated, "Defining professional competence is the cornerstone upon which a competency-based programme of medical education is built" (WHO, 1978, p. 21). The report went on to say, "Unless this task is approached both thoughtfully and systematically the medical curriculum is more likely to be a reflection of faculty interests than of student and public needs" (WHO, 1978, p. 21). The Institute of Medicine (IOM) 2003 report *Health Professions Education: A Bridge to Quality* spoke to the importance of a competence-based approach to all the health care professions. This report detailed five core competences to which all the health care professions should aspire.

The proliferation of reports, books, and articles identifying or calling for the establishment of core competencies can leave the consumer of this knowledge quite confused. As such, each of the health disciplines has followed an extensive process similar to that of social work. Surveys, focus groups, and Delphi panels are all used in an iterative, consensus-building process that ultimately declares the core competencies identified with a profession or specialty section within the discipline. Regardless of the profession, the process of arriving at a short list of competencies requires a winnowing down of a broad range of skills and behaviors. In one of the more comprehensive approaches to arriving at a short list of core competencies, Englander and colleagues (2013) started with 153 statements found in a Web search of different competency statements. After eliminating redundancy and overlap of statements, they presented eight competency domains that include a total of 58 subdomains. The eight domains and subdomains are patient care (11 subdomains), knowledge for practice (six subdomains), practice-based learning and improvement (10 subdomains), interpersonal communication and communication (seven subdomains), professionalism (six subdomains), systems-based practice (six subdomains), interprofessional collaboration (four subdomains), and personal and professional competency (eight subdomains).

In addition to the variation in the number and content in each of the health professions, there is a growing trend in CBE within many professions' substantive specialty areas. For example, in addition to general competencies that apply to social work education, there are competency statements that are specific to gerontological social work. Other examples can be found in the John A. Hartford Foundation's collaboration with the discipline of nursing, which developed a series of competency statements specifically focused on geriatric nursing, and the Social Work Leadership Institute's collaboration with the CSWE, which developed foundation and advanced practice competencies in geriatric social work. Both interprofessional and person-centered care are recognized as competencies in geriatric social work and nursing.

Last, it is important to note that in addition to CBE throughout the health professions, there is a growing demand for practitioners to be competent in the delivery of patient-centered care. Although multiple reports from IOM and WHO have addressed the importance of patient-centered care, it has taken policy initiatives such as the Patient Protection and Affordable Care Act of 2010 (ACA; specifically Section 2402a and Section 3506) to ensure that states develop and/or evaluate patient-centered models of care.

Although the concept of patient-centered, participant-directed (PC/PD) care is relatively new in the majority of health professions, the social work profession has historically identified a person-centered approach as the foundation of all competent practice. In her seminal text *Social Diagnosis* (1917), social worker Mary Richmond discusses the importance of the client being in the center of all care. Using concentric circles moving from the client out to the larger environment, Richmond stresses six power sources for the social worker and client: within the household, in the person of the client, in the neighborhood and wider social network, in civil agencies, and in private and public agencies.

CSWE and the National Center for Participant Directed Services collaborated to develop PC/PD competencies in 2013. The PC/PD competencies were designed to be compatible with and expand the previously mentioned social work gero-competencies that were developed in 2008–2009 (National Center for Gerontological Social Work Education, n.d.).

Given that client empowerment and advocacy have a long tradition in social work, it is not surprising that PC/PD principles and competencies in social work education are not new. However, in many of the allied health professions, where the professional has traditionally been considered the expert, PC/PD competencies are not nearly as developed. The specific mention of PC/PD competencies in the ACA has increased the importance of PC/PD. Consequently, PC/PD competencies will be infused into the curriculum of all the health professions.

POST-CERTIFICATE CBE

The health care workforce accounts for more than 10 percent or approximately 14 million health care workers in the United States (U.S. Department of Health and Human Services, Health Resources and Services Administration, National Center for Health Workforce Analysis, 2013). The vast majority of this workforce has had little or no prior interprofessional education or training (Advisory Committee on Interdisciplinary, Community Based Linkages, 2014; IOM, 2008). Given the size of the current workforce (many of whom had no pre-certificate training in interdisciplinary practice), the potentially decades-long span of a practice career, and the rapid development of knowledge, the importance of continuing education (CE) cannot be overstated. Consequently, there has been a growing focus on post-certificate continuing education. Unfortunately, pre-certificate interprofessional education and interprofessional post-certificate CE have evolved in separate silos with little relationship to each other (Barr, 2013). The IOM (2010) report *Redesigning Continuing Education in the Health Professions* stated that the current models of continuing education do not adequately promote the acquisition of the five core competencies for health care: providing patient-centered care, working in interdisciplinary teams, employing evidence-based practice, applying quality improvement, and utilizing informatics.

There are a number of other factors that complicate the provision and regulation of post-certificate CE. In addition to differences in CE requirements by profession, CE requirements and delivery methods also differ by state. For example, at the time of this writing, New York State requires 36 contact hours of continuing education every three years, while Illinois requires 30 contact hours every two years. New Jersey and Pennsylvania require 100 continuing medical education (CME) hours for physicians every two years, while Arizona, Florida, and Delaware require physicians to obtain 40 CME hours per year.

Interprofessional CE becomes even more complicated because of the lack of a single regulatory authority that spans multiple professions. Consequently, a CE program seeking to provide interprofessional CE must meet the regulatory requirements of each profession. Although there has been a call for a single regulatory body that could credential continuing education across professional disciplines (Hager, Russell, & Fletcher, 2008), there is no consensus as to how this can be accomplished given the multiple professional and state licensing authorities. With such a large number of subspecialties in medicine alone, it is easy to understand the challenge to developing a universal certification of continuing education (Jackson et al., 2007).

EVALUATION OF CBE

Evaluation and assessment of competence is at the root of all CBE for the health professions. Unfortunately, the assessment and evaluation of CBE is a complicated process. Competence is not directly observable, as it can only be inferred from performance that relies on "the integration of general capacities, such as reasoning and making judgments, as well as specific knowledge and individual dispositions" (Gonczi, 2013, p. 1291). The lived experience of practice often requires instantaneous decisions and actions that seldom provide adequate time for reflection. Evaluating competence requires an integrated approach that includes both the evaluation of classroom learning and evaluation of the lived experience of field practicums and internships.

Although methods for evaluation and assessment vary, all share some common elements. The 2015 EPAS identifies six areas of assessment for generalist and specialist levels of education. These include a detailed description of the assessment procedures, a minimum of two measures of assessment, an explanation of how the institution achieves its benchmark, and copies of all assessment measures. Evaluation and assessment strategies include patient surveys, 360-degree evaluation instruments, portfolios, objective structured examinations, and simulation. These strategies can be found in many of the other health professions. Discussions of the evaluations that were used by each of the academic programs featured in this book can be found in chapter 12.

CONCLUSION

Although health education has made tremendous strides in developing and, more recently, evaluating CBE, there remains much work to be done. Integrating PC/PD competencies into the core competencies in the health professions presents a challenge to future health care education. Developing strategies to break down the silos between pre-certificate education and post-certificate education is also essential. This brief review of the growth of CBE is not intended to be comprehensive but rather to set the stage for understanding the growth and development of interprofessional CBE.

Recognition of the importance of interprofessional education and practice dates as far back as some of the early writing on CBE. IOM called for the advancement of interprofessional practice as far back as 1972, and WHO identified interprofessional (collaborative) practice as a priority as far back as 1978 (see, for example, IOM, 1972, 2000, 2001, 2003; WHO, 1978, 1988, 2006). Yet as recently as 2013, Barr noted, "Designing the learning environment for the health care professionals of tomorrow is less than complete unless and until it includes interprofessional education (IPE)" (p. 9).

As will be discussed in subsequent chapters, terms such as *collaborative*, *multidisciplinary*, and *interdisciplinary* can be found throughout most, if not all, of the health disciplines' competency statements. The degree of specificity and the scheduling of interprofessional learning varies from discipline to discipline. It is common for most interprofessional CBE to include a variety of experiential learning, observational-based learning, case-based learning, and problem-based learning methods (Barr, 2013).

There are many factors contributing to the current push for the inclusion of interprofessional content into health curricula. In addition to being included as a core competency in all health professions, competencies in interprofessional collaboration currently exist in medical specialties such as geriatrics, pediatrics, oncology, and pain management. Similar competencies can be found in the specialty practices of nursing, public health, and social work.

As discussed in Part 3, there are a number of systemic challenges and barriers that must be overcome to support and sustain true interprofessional learning. The exemplars of the five academic programs included in this text are but a sample of what can be accomplished with adequate time and support.

REFERENCES

Advisory Committee on Interdisciplinary, Community Based Linkages. (2014, October). *Transforming interprofessional health education and practice: Moving learners from the campus to the community to improve population health* (13th annual report). Retrieved from http://www.hrsa.gov/advisorycommittees/bhpradvisory/acicbl/acicbl.html

American Nurses Association. (2013, August). *Competency model*. Retrieved from https://learn.ana-nursingknowledge.org/template/ana/publications_pdf/leadershipInstitute_competency_model_brochure.pdf

Barr, H. (2013). Enigma variations: Unraveling interprofessional education in time and place. *Journal of Interprofessional Care, 27*(Suppl. 2), 9–13.

Bennett, J. D., & Watson, S. L. (2015). Improving the use of competencies in public health education. *American Journal of Public Health, 105*(Suppl. 1), S65–S67.

Berkman, B. J. (2011). Seizing interdisciplinary opportunities in the changing landscape of health and aging: A social work perspective. *Gerontologist, 51*, 433–440.

Council on Social Work Education. (2008). *Educational policy and accreditation standards*. Retrieved from http://www.cswe.org/File.aspx?id=13780

Council on Social Work Education. (2015). *Educational policy and accreditation standards.* Retrieved from http://www.cswe.org/File.aspx?id=81660

Damron-Rodriguez, J. (2008). Developing competence for nurses and social workers. *Journal of Social Work Education, 44*(Suppl.), 27–37. doi:10.5175/JSWE.2008.773247708

Educational Commission for Foreign Medical Graduates. (2012). *ACGME core competencies.* Retrieved from http://www.ecfmg.org/echo/acgme-core-competencies.html

Englander, R., Cameron, T., Ballard, A. J., Dodge, J., Bull, J., & Aschenbrener, C. A. (2013). Toward a common taxonomy of competency domains for the health professions and competencies for physicians. *Academic Medicine, 88,* 1088–1094.

Frank, J. R., Snell, L. S., Cate, O. T., Holmboe, E. S., Carraccio, C., Swing, S. R., et al. (2010). Competency-based medical education: Theory to practice. *Medical Teacher, 32,* 638–645.

Gonczi, A. (2013). Competency-based approaches: Linking theory and practice in professional education with particular reference to health education. *Educational Philosophy and Theory, 45,* 1290–1306.

Hager, M., Russell, S., & Fletcher, S. W. (Eds.). (2008). *Continuing education in the health professions: Improving healthcare through lifelong learning.* Retrieved from http://www.macyfoundation.org/docs/macy_pubs/pub_ContEd_inHealthProf.pdf

Iglar, K., Whithead, C., & Takahashi, S. G. (2012). Competency-based education in family medicine. *Medical Teacher, 35,* 115–119.

Institute of Medicine. (1972). *Educating for the health team.* Washington, DC: National Academies Press.

Institute of Medicine. (2000). *To err is human: Building a safer health system.* Washington, DC: National Academies Press.

Institute of Medicine. (2001). *Crossing the quality chasm.* Washington, DC: National Academies Press.

Institute of Medicine, Committee on the Future Health Care Workforce for Older Americans. (2008). *Retooling for an aging America: Building the health care workforce.* Washington, DC: National Academies Press.

Institute of Medicine, Committee on the Future Health Care Workforce for Older Americans. (2010). *Redesigning continuing education in the health professions.* Washington, DC: National Academies Press.

Institute of Medicine, Committee on the Health Professions Education Summit. (2003). *Health professions education: A bridge to quality.* Retrieved from http://iom.edu/Reports/2003/Health-Professions-Education-A-Bridge-toQuality.aspx

Jackson, M. J., Gallis, H. A., Gilman, S. C., Grossman, M., Holzman, G. B., Marquis, D., & Trusky, S. K. (2007). The need for specialty curricula based on core competencies: A white paper of the Conjoint Committee on Continuing Medical Education. *Journal of Continuing Education of Health Professions, 27,* 124–128.

Leung, K., Trevena, L., & Waters, D. (2016). Development of a competency framework for evidence-based practice in nursing. *Nurse Education Today, 39,* 189–196. doi:10.1016/j.nedt.2016.01.026

National Center for Gerontological Social Work Education. (n.d.). *Gero competencies.* Retrieved from http://www.cswe.org/CentersInitiatives/GeroEdCenter/TeachingTools/Competencies.aspx

Richmond, M. E. (1917). *Social diagnosis.* New York: Russell Sage Foundation.

Rudin, N. J., Bebeau, M., Leigh, I. W., Lichtenberg, J., Smith, I. L., Nelson, P. D., et al. (2007). The competency movement within psychology: An historical perspective. *Professional Psychology: Research and Practice, 38,* 452–462.

U.S. Department of Health and Human Services, Health Resources and Services Administration, National Center for Health Workforce Analysis. (2013). *The U.S. health workforce chartbook.* Rockville, MD: Author.

World Health Organization. (1978). *Competency-based curriculum development in medical education.* Geneva: Author.

World Health Organization. (1988). *Learning together to work together for health. Report of a WHO Study Group on Multiprofessional Education for Health Personnel: The Team Approach* (Technical Report Series 769). Geneva: Author.

World Health Organization. (2006). *Rapid scaling up of health workforce production.* 59th World Health Assembly. Geneva: Author.

2

THE HISTORY OF INTERPROFESSIONAL EDUCATION

Carmen Morano

Dating back to the first Institute of Medicine (IOM) conference in 1972, leaders from allied health, dentistry, medicine, nursing, and pharmacy have raised questions about the role of interprofessional education across the health disciplines (Interprofessional Education Collaborative [IPEC] Expert Panel, 2011). An early effort by the American Nursing Association and the American Medical Association in 1982 collapsed because of conflicts, particularly concerning issues of nurses' role expansion and salaries (Fagin, 1992, as cited in Hall & Weaver, 2001). The World Health Organization (WHO) published its report of the International Conference on Primary Health Care in 1982 and followed up in 1988 with *Learning Together to Work Together for Health*. More recently the WHO (2010) published the *Framework for Action on Interprofessional Education and Collaborative Practice*. These reports emphasize the importance of interdisciplinary educational opportunities. Interdisciplinary practice has the potential to be a dynamic interpersonal process applying shared values and a commitment to learning from other disciplines, with the goal of achieving common purposes (Hanson & Spross, 1996).

In the last decade, a number of published reports have called for significant changes to the education of all health care professionals across the globe. In the United States, WHO, IOM, and the federal government have all emphasized the need to develop interdisciplinary models of training and education. Reports from IOM (see, for example, IOM, 2003, 2008, 2010, 2012) and from the Health Resources and Services Administration's Advisory Committee on Interdisciplinary, Community-Based Linkages (2013), and WHO (2010) have all continually emphasized the importance of interdisciplinary practice, education, and training.

Presented more than a decade ago, the chronic care model (Wagner et al., 2001) provides a clear and convincing rationale for the importance of system changes that support an interprofessional approach to disease management. Although Wagner and colleagues (2001) did not specifically refer to interprofessional teams, they noted the importance of a "practice team" that is composed of physicians, nurses, and other relevant health care professionals working in collaboration with patients. I concur with Kodner and Spreeuwenberg (2002) that it is time to expand the concept of the practice team beyond the medical team of the doctor and nurse to include a more comprehensive team that crosses the historically rigid boundaries of multiple systems, including but not limited to medical, behavioral, and social systems of care.

In the 2009 report *Revisiting the Medical School Educational Mission at a Time of Great Expansion* (cited in Brenner, Sutphen, Leonard, & Day, 2009), the Josiah Macy Jr. Foundation called for reform in the educational model of medical curricula because of its failure to provide new physicians with the right mix of competencies to practice effective medicine in the 21st century. The Carnegie Foundation for the Advancement of Teaching report *Educating Physicians: A Call for Reform of Medical School and Residency* called for a change in physician educational programs (Cooke, Irby, & O'Brien, 2010). Other disciplines have made similar arguments for their fields, notably IOM's report on the future of nursing (2010) and the National League for Nursing 2009 report on transforming clinical education (cited in Brenner et al., 2009). Although the health professions have each made efforts to infuse interdisciplinary content into their curriculum, a variety of institutional and structural challenges have made implementation and evaluation of these efforts challenging and difficult to sustain.

A REVIEW OF INTERDISCIPLINARY EDUCATION

The terms *interdisciplinary, transdisciplinary, interprofessional*, and *multidisciplinary* have been defined in a variety of ways and at times have been incorrectly used interchangeably (Choi & Pak, 2008). In a series of monographs published in *Clinical and Investigative Medicine*, Choi and Pak (2006, 2008) provided a detailed review of literature that explored definitions, objectives, education, practice, and policy factors from these multiple perspectives. They offered the following definitions:

> Multidisciplinarity draws on knowledge from different disciplines but stays within their boundaries. Interdisciplinarity analyzes, synthesizes and harmonizes links between disciplines into a coordinated and coherent whole. Transdisciplinarity integrates the natural, social and health sciences in a humanities context, and transcends their traditional boundaries. (Choi & Pak, 2008, p. 351)

I have used "interdisciplinary" when speaking about disciplines, such as medicine, nursing, and social work, and "interprofessional" when discussing the interaction among individual professionals representing the disciplines. (However, in the attempt to honor the voice of referenced materials, the term appearing in that referenced work will be used.) Oandasan and Reeves (2005) proposed the distinction that interdisciplinary teams result in an exchange of knowledge and information from two or more professions, whereas interprofessional teams integrate different professional perspectives to achieve a unified set of values, language, and goals.

In an early study on the lack of interdisciplinary education, McPherson and Sachs (1982) reported that fewer than 30 percent of medical schools in the United States and Canada were offering or had formal course work or components of interdisciplinary practice. Of the 105 programs responding to the survey, fewer than 50 percent indicated that interdisciplinary courses were required. There were some models of interprofessional instruction that were housed in the discipline's educational silo, with curricular content that included class instruction about interdisciplinary practice. A common practice was having a featured guest lecturer from one of the allied health disciplines present information about the roles and functions from that discipline's perspective. Although this model of delivery can be effective for a multidisciplinary education program, it lacks an interprofessional learning experience that provides students with opportunities to develop a set of shared values. Consequently, practitioners will continue to lack adequate knowledge and skills to move beyond disciplinary values to a shared value of the interprofessional team.

In their review of interdisciplinary education by systemic and content issues, Hall and Weaver (2001) identified systemic issues, including institutional support, timing, faculty development, method of delivery, and participant characteristics. Content issues included the curriculum and general learning experience. Harnessing the institutional support required to launch an interprofessional education continues to be one of the greatest and most important hurdles to developing an interprofessional education program. The organizational structure in academic settings varies from school to school and program to program. For example, a school of social work would answer directly to a provost or president of a college, university, or department, but a program or department of social work would answer to a dean of health or social sciences. Crossing boundaries to collaborate with a school housed in a separate silo will be more complex than crossing boundaries in those settings where multiple disciplines are located in a single structure. Issues such as faculty workload, budgets, or curriculum design would be specialized to achieve the competencies of each profession. Although there appears to be a trend developing with multiple professional health disciplines being housed in a broader department or school of health sciences, the tradition of academic independence (curricular, faculty workload, and budgetary) that exists in many schools could easily temper the enthusiasm required to work out the complicated logistics of sharing the expensive startup costs, the curriculum space, faculty, and scarce resources required to develop and sustain a successful interprofessional program.

THE TIMING OF INTERPROFESSIONAL EDUCATION (IPE)

The timing of the exposure to IPE intervention is another challenge to developing any program. Is exposure to an interdisciplinary milieu early in the education of the learner more effective than exposure later in the professional development life cycle of the learner? Developing awareness of the roles and responsibilities of allied professionals early should help to make interprofessional practice more acceptable later in practice. Introducing IPE early on in the learning process can help to provide a foundation of knowledge, skills, and values that has potential to expand the student learner's world view, before he or she becomes closed off to other ways of thinking. However, there is some evidence that incorporating learners early on in their educational process can be especially challenging (Petrie, 1976). This supports the much earlier belief that the individual embarking on interdisciplinary teamwork and interprofessional learning must first be secure in his or her discipline competency (Petrie, 1976). Knowledge of one's own discipline is essential to understanding its potential contributions to the team effort (Cooke, Irby, Sullivan, & Ludmerer, 2006; Irby & Wilkerson, 2003; Mariano, 1989). The debate about the timing of exposure remains unresolved, but all indicators suggest that it remains an important consideration (Hall & Weaver, 2001).

FACULTY DEVELOPMENT

One of the long-standing challenges to developing an interdisciplinary program of instruction is engaging faculty who are motivated and committed to engage in a genuine interdisciplinary process at all stages of program development, implementation, and evaluation (McPherson & Sachs, 1982). From conceptual design to establishing a strategy for program evaluation, all members of the interprofessional faculty team must move beyond their unique disciplinary lens to an informed shared process that takes on the team's interdisciplinary identity and is truly interprofessional in application. Unfortunately, the majority of the current health professions faculty have been classically trained in their profession's silo of education. Developing the team's identity and competency to engage in designing an interdisciplinary program of instruction requires the faculty to spend enough time together to mature into a truly interprofessional team with shared interprofessional values. This time can be achieved only with an institutional commitment of resources and support. Without this support, even the best of efforts to launch an IPE program becomes extremely difficult. As faculty come together and experience the normative stages of group development (Yalom & Leazcs, 2005), they initially struggle through the forming stage. Next, members of the team develop the norms for how they will interact (norming stage). The storming stage can occur when the team experiences struggles or disagreements or vying for control. When the team successfully navigates these stages, the stage of performing is reached. Finally, when the team has concluded their task, the final stage of the process is termination (Yalom & Leazcs, 2005).

The team is seldom prepared to model an interprofessional team of educators with the skills to educate their students. The curriculum in social work programs does include content and practice experience in facilitating groups. Yet in most medical settings, although the social worker could be asked to facilitate a group for patients, it is unlikely that a medical director would request the social worker to lead the effort to develop an interprofessional team.

MODELS OF IPE

The renewed interest in interprofessional practice has resulted in a growing number of educational program models. Traditional didactic lectures using an interdisciplinary problem-based learning (PBL) model (Bruhn, 1992; Lary, Lavigne, Muma, Jones, & Hoeft, 1997) and the service/learning models (Carpenter, 1995; Clark, Spence, & Sheehan, 1996) are two team approaches to education presented in the Hall and Weaver (2001) review. The PBL model was frequently delivered in a small-group format as a means of integrating theory with clinical components. It was also used in a structured educational activity drawing on case presentations as the stimulus to learning. This approach helped students learn to listen to each other and to collaborate while resolving problems (Makaram, 1995). This approach also develops the skills and confidence for team members to identify and respond to the presenting problems.

The poststructuralist model requires a critical appraisal of the presenting situation by using reflective or questioning techniques. The social construction of the professionals' lived experience intersects with the patients' lived experience. This interconnection occurs within a complex system of hierarchical structures that have a history of asserting power and privilege. The poststructuralist approach to care confronts the traditional top–down approach, facilitates working across professional and cultural differences, and has the potential to make a significant contribution to interdisciplinary education and interdisciplinary practice (Hall & Weaver, 2001). The relevance of this model will grow in importance given the recent focus on providing person-centered, participant-directed care (Sciegaj & Selkow, 2011). Patients and professionals frequently have different social constructions of their lived experiences. These differences must be understood when engaging individuals in a team approach to care.

CURRICULUM FOR IPE

A number of key topical areas have been found to be critical to interdisciplinary instruction, including (a) knowledge and skills, (b) communication skills, (c) group dynamics, (d) conflict resolution, (e) role delineation, and (f) leadership. Knowledge in each of these areas provides a critical foundation to development and functioning of interdisciplinary teams. As will be discussed in a subsequent section of this text, these six areas are frequently embedded into IPE programs. Thus, to provide an instructional curriculum, it is important that faculty and instructors have established competency in each of these areas to model an interdisciplinary team approach to teaching.

With representatives from medicine, nursing, pharmacy, and public health, the IPEC (2016) has "reaffirmed the value of the established core competencies" with the intention to "organize the competencies within a singular domain of Interprofessional Collaboration, encompassing the topics of values and ethics, roles and responsibilities, interprofessional communication, and teams and teamwork" (p. 1). These core competencies mirror the development of competency-based education in other curricular areas. The chapters in Part 2 provide a more detailed discussion of the core competencies.

It has become almost impossible to keep up with the growing number of curricular resources focusing on IPE in the United States and Canada. In addition to the resources provided throughout this text, there are many international meetings on interprofessional education and practice, such as the Collaborating Across Boarders series of conferences, as well as a growing number of curricular resources that are made available at conferences such as the Annual Program Meeting of the Council on Social Work Education, the Society for Social Work Research, the American Geriatrics Society Annual Conference, and the Annual Meeting of the Gerontological Society of America, to name a few. The National Center for Interprofessional Practice and Education at the University of Minnesota, the Center for Interprofessional Learning at the University of Toronto, and the Interprofessional Educational Collaborative represent a growing trend of centers with a mission to facilitate the exchange of interprofessional curricular materials. There are also a growing number of curricular resources, learning assignments, classroom videos, and exercises available on the Web (see, for example, http://www.aihc-us.org/program-resources/ or http://www.ttuhsc.edu/ipe/).

DISCIPLINARY PERSPECTIVES ON INTERPROFESSIONAL EDUCATION

In their review, Choi and Pak (2006) found that many professional health programs referred to interprofessional (as well as interdisciplinary, multidisciplinary, and transdisciplinary) education in literature dating back to the early 1970s. For example, Abramson and Mizrahi (2003) found that social work, nursing, medicine, and public health have each mentioned interprofessional practice in their respective code of ethics or discipline-specific competencies. To name just a few, the codes of ethics for the National Association of Social Workers, the American Medical Association (2001), the American Nursing Association, and the American Public Health Association each speak to interprofessional practice. It is interesting, however, that the most recent Educational and Policy Accreditation Standards of the Council on Social Work Education (CSWE, 2008) do not include a specific section on collaboration with other professionals. Although not mentioned in the most recent accreditation standards, interprofessional practice is mentioned as an intervention strategy in the CSWE Gero-Ed Center (2008) Advanced Gerontology Competencies.

It appears that all health professions have struggled with ways to design, deliver, and evaluate interprofessional education and practice on an institutional level. All the health professions are challenged to embrace working across multiple disciplines while continuing to maintain or modify their own professional identity (IPEC, 2016). The long-held tradition of rigid separation among professional groups is becoming less fixed as academic silos evolve into academic centers combining a number of professional health disciplines (Reynolds, 2005).

Nurse educators have recognized for some time that traditional models of clinical education are no longer adequate in preparing nurses for the challenges they are faced with shortly after graduation, including increased patient acuity, shortened hospital stays, the shift to community health care, and the demand for quick, sophisticated clinical reasoning. The Carnegie National Study of Nursing Education, recently completed by the Carnegie Foundation for the Advancement of Teaching, describes the need for student apprenticeships in intellectual training, clinical reasoning, and ethical comportment (Brenner et al., 2009). This report describes uneven and inadequate teaching across types of schools, limited consultation of evidence-based literature, almost no interdisciplinary teaching, uneven classroom integration, and clinical overreliance on staff nurses as teachers. It is also noteworthy that the recent comprehensive national reform on the future of nursing education by Brenner and colleagues (2009) mentions the term *interdisciplinary collaboration* only once.

Cooke and colleagues (2010) stated that there is an expectation that physicians play a broad role in society where engagement in policy must be collaborative and coordinated among all stakeholder groups. Although some of this may be attributable to the fragmented and problematic nature of the health care delivery system in the United States (Wagner et al., 2001), it is generally acknowledged that most medical schools do not prepare students with the skill set needed to provide collaborative patient care with other health care professionals and also do not provide sufficient experiential educational training in community-based settings. The most recent national efforts to reform medical education are promising. The roles and responsibilities of public health professionals on interprofessional teams have grown in importance in response to the need for a health care workforce that can recognize and respond to population-level health and well-being (Advisory Committee on Interdisciplinary, Community-Based Linkages, 2013).

The public health framework recognizes that the health of populations and individuals is shaped by a wide range of factors in the social, economic, natural, built, and political environments. However, this recognition is rarely integrated into mainstream health care delivery systems. In the face of 21st century health and public health challenges, the integration of public health professionals directly into interprofessional clinical teams can better facilitate achieving the goals articulated by the Centers for Disease Control and Prevention in their Healthy People 2020 initiative (see https://www.healthypeople.gov). This same urgency to expand opportunities for interprofessional education is also starting to take hold in schools of pharmacy, physical and occupational therapy, and other disciplines.

HISTORY OF EVALUATION OF IPE

The number of evaluations of interdisciplinary learning activities is growing, as is the sophistication of the rigor of the methodology. In one of the more recent comprehensive meta-analyses of evaluation studies, Gillian, Lovrics, Halpern, Wiljer, and Harnett (2011) reviewed more than 1,600 abstracts and included 202 full-text articles in their analyses. Approximately 44 instruments containing more than 500 items were identified. The most frequently evaluated outcomes appear to be participant satisfaction with program content or presentation modality and changes in participant perception of interdisciplinary practice (Gillian et al., 2011). A deeper level of understanding of the impact of interdisciplinary education and training on practice behavior and patient-level outcomes has proven much more difficult to capture (Gillian et al., 2011). As previously mentioned, the logistical challenges of coordinating the schedules of multiple cohorts of students are further complicated by the shortage of clinical preceptors with experience in interprofessional education or practice. As will be reflected in subsequent chapters of this book, a number of challenges to both the conceptual design and desired level of evaluation is an inevitable part of the early development of any program.

REFERENCES

Abramson, J. S., & Mizrahi, T. (2003). Understanding collaboration between social workers and physicians: Application of a typology. *Social Work and Health Care, 37,* 71–100.

Advisory Committee on Interdisciplinary, Community-Based Linkages. (2013, August). *Redesigning health professions education and practice to prepare the interprofessional team to care for populations* (12th annual report). Retrieved from http://www.hrsa.gov/advisorycommittees/bhpradvisory/acicbl/Reports/twelfthreport_.pdf

American Medical Association. (2001). *Principles of medical ethics.* Retrieved from https://www.ama-assn.org/ama/pub/physician-resources/medical-ethics/code-medical-ethics/principles-medical-ethics.page

Brenner, P., Sutphen, M., Leonard, V., & Day, L. (2009). *Educating nurses: A call for radical transformation.* San Francisco: Jossey-Bass and the Carnegie Foundation for the Advancement in Teaching.

Bruhn, J. G. (1992). Problem-based learning: An approach toward reforming allied health education. *Journal of Allied Health, 21,* 161–173.

Carpenter, J. (1995). Interprofessional education for medical and nursing students: Evaluation of a programme. *Medical Education, 29,* 265–272.

Choi, B.C.K., & Pak, A.W.P. (2006). Multidisciplinarity, interdisciplinarity and transdisciplinarity in health research, services, education and policy: 1. Definitions, objectives, and evidence of effectiveness. *Clinical and Investigative Medicine, 29,* 351–364.

Choi, B.C.K., & Pak, A.W.P. (2008). Multidisciplinarity, interdisciplinarity, and transdisciplinarity in health research, services, education and policy: 3. Discipline, interdiscipline distance, and selection of discipline. *Clinical and Investigative Medicine, 31,* E41–E48.

Clark, P. G., Spence, D. L., & Sheehan, J. L. (1996). A service/learning model for interdisciplinary teamwork in health and aging. *Gerontology & Geriatrics Education, 6*(4), 3–16.

Cooke, M., Irby, D., & O'Brien, B. (2010). *Educating physicians: A call for reform of medical school and residency.* San Francisco: Jossey-Bass.

Cooke, M., Irby, D., Sullivan, W., & Ludmerer, K. (2006). American medical education 100 years after the Flexner report. *New England Journal of Medicine, 355,* 1339–1344.

Council on Social Work Education. (2008). *Educational policy and accreditation standards.* Retrieved from http://www.cswe.org/File.aspx?id=13780

Council on Social Work Education Gero-Ed Center. (2008). *Gero competencies.* Retrieved from http://www.cswe.org/CentersInitiatives/GeroEdCenter/EducationalResources/Competencies.aspx

Gillian, C., Lovrics, E., Halpern, E., Wiljer, D., & Harnett, N. (2011). The evaluation of learner outcomes in interprofessional continuing education: A literature review and an analysis of survey instruments. *Medical Teacher, 33,* 461–470.

Hall, P., & Weaver, L. (2001). Interdisciplinary education and teamwork: A long and winding road. *Medical Education, 35,* 867–875.

Hanson, C. M., & Spross, J. A. (1996). Collaboration. In A. B. Hamric, S. Ja, & C. M. Hanson (Eds.), *Advanced nursing practice: An integrative approach* (pp. 229–248). Philadelphia: Saunders.

Institute of Medicine. (2012). *Primary care and public health: Exploring integration to improve population health.* Washington, DC: National Academies Press.

Institute of Medicine, Committee on the Future Health Care Workforce for Older Americans. (2008). *Retooling for an aging America: Building the health care workforce.* Washington, DC: National Academies Press.

Institute of Medicine, Committee on the Future Health Care Workforce for Older Americans. (2010). *Redesigning continuing education in the health professions.* Washington, DC: National Academies Press.

Institute of Medicine, Committee on the Health Professions Education Summit. (2003). *A bridge to quality.* Washington, DC: National Academies Press.

Interprofessional Education Collaborative. (2016). *Core competencies for interprofessional collaborative practice: 2016 update.* Washington, DC: Author.

Interprofessional Education Collaborative Expert Panel. (2011). *Core competencies for interprofessional collaborative practice: Report of an expert panel.* Washington, DC: Interprofessional Education Collaborative.

Irby, D., & Wilkerson, L. (2003). Educational innovations in academic medicine and environmental trends. *Journal of General Internal Medicine, 18,* 370–376.

Kodner, D. L., & Spreeuwenberg, C. (2002): Integrated care: Meaning, logic, applications, and implications—A discussion paper. *International Journal of Integrated Care, 2*(4), e12.

Lary, M. J., Lavigne, S. E., Muma, R. D., Jones, S. E., & Hoeft H. J. (1997). Breaking down barriers: Multidisciplinary education model. *Journal of Allied Health, 26,* 63–69.

Makaram, S. (1995). Interprofessional cooperation. *Medical Education, 29*(Suppl. 1), 65S–69S.

Mariano, C. (1989). The case for interdisciplinary collaboration. *Nursing Outlook, 37,* 285–288.

McPherson, C., & Sachs, L. A. (1982). Health care team training in U.S. and Canadian medical schools. *Journal of Medical Education, 57,* 282–287.

Oandasan, I., & Reeves, S. (2005). Key elements for interprofessional education. Part 1: The learner, the educator and the learning context. *Journal of Interprofessional Care, 19*(Suppl. 1), 21–38.

Petrie, H. G. (1976). Do you see what I see? The epistemology of interdisciplinary inquiry. *Journal of Aesthetic Education, 10,* 29–43.

Reynolds, F. (2005). *Communication and clinical effectiveness in rehabilitation.* Edinburgh: Elsevier Butterworth-Heinemann.

Sciegaj, M., & Selkow, I. (2011). *Growth and prevalence of participant direction: Findings from the National Survey of Publically Funded Participant-Directed Services Programs*. Retrieved from http://web.bc.edu/libtools/details.php?entryid=340

Wagner, E. H., Austin, B. T., Davis, C., Hindmarsh, M., Schaefer, J., & Bonomi, A. (2001). Improving chronic illness care: Translating evidence into action. *Health Affairs, 20*(6), 64–78. doi:10.1377/hlthaff.20.6.64

World Health Organization. (1988). *Learning together to work together for health. Report of a WHO Study Group on Multiprofessional Education for Health Personnel: The Team Approach* (Technical Report Series 769). Geneva: Author.

World Health Organization. (2010). *Framework for action on interprofessional education and collaborative practice*. Retrieved from http://www.who.int/hrh/resources/framework_action/en/

Yalom, I. D., & Leazcs, M. (2005). *Theory and practice of group psychodynamics* (5th ed.). Cambridge, MA: Basic Books.

Part 2

CORE COMPETENCIES OF INTERPROFESSIONAL EDUCATION

3

VALUES AND ETHICS

Kenya V. Beard

Case Study: Mrs. Garcia

The health care team ignores the importance of familial values and culture to Mrs. Garcia, who sees her role as the maternal grandmother to provide care to grandchildren, as well as the professional ethics of professional collegiality. Not only do they ignore the new team member who is arriving at her first meeting with the team, but they also criticize the Garcia family for being late to a meeting. Yet, they saw nothing wrong with the doctor being late. The team dismisses their ethical obligation to make sure that Mrs. Garcia gives an informed consent by suggesting that in lieu of having a reliable translator available, they are satisfied that she appears to understand her treatment by her nodding when they give her instructions. The team also violate Mrs. Garcia's right to confidentiality by speaking in a public place about Mrs. Garcia as a "frequent flyer" who is incapable of complying with the medical orders.

This chapter focuses on how the behavior and comments made by the team with each other repeatedly demonstrate a disregard for the core competency of values and ethics to both their colleague and the Garcia family.

CORE COMPETENCIES

Health care providers are charged with demonstrating the competencies of their profession. Although each health care discipline has independently constructed unique competencies, some groups (nursing, pharmacy, dentistry, public health, medicine, and osteopathic medicine) have partnered through the auspices of the Interprofessional Education Collaborative (IPEC) Expert Panel and developed core competencies for interprofessional collaborative practice (IPEC Expert Panel, 2011); the competencies were updated five years later (IPEC, 2016). The core competencies generate an ethos that cultivates a shared purpose and strengthens the capacity of the interprofessional team to work collectively in providing high-quality health care.

There are four core interprofessional collaborative practice competencies: (1) values and ethics for interprofessional practice, (2) interprofessional communication, (3) roles and responsibilities, and (4) teams and teamwork. This chapter focuses on the competency of values and ethics for interprofessional practice (see Appendix A for a complete list of the nine VE subcompetencies). Values undergird our thoughts and influence our decisions. Ethics are the principles that help us determine what is right or wrong. Collectively, the competency of values and ethics sets a fundamental tone of mutual respect and shared values, which fosters a professional climate (IPEC Expert Panel, 2011). In addition, the competency underscores the need for interprofessional relationships that value mutual respect and trust to improve patient care.

These competencies are threaded throughout this chapter to operationalize the concepts of values and ethics and guide discussions on interprofessional professionalism.

VE1: Place interests of patients and populations at center of interprofessional health care delivery and population health programs and policies, with the goal of promoting health and health equity across the life span.

The health care system has been described as a fragmented and complex system that was fraught with opportunities to undermine patient safety. Today, numerous changes have been made to create environments that promote the delivery of safe, quality health care that is patient centered. As institutions shift from provider-centered to patient-centered systems, greater emphasis is being placed on the importance of identifying and meeting the needs of patients and the populations served. The Institute for Healthcare Improvement (IHI, 2015) has provided a three-dimensional framework to address current health care challenges and produce healthier populations. One of the three aims underscores the importance of improving the quality of care that is experienced by the patient. IHI adds that there needs to be an intentional focus on individuals and families to improve outcomes.

Students in the health care disciplines are entering a new health care delivery system that requires them to be trained in a way that supports interdependence and embodies the four core interprofessional competencies. Working in professional silos has proven to be detrimental to patient outcomes. Thus, students should engage in interprofessional opportunities that allow them to demonstrate the core competencies so they are better prepared for their future role as safe and effective health care providers. Students should understand that health equity, the right of every patient to achieve his or her full health potential (Centers for Disease Control and Prevention, 2015), dictates that all members of the health care team work collectively in delivering optimal care to all individuals.

The following three subcompetencies represent intersecting concepts that can be demonstrated only collectively.

VE2: Respect the dignity and privacy of patients while maintaining confidentiality in the delivery of team-based care.

VE3: Embrace the cultural diversity and individual differences that characterize patients, populations, and the health team.

VE4: Respect the unique cultures, values, roles/responsibilities, and expertise of other health professions and the impact these factors can have on health outcomes.

Achieving health equity and eliminating health care disparities has proved to be quite challenging for the United States (Agency for Healthcare, Research, and Quality, 2015). There are numerous factors that undermine health equity initiatives and lead to health care disparities. The two overarching factors are differences in both accessibility and quality of care (Agency for Healthcare, Research and Quality, 2015). It is widely accepted that efforts to improve health care quality hinge on a care delivery model that stresses the significance of cultural competence. Thus, the critical need to improve health care quality has led to a greater emphasis on graduating health care providers who are prepared to effectively engage in cross-cultural encounters. Regardless of the health care discipline, it is essential that all providers continuously broaden their cultural competence and possess the knowledge, skills, and attitudes that reflect an ongoing commitment to person-centered care. Indeed, all patients should have access to culturally sensitive health care providers who possess the skill sets to deliver unbiased quality care that considers the patients' values and beliefs. To limit the risk of stereotyping individuals and undermining the goals of patient-centered care, providers should not attempt to link certain values and beliefs to specific groups without considering the diversity within groups.

The term *cultural competence* is defined as a set of congruent behaviors, attitudes, and policies that come together in professionals, systems, and agencies and enable those professionals, systems, or agencies to work effectively in cross-cultural situations (Cross, Bazron, Dennis, & Isaacs, 1989). The term *diversity competence* could be used as an alternative to cultural competence because the former captures the differences in race and ethnicity, in sexual orientation and identification, and in persons with disabilities that cultural competence encompasses. However, this chapter's intentional use of the term *cultural competence* echoes that the differences embedded in cultural competence should never be limited to race and ethnicity alone.

The effects of poor interprofessional communication are well documented in the literature and can result in patient harm. Intentional intergroup dialogues can enhance confidence in working with members from different professions. Intergroup dialogues can also be used to help decrease anxiety and improve provider confidence in clinical encounters (Burgess, van Ryn, Dovidio, & Saha, 2007). Students can subsequently transfer the communication skills they learned to improve patient–provider, interprofessional, and personal relationships.

As health care institutions seek to create healthier populations, institutional climates must support the growth of collaborative teams that embody trust and respect. For example, to reduce surgical errors (wrong site, wrong side, and wrong patient surgical procedures), the Center for Transforming Healthcare has called on the surgical team to conduct pre-surgical time-out discussions (Joint Commission Center for Transforming Healthcare, 2013). For communication efforts to be successful, members of the team must value and respect each other's voices and feel empowered to speak up (Joint Commission Center for Transforming Healthcare, 2013). These changes require an organizational culture that fosters collaboration between health care providers and respect for each other's role.

> VE5: Work in cooperation with those who receive care, those who provide care, and others who contribute to or support the delivery of prevention and health services and programs.

When ethical and practice dilemmas occur, they can threaten interprofessional relationships and jeopardize the quality of care that is delivered. A focus on behaviors that generate positive patient–provider, interprofessional, and cross-professional relationships helps to create safe and effective health care systems. IPEC (2011) has identified values and ethics as one of its four core competencies for interprofessional practice. Developing shared values and ethics is critical for balancing professional and interprofessional identity. Students should graduate with the knowledge, attitudes, and skills that permit them to create effective interprofessional relationships that reflect shared values and ethics.

> VE6: Develop a trusting relationship with patients, families, and other team members (Canadian Interprofessional Health Collaborative, 2010).

As is the case with many of the subcompetencies, there is an overlapping or coming together of other competencies. Developing trusting relationships with patients, families, and colleagues can occur only though behavior. Health care professionals should demonstrate trust by being open to understanding the perceptions, thoughts, and feelings of patients and colleagues and reinforce that openness with behaviors that fulfill their words.

> VE7: Demonstrate high standards of ethical conduct and quality of care in one's contributions to team-based care.

Health care professions have created standards on how to best resolve ethical dilemmas. The ethical principles of autonomy, beneficence, and justice should be considered when attempting to balance dissimilar opinions surrounding an ethical dilemma. Autonomy underscores the saliency in providing individuals with information so that they can make an informed decision. Providers should respect the individual's right to determine the course of action he or she wants to follow. Beneficence captures the essence of doing good and helping others. However, the principle of beneficence is not always easily operationalized. Last, providers should be advocates for justice. Resources should be distributed in a way that is equitable and meets the needs of the community, population, or individual. Although all patients should have access to quality health care, it is not always the case that they do. Some patients receive less than optimal health care because of provider biases, stereotypes, social determinants of health, or institutional barriers (time constraints) (Agency for Healthcare, Research, and Quality, 2015).

VE8: Manage ethical dilemmas specific to interprofessional patient/population centered care situations.

Difference is inherently linked to diversity and reflected in one's thoughts, actions, beliefs, and opinions. When individuals share differences in what they value or believe to be true, moral imperatives are argued and ethical dilemmas can ensue. Ethical dilemmas, also described as moral dilemmas, are complex situations that stem from difference and result in dissonance. Polarizing beliefs in regards to how best to respond to an issue is at the core of ethical dilemmas. Note that ethical dilemmas are not discipline specific. Conversely, it is likely that all providers will encounter some type of ethical dilemma in the health care arena. As a matter of professionalism, all providers should be prepared to use best practices to achieve resolution and demonstrate a commitment to values and ethics.

Resolving an ethical dilemma requires that a choice be made between two opposing views; one response is likely to bring about a resolution that occurs at the expense of the other. Oftentimes an ethical dilemma emerges from a complex situation whereby individuals have a difference in beliefs. Take, for example, a child who is hospitalized for a routine surgical procedure. The child suffers complications, is found in cardiac arrest, is resuscitated, and is subsequently placed on life support. The hospital wants to remove life support once the child is declared brain dead. The family argues that the child is still alive and declares that any intentional actions to end the child's life are nothing short of murder. In this situation, it is clear that a difference in beliefs about what constitutes life has created an ethical dilemma. The family believes the child is still alive because the child is breathing and has a pulse, albeit with the aid of a ventilator. Health care providers attempt to explain that because there is no brain stem activity, the child has essentially died.

Should the child be removed from life support? This example helps to illustrate the layers of an ethical dilemma and reveals the complexities that can be embedded in a simply stated yes-or-no question. Though not all ethical dilemmas rise to the level of life-or-death decisions, health care providers should be able to collectively identify, develop a plan, and engage in actions that seek to effectively resolve ethical dilemmas. Keep in mind that how providers respond to dilemmas in health care is likely to influence health care outcomes.

So how does one develop a capacity to demonstrate shared values and ethics? First, defining what values and ethics are is essential. The IPEC Expert Panel (2011) stated that values should promote public trust. In addition, professionals should consistently demonstrate the core values by applying "principles of altruism, excellence, caring, ethics, respect, communication, [and] accountability to achieve optimal health and wellness in individuals and communities" (IPEC Expert Panel, 2011, p. 17). Ethics deal with the rules of behavior and are typically based on what is considered morally right and good or wrong and bad. Members of the health professions should be ready to address the difficulties involved with achieving greater competency in values and ethics. Being mindful of the common purpose, patient-centered care, which links all health professions together is key to improving the quality of health care and achieving optimal patient outcomes.

It is essential that students understand the shared interprofessional competencies and commit to adopting behaviors that are critical to professionalism. Consider the case example of Maria Garcia. At the beginning of the meeting, there was one member who was late. The different responses to the lateness were obvious. Some members of the heath care team appeared frustrated, while others did not show any signs of being disturbed by the individual's lateness. How lateness is perceived by colleagues and by the individual who is late could be influenced by title and degree of respect.

Take, for example, a meeting where you are waiting for the physician. Do you pardon the lateness and consider it an oversight that is beyond the physician's control because that position can be quite demanding? Or do you disregard the position and get frustrated and annoyed because you believe the physician does not value your time? Placing a high value on the physician's role and having a high level of respect for that individual could raise your level of acceptance and influence your attitude toward the lateness.

Now consider a similar situation in which the one who is late is someone who has a position that is not viewed as one of great importance. The attitude could now switch to one of great frustration and a feeling that the individual is rude and discourteous. The important message here is that the same transgression resulted in different responses that were shaped by beliefs and attitudes.

The team meeting scenario could also suggest that the physician who was late could view her position as more valuable than that of the other members of the team. Moreover, the individual may not recognize the effect that being late has on her colleagues. In this case, the individual may not even apologize for her tardiness. This creates interprofessional tensions that could spill out into the meeting and thwart efforts to achieve desirable outcomes for the patient.

Is it acceptable to be late because your position is one that you or others value highly? Is it less acceptable to be late if your position is not valued? Professionalism, specifically the competencies of values and ethics, reminds us that all roles should be respected (IPEC Expert Panel, 2011). Members of the health care team should appreciate the goals of collaboration and work together to optimize health. Of course, as the scenario depicts, there are numerous behaviors that undermine the ideals of interprofessional environments and make it difficult to create environments of mutual respect. Members of the health team should reflect on how they respond to colleagues and consider the attitudes and beliefs that influence their behaviors.

VE9: Act with honesty and integrity in relationships with patients, families, communities, and other team members.

The expertise that all members bring to the health team should be valued. Collectively, members of the group work toward a common purpose that is patient centered and produces the best outcomes. But as human nature dictates, this may not always be the case. Sometimes individuals develop negative beliefs or assumptions toward an individual or a discipline that influence their attitude and predict their behavior. Attitudes can also be shaped by past experiences with people who belong to a specific profession. Biases are created when preconceived beliefs and attitudes are presented with a disregard to alternative views. Regardless of the cause, negative attitudes and behaviors can quickly derail the agenda and shift the attention away from the patient.

Implicit assumptions about members of the health care team should be examined. What are some of the potential assumptions toward the physician being late? Is the lateness readily assumed to be due to a patient encounter? Perhaps the assumption is discipline specific, and there is an unconscious belief that physicians do not value the other members of the team. The culture of the organization can also contribute to negative attitudes. Does the institution demand a certain level of punctuality from only certain members of the team? When individuals are late, are members from only some groups held accountable and subjected to disciplinary measures? If individuals believe that the culture of the institution is such that rules apply only to certain individuals or disciplines, resentment toward the discipline could develop. Again, this could affect the team's dynamics.

Biases are attitudes that can be shaped by past experiences or beliefs about individuals or groups. Once formed, attitudes that are desirable or undesirable are projected onto others. Forming preconceived opinions toward a discipline or an individual can have disastrous results. Assumptions and implicit or conscious bias can easily manifest into behaviors that shape the way we interact with others. Thus, it is crucial that members of the health team examine what, if any, assumptions they hold.

Positive attitudes, trust, and respect are key to effective interprofessional relationships. The recognition of implicit biases and how they inform behaviors is also essential. Although many individuals may readily admit to holding explicit biases, few may realize that implicit biases are quite common (Banaji & Greenwald, 2013). To improve relationships, members should seek to identify whether they possess implicit biases. Strategies that assist individuals in bringing unconscious biases to the forefront and mitigating them do exist and should be applied. Recognizing implicit biases can help motivate individuals to reconstruct their truths and strengthen relationships (Burgess et al., 2007). Learning alongside colleagues helps to facilitate an understanding of their role as health care providers. However, knowing what members of the health care team do is not enough to ensure that roles are respected.

In the scenario with Mrs. Garcia, the members of the health care team knew the role of the physician. Despite this understanding, some were more disturbed by the lateness. Members should be willing to extend a degree of respect and understanding toward colleagues based on an appreciation for the services they bring to the health care arena. Attempts should be made to adopt a positive attitude and demonstrate a willingness to believe that the lateness was unintentional. Giving an individual the benefit of the doubt can create an ethos that is conducive to respectful encounters and effective communication. This is to say not that negative behaviors should be overlooked but rather that all members should seek to create positive environments to maintain a climate of mutual respect. That being said, all members of the team should exhibit a respect for each other's time and make great attempts to adhere to scheduled meeting times.

> VE 10: Maintain competence in one's own profession appropriate to scope of practice.

Members of the health professions should engage in role development activities that help to strengthen their ability to provide high-quality care in accordance with their scope of practice. Knowing and sharing information about one's professional role can help to create a climate that supports safe and effective relationships. So how do students model an appreciation for the skills that members of the health care team bring? Being competent in one's own role helps to minimize the risk of devaluing the contributions of others. Thus, students should participate in activities that support life-long learning and adhere to their scope of practice.

Service-based learning is one method that can be used to help foster role development and an appreciation for the skill sets of other members of the team. Collectively, students work toward a common goal and engage in conversations that challenge them to think broadly and consider each member's role in improving patient outcomes.

OPPORTUNITIES AND CHALLENGES TO EVALUATING COMPETENCY

Knowledge

Conflicts that involve interprofessional values and ethics can contribute to high levels of stress in the workplace environment. In addition, value incongruence can occur when members of the group have values that do not align with those of other members of the team. Members of the health professions should know the role of their colleagues and recognize factors that influence their beliefs about others to reduce the risk of jeopardizing interprofessional relationships.

Attitude

Not all students enter school with attitudes that facilitate collaboration and partnerships with members of other professions. Some students may not know how to best model the specific values and ethics competencies. Opportunities that allow students to challenge their beliefs about the professional roles of different disciplines and engage in dialogues that foster positive attitudes can be provided.

Skills

When members of the health professions work together to provide person-centered care, they are presented with both unique opportunities and challenges. The opportunity to learn from each other and share expertise helps to promote positive patient outcomes. Metrics should be used to determine the extent to which members use their skills to create an environment that fosters mutual respect.

CLASSROOM EXERCISES

Having shared values and ethics is essential to establishing an interprofessional identity. The team can only come to develop their interprofessional identity by engaging in a process of exploration and understanding the values and ethics of its members. The following list provides a guide for developing the knowledge, attitudes, and skills associated with achieving competence in values and ethics:

Knowledge
a. Understand the role of your colleagues
b. Recognize the factors that shape your opinion of others
c. Prevent actions that compromise patient confidentiality
d. Know the steps to resolving an ethical dilemma

Attitude
a. Respect the roles and expertise of colleagues
b. Appreciate differences in thoughts and beliefs
c. Believe that patients and colleagues know something that you do not

Skills
a. Engage in activities that help to eliminate biases
b. Create an environment that fosters mutual respect
c. Model behaviors that build effective teams

The following set of reflective questions can help to provide insight into our own internal processes and those of the members of the team and patient:

- What other values do members of the health care team share?
- What behaviors undermine efforts to create a climate that fosters mutual respect? How can members of the team address these issues in an attempt to build effective interprofessional relationships?
- What skills would you use to identify whether you have implicit biases, and how would you address them?
- What advice would you give to peers regarding the effects of bias and how to mitigate bias?
- What type of ethical dilemmas must be addressed in an objective manner that demonstrates professionalism?
- What model would you use to determine the steps in resolving an ethical dilemma?

As the shared values of the team are established it is also important that one of those shared values include a commitment to cultural competency, although no one is ever totally competent regarding every culture. Accreditation guidelines in all the health disciplines typically include standards that address cultural competency to ensure that students are prepared to respond safely to the different cultural beliefs and traditions of the populations they serve. However, being able to model cultural competency should never be limited to just patients or communities. Schools should provide students with opportunities to demonstrate an appreciation for difference and model respect for the unique cultures of members of the health care team as well.

Values and ethics is one of the four core interprofessional collaborative practice competencies. It is believed that providers who are able to model this competency are better positioned to improve the quality of health care. For students to become effective members of the health care team, they must seek opportunities that allow them to learn about shared values and ethics with and from different members of the health professions. Shared values include but are not limited to accountability, approachability, dependability, and fidelity. These values are likely to facilitate positive intergroup relationships.

Activities that include different members of the health team are likely to assist students with developing healthy interprofessional relationships that could transfer to patient–provider relationships. Students and providers should examine the extent to which they uphold the 10 specific competencies that help operationalize the concept of value and ethics.

REFERENCES

Agency for Healthcare, Research, and Quality. (2015). *2014 national healthcare quality & disparities report*. Retrieved from http://www.ahrq.gov/research/findings/nhqrdr/nhqdr14/index.html

Banaji, M. R., & Greenwald, A. G. (2013). *Blindspot: Hidden biases of good people*. New York: Delacorte Press.

Burgess, D., van Ryn, M., Dovidio, J., & Saha, S. (2007). Reducing racial bias among health care providers: Lessons from social-cognitive psychology. *Journal of General Internal Medicine, 22*, 882–887.

Canadian Interprofessional Health Collaborative. (2010, February). *A national interprofessional competency framework*. Retrieved from www.cihc.ca/resources/publications

Centers for Disease Control and Prevention. (2015). *Health equity*. Retrieved from http://www.cdc.gov/chronicdisease/healthequity/

Cross, T., Bazron, B., Dennis, K., & Isaacs, M. (1989). *Towards a culturally competent system of care: A monograph on effective services for minority children who are severely emotionally disturbed*. Washington, DC: Georgetown University Child Development Center, Child and Adolescent Service System Program Technical Assistance Center.

Institute for Healthcare Improvement. (2015). *IHI Triple Aim Initiative*. Retrieved from http://www.ihi.org/engage/initiatives/TripleAim/Pages/default.aspx

Interprofessional Education Collaborative. (2016). *Core competencies for interprofessional collaborative practice: 2016 update.* Washington, DC: Author.

Interprofessional Education Collaborative Expert Panel. (2011). *Core competencies for interprofessional collaborative practice: Report of an expert panel.* Washington, DC: Interprofessional Education Collaborative.

Joint Commission Center for Transforming Healthcare. (2013). *Reducing the risk of wrong site surgery.* Retrieved from http://www.centerfortransforminghealthcare.org/assets/4/6/CTH_WSS_Storyboard_final2011.pdf

4

INTERPROFESSIONAL COMMUNICATION

Kathleen M. Nokes

Case Study: Mrs. Garcia

After being treated and discharged from the hospital for an ischemic stroke a few weeks ago, Maria Garcia arrives for a routine follow-up appointment at an outpatient stroke rehabilitation center. Maria's rehabilitation team is very enthusiastic about her recovery.

INTRODUCTION

Interprofessional communication is the next domain of the general competencies described by the Interprofessional Education Collaborative (IPEC) Expert Panel (2011) and updated five years later (IPEC, 2016) to be covered in this text. The competency states, "Communicate with patients, families, communities, and professionals in health and other fields in a responsive and responsible manner that supports a team approach to the promotion and maintenance of health and the prevention and treatment of disease" (IPEC, 2016, p. 10) (see Appendix A for a complete list of the eight CC subcompetencies). Health and social care–related communication can be conceptualized broadly into two domains: interpersonal and interprofessional communication (Hagemeir, Hess, Hagen, & Sorah, 2014). There are three types of communication: verbal, written, and paraverbal, which refers to the emotions behind our words (Windle &

Warren, n.d.). Language competency evolves from a person's cultural and educational background. Health and social care providers use language from their personal history in conjunction with language from their professional development when they communicate. Within the health care setting, diverse personal languages exist alongside more dominant discipline-specific languages. As part of the professional education processes, students are taught how to communicate according to their role on the health care team. These professional language skills are taught through a variety of strategies (including role modeling and immersion within clinical areas) and evaluated and refined throughout the educational process. It is expected that a beginning professional is competent in the language used by his or her specific professional group.

Interprofessional communication differs from professional communication. The concept emerged from the recognition that the failure of practitioners in different professions to communicate with each other caused significant harm in health care settings. One particularly glaring consequence emerged during the fall of 2014 when an ill person who had recently traveled from a western African country went to the emergency room of a Texas hospital. Although the nurse recorded the recent travel in the electronic health record, that information was not provided in the part of the medical record available to the treating physician. The person was discharged only to return two days later and subsequently die from Ebola. Two nurses who cared for him were also infected with the Ebola virus (Villasenor, 2014). Although the consequences resulting from this communication gap were highly significant, the gap was rather routine. It is not unusual for health and social care providers to neglect reading the notations of other professionals because of a variety of factors in a highly complex health care setting. The domain calls for communication in a responsive and responsible manner, but more than that, it calls for communication that supports a team approach that recognizes that health and social care providers do not work in isolation. Team communication provides a unique window into how the team is functioning (Patterson et al., 2013).

INTERPROFESSIONAL COMMUNICATION COMPETENCIES

The interprofessional communication domain has eight competencies that address the skills required to communicate effectively with different members of the health and social care team.

> CC1: Choose effective communication tools and techniques, including information systems and communication technologies, to facilitate discussions and interactions that enhance team function.

Paper-based medical records are quickly being replaced by electronic medical records (EMRs). To accelerate the adoption and use of health information technology systems, the Health Information Technology for Economic and Clinical Health (HITECH) Act was signed into law as part of the American Recovery and Reinvestment Act of 2009. The HITECH Act authorized the Centers for Medicare and Medicaid Services (CMS) to provide financial incentives to eligible hospitals, Critical Access Hospitals, and eligible professionals to adopt and meaningfully use certified technology to improve patient care (Office of the National Coordinator for Health Information Technology, 2014). The EMR is a digital version of a paper chart that contains all of a patient's medical history from one clinical setting or network (HealthIT.gov, n.d.).

Different health care settings have purchased different EMR systems, which are password protected because the information is highly private and sensitive. Although password protection may promote privacy, it can also serve as a barrier to accessing information when a provider does not have the necessary password. This has been a major challenge for educational systems because students are often not given passwords but need to document care provided. Like any other innovation, widespread adoption of EMRs has been characterized by challenges and obstacles, but it is hoped that the overall benefits will outweigh the limitations. All health and social care providers in the 21st century will use EMRs to communicate. Handwritten narrative notes are being replaced by clicks and links. The Ebola situation in the Texas hospital highlights what can happen when different providers are unable to access different components of the EMR.

The specific EMR system used in a health care setting is often selected by administrators on the basis of a number of variables, including cost and history. EMR companies are frequently purchased by larger companies, which can lead to the introduction of new systems at less than convenient times. These realities within the health care settings of the 21st century need to be recognized. Health and social care providers need to be supported as they integrate use of these electronic systems to communicate between providers and consumers.

One strategy that can promote interprofessional communication is the use of a shared framework for documentation, such as SOAP (subjective, objective, assessment, plan) or SBAR (situation, background, assessment, recommendation) notes. Health and social care providers can continue to use their unique frameworks for profession-specific communication but rely on a more generic framework when interprofessional collaboration is essential. Because the health care setting is active over the 24-hour period, care providers routinely change and patients can be transferred to a number of units within the health care setting. In our case study, Maria Garcia received services in the emergency department and the neurology step-down unit before discharge. When there is a consistent team, team checklists may be helpful in promoting comprehensive health and social care. Chen, Green, and McCollum (2014) described graded team checklists as an effective method for increasing teamwork in an anatomy dissection course in which the team members were stable and the learning objectives relatively controllable. Health care settings are characterized by more fluid teams and great uncertainty generated by the complexity of the patients being served.

Changes in a patient's condition or plan of care need to be communicated in a timely fashion. Traditionally, one-way pagers have been used to contact the provider who is not at the point of care. Use of these pagers has been associated with interrupted patient care, long waiting periods by the phone (either on hold or waiting for the returned call), and missed calls. Whitlow, Drake, Tullmann, Hoke, and Barth (2014) gave smartphones to physicians and nurses on a busy inpatient unit to address these issues. After a two-month period, there was a 79 percent decrease in minutes that the clerical staff spent locating a nurse, a 94 percent decrease in the nurse being away from patient care to answer a call, and a 54 percent decrease in physician time away from task, in addition to the 100 percent decrease in time to travel to answer the call and time spent on hold. These results are promising and point to a setting-wide need for technology that smartly increases provider communication. Other workplaces have adopted communication tools that foster teamwork. The type of sensitive, private information that needs to be communicated within the health care setting requires special adaption (such as encrypted systems) to ensure confidentiality. As decision makers are often not immediately accessible for an in-person consultation, technology is an important consideration. Consumers often use technology such as smartphones to report dissatisfaction with care or long waiting periods. Thus, health and social care providers need to pilot viable solutions that promote team communication through innovation.

> CC2: Communicate information with patients, families, community members, and health team members in a form that is understandable, avoiding discipline-specific terminology when possible.

Social marketing research has found that different cultural groups prefer to receive information through different media. Although there are many definitions of health literacy, the Patient Protection and Affordable Care Act states that health literacy is the degree to which individuals have the skills and competencies needed to obtain, communicate, process, and understand basic health information and services needed in order to make appropriate health decisions (Serensen et al., 2012; Wizemann & Institute of Medicine, 2011). Culture and health literacy need to be considered by the team as they interact with patients and families. Although the health and social care team believed that our case, Maria Garcia, would benefit from inpatient rehabilitation, her immediate family wanted her to be discharged to her home and was willing to make the adjustments needed for her to be successful in regaining function after her stroke.

The Joint Commission accredits health care settings. This accreditation is often tied to federal government health insurance reimbursement through Medicare and Medicaid. Launched in 2002 with the Centers for Medicare and Medicaid Services, the Joint Commission's (n.d.) Speak Up program urges patients to take an active role in preventing health care errors by becoming involved and informed participants of their health care team. The Speak Up program has infographics, brochures, posters, animated videos, and podcasts that can be downloaded for free. This resource could be offered through patient-accessible computers within health care settings. Additionally, posters could be placed in prominent places, which would establish a climate supporting the active involvement of patients and families in care decisions. Communication about this resource could be integrated into a team checklist to ensure that patients and families are aware that the agency has a serious commitment to patient involvement in care decisions.

Hospice teams who care for persons in their last stage of life have relatively consistent provider membership compared with teams within acute health care settings. Factors related to impaired communication with family care providers include the caregiver's impaired concentration, propensity to remain silent, desire not to bother clinicians, rejection of support services, and the timing and amount of information received during an in-person encounter (Wittenberg-Lyles et al., 2013). To address some of these difficulties, Assessing Caregivers for Team Intervention through Video Encounters (ACTIVE) team meetings, in which family caregivers participated virtually through the use of video technology, were compared with regular team meetings (Wittenberg-Lyles et al., 2013). The video conferencing used a secure, encrypted, and password-protected service. The Roter Interaction Analysis System (RIAS), adapted for telemedicine, was used to measure the dialogue. This computerized system is applied to the smallest unit of spoken expression to which a meaningful code can be assigned (Roter & Larson, 2002). These units of spoken expression can be coded into socioemotional talk, which captures the affective dimension, and task-focused behaviors, which include data gathering and patient education and counseling. The participation of all team members significantly changed in ACTIVE compared with standard team meetings for all providers, but there was a significant increase for family caregivers to 41 percent participation in each conversation (Wittenberg-Lyles et al., 2013).

The method of content delivery, such as print or visual media, needs to be based on cultural preferences and health literacy. Health and social care providers have learned about different phenomena through the use of profession-specific terminology and may find it easy to explain the problem using these terms. However, most consumers are not familiar with this language, and terms need to be translated and explained until they are understood.

> CC3: Express one's knowledge and opinions to team members involved in patient care and population health improvement with confidence, clarity, and respect, working to ensure common understanding of information, treatment, care decisions, and population health programs and policies.

Health care settings operating 24 hours a day and seven days a week require creation of patient care teams with highly variable composition. Because the health status of patients is often unstable, planning is difficult. Compared with many other work settings, emergencies do have life-and-death consequences. The range of adverse outcomes includes compromised patient care, sentinel events resulting from medical errors, and staff distress, tension, and inefficiency (Weller, Boyd, & Cumin, 2014). Gaps in interprofessional communication are not surprising in this chaotic context. Hills (2013) identified 10 common barriers to effective team communication: (1) physical separation and lack of contact among team members, (2) gender differences, (3) generational differences, (4) cultural diversity, (5) language differences, (6) differences in values and beliefs, (7) lack of trust, (8) noise, (9) information overload, and (10) personal biases and prejudices. Patients and families often express frustration with the inability to identify the team member who can provide needed information. Although the competency of expressing one's knowledge and opinions seems simple, figuring out which members are on the team and can use the information being communicated can be more challenging. Mrs. Garcia's team consisted of representatives from medicine, nursing, social work, physical therapy, occupational therapy, speech therapy, and the business office. Each of those professional groups have their own language and preferred ways of interacting. Once Mrs. Garcia's health status stabilized, the team was able to meet to identify discharge plans. However, because family input was not actively sought, the identified plan needed to be amended.

CC4: Listen actively, and encourage ideas and opinions of other team members.

This competency can best be achieved in an organization that supports open communication. Morrison (2014) proposed a model of antecedents and outcomes of employee voice and silence (p. 185) that identified the complexity of team communication. She argued that voice and silence are two responses to the same opportunity. A team member may be aware of a problem or opportunity and have an idea, concern, or perspective that might be relevant to share or important to convey. Motivation affects whether the team member voices input or remains silent. Morrison also identified a number of variables that can motivate or inhibit voice, specifically individual dispositions; job and organizational attitudes and perceptions; emotions, beliefs, and schemas; supervisor and leader behavior; and other contextual factors, such as group voice climate, caring climate, and formal voice mechanisms.

Team leaders can support development of this competency by creating environments that support motivators of voice rather than silence. Meetings can be structured to ensure that each team member has the opportunity to provide input and contribute to the discussion and that silence is clarified and emerges from not having anything additional to contribute.

CC5: Give timely, sensitive, instructive feedback to others about their performance on the team, responding respectfully as a team member to feedback from others.

Health and social care provider students receive regular formative assessments as they learn new roles and acquire knowledge and skills. Faculty are cognizant about how to give instructive feedback, and grading rubrics are increasingly used to promote consistency and clarity about course expectations. Once the person transitions into a professional role and is employed by a health care setting, these frequent opportunities for instructive feedback often become episodic and associated with adverse behaviors. Formal evaluation periods may be mandated by personnel procedures, but these periods are often associated with increasing compensation and status. The opportunity for informal evaluation is often superseded by more urgent, patient-centered, or organizational needs. The transition period from novice to expert practitioner is often characterized as being lost in a forest with few guideposts. There are assumptions that the novice is receiving feedback, but there are few organizational structures to support regular formative evaluations. Conferences are usually called when there are gaps in expectations. Changes in organizational ownership frequently occur as more extensive health care delivery systems are created through mergers with smaller institutions. For practitioners with extensive experience, this often results in greater expectations. There is no doubt that regular implementation of this competency by teams would benefit everyone, but the method of operationalizing this expectation is unclear.

Research could be used to assess team communication processes in a relatively neutral, objective way that could identify the complexity of team communication along with its strengths and gaps. Social network analysis (SNA) graphically depicts patterns of team communication and interaction and generates statistics that quantify communication between team members (Patterson et al., 2013). Three standard measures can be computed to characterize the structural patterns of communication flow: network density, network centralization, and in-degree centralization. Network density acts as an overall measure of interaction as it measures affiliation between team members; centralization measures the concentration of communication within the team, with low centralization indicating greater communication among team members; and in-degree centrality ranks individuals on the basis of their position and influence on the team.

SNA has been used by different researchers to examine interprofessional communication in a variety of discrete services within the health care setting. Patterson et al. (2013), who examined team communication in an emergency department across the 24-hour period over eight weeks, found great variation based on team composition and time of day and concluded that much about communication in the emergency department is unknown. Mundt et al. (2015) used SNA to examine team communication in primary care settings for patients with cardiovascular disease. They identified a team leader as the health care provider (physician, nurse practitioner, or physician assistant) who prescribed treatment. The median team size was 19 members, and other than the team leader, team members belonged to four teams on average. The researchers found that teams with a higher density of face-to-face interactions and lower centralization were associated with better quality of care and an average of $594 less spent in patient costs over the preceding 12 months.

Pinelli, Papp, and Gonzalo (2015) used SNA to analyze team communication during the process of discharging a person from a hospital-based medicine unit. They found that an average of 11 different roles were required in the interaction with the patient. These roles were related to medicine, nursing, social work, transport, and case management, and different people in those roles conversed with the patient being discharged. Pinelli et al. (2015) screened 46 patients for inclusion in the network analysis and found that only seven patients were fully oriented and able to complete an interview. The number of different providers in different roles with different goals seen on the day of discharge as identified in the SNA research illuminates the chaos. Although a complex research method, SNA is shining light onto the complexity of team communication, a light that is needed to develop and pilot effective interventions. Health care facilities might have increased motivation to focus on communication during the day of discharge because for some conditions readmissions into an acute care facility within 30 days after discharge are no longer being reimbursed by Medicare. Communication gaps or overload are probably adding to the rehospitalizations because patients find themselves at home, getting sicker, and confused about next steps.

CC6: Use respectful language appropriate for a given difficult situation, crucial conversation, or interprofessional conflict.

Health care teams with multiple professions need to anticipate that conflict will occur. Team science has demonstrated that how conflict is managed may have more influence on tensions and ongoing relationships than the conflict itself. Maxwell, Odu-koya, Stone, and Chui (2014) conducted a qualitative study with pharmacists and physi-cians and found that most of the conflicts arose from the context of real-life challenges facing health care professionals, including scarce resources (time and information), technology design and usability, insurance constraints, and laws and policy governing patient care. Using respectful language can be difficult when the team is overwhelmed by frustrating, adverse outcomes that seem particularly unfair or unjust. However, if team members do not speak respectfully, the focus of the conflict will drift from the fundamental cause of the conflict (which could be, for example, laws or policies gov-erning patient care) and onto the disrespectful behavior of a frustrated team member.

> CC7: Recognize how one's own uniqueness, including experience level, exper-tise, culture, power, and hierarchy within the health team, contributes to effec-tive communication, conflict resolution, and positive interprofessional working relationships (University of Toronto, 2008).

Team members who are committed to provision of quality patient care and pro-motion of safe environments bring their unique contributions to team processes to promote conflict resolution and team productivity. These team members could be considered as boundary objects that are plastic enough to adapt to both local needs and the constraints of several parties using them, yet robust enough to maintain a common identity. Keshet, Ben-Arye, and Schiff (2013) used the concept of boundary actors to denote individuals who mediated between incommensurable paradigms in the context of power differences arising from practices of complementary and conventional health care. Communication at the edge of the boundaries between professionals and between caregivers and patients can be challenging and require skillful and empathetic risk-takers.

> CC8: Communicate the importance of teamwork in patient-centered care and population health programs and policies.

In contrast to the communication gaps related to the Ebola outbreak in 2014, the *New York Times* extensively reported on how teams caring for persons who experienced a heart attack have reduced mortality by 38 percent over a 10-year period through seam-less communication (Kolata, 2015). The article makes a point to emphasize that the new care standards have been implemented not only in famous institutions or major medical centers but also in community hospitals far from population centers and set-tings serving economically depressed areas where patients had multiple comorbidities. These teams spanned institutional and professional boundaries with a mutual target of time to open up a clogged heart artery, thus providing an easily measurable outcome. Either the goal of approximately one hour from heart attack to reopened blood supply was reached, or teams could analyze breaches in reaching the goal. The visibility given to this success points to the value that consumers give to health and social care provid-ers' ability to save their lives and improve their quality of life.

In summary, interprofessional communication is at the heart of team functioning. High-functioning teams reduce adverse outcomes and costs and improve quality of care. Although the need for interprofessional collaboration has been recognized for more than 40 years, most practicing health and social care providers are educated in silos. Although interventions can be most effectively targeted toward preprofessional students, knowledge and skills will regress if these students go on to practice in settings where communication is not facilitated.

STRATEGIES TO DEVELOP COMPETENCIES

Preprofessional

Hagemeir et al. (2014) described a two-credit interprofessional communication course completed by medical, nursing, and pharmacy students at East Tennessee State University. During the spring of 2012, 192 medical, nursing, clinical psychology, and second-year pharmacy students were enrolled in this course. Teaching strategies included creation of interprofessional small groups that had regular graded assignments and facilitation by faculty from the different disciplines. Faculty participated in a three-hour pre-course training workshop that addressed small group mediation and formative and summative assessment. Videos, standardized patient cases, and objective structured clinical examinations were some of the strategies used in this blended course. Student evaluations demonstrated that the biweekly blended learning interpersonal and interprofessional communication skills course positively affected communication self-efficacy of medical, nursing, and pharmacy students.

Simulation is another strategy used to teach interprofessional communication skills and often includes the use of mannequins and standardized actors along with cases. Brock et al. (2013) described how medical, nursing, pharmacy, and physician assistant students ($N = 306$) participated in a four-day interprofessional team capstone experience. Students could choose from an acute adult, pediatric, or obstetric case and, as a group, participated in a didactic session and three simulated exercises. The organizing framework focused on safety and the researchers developed evaluation instruments around safe health care delivery. Communication-related attitudes significantly improved after the capstone experience.

Practicing Providers

Root cause analysis is a structured method used by a multidisciplinary team to analyze the sequence of events leading to the error that caused a serious adverse event (Agency for Healthcare Research and Quality, n.d.). The focus is on uncovering the multiple factors that led to the event rather than placing blame on one individual or department. Gaps in interprofessional communication are often associated with serious adverse events, and one strategy to closing these gaps is the focus on interprofessional communication. Through the Agency for Healthcare Research and Quality, the federal government developed TeamSTEPPS. This evidence-based program was developed to improve safety within health care settings. Communication is an essential component of the program, which includes the development of a communication plan outlining what will be done and how the goal of improved patient safety will be achieved. The Web page provides resources on training and how health care settings have implemented TeamSTEPPS (http://teamstepps.ahrq.gov/about-2cl_3.htm).

Different strategies, such as bedside interprofessional rounds, have been described. During these rounds, the team of providers discusses the case at the bedside with the patient. Researchers (Gonzalo, Wolpaw, Lehman, & Chuang, 2014) did not assess the quality of the team–patient interactions but noted that two-thirds of the patients received interprofessional rounding for an average of eight minutes.

Although there is no denying that safety within health care settings could be improved, the vast majority of consumers receive evidence-based care. Health and social care providers have established patterns of communication over time, and it is somewhat unrealistic to expect a total paradigm shift. Although status-based communication models (Matzke, Houston, Fischer, & Bradshaw, 2014) may be less than collegial, they are comfortable, familiar, and somewhat effective in arriving at a clear treatment decision. As in most other situations, issues occur when a team member dominates and verbally abuses his or her colleagues and more specifically the team members (Budin, Brewer, Chao, & Kovner, 2013). This verbal abuse has been described as bullying and seems to be widespread within health care settings at a variety of levels. In light of the complexity of team communication, research is needed to elucidate the patterns so that appropriate solutions can be suggested.

Anthoine, Delmas, Coutherut, and Moret (2014) described the development of a short, easily administered tool to measure the sharing of medical information and interprofessional communication. The 13-item communication and sharing of information (CSI) scale measures elements of interprofessional communication between medical and nursing staff with items such as *physicians and nurses share medical information received from or delivered to the patient.* This item would not be rated highly by the nurses and physicians treating the Texas Ebola patient during the first visit to the emergency department. Although CSI assesses communication only about clinical information, additional tools could be developed that include a broader representation of the interprofessional team.

Communication emerges from interpersonal and interprofessional factors. Interpersonal factors can facilitate or alienate communication and need to be considered in models that support open expression. Professional factors can affect communication by reflecting role expectations, including who leads the team, who truly knows the patient, and who is most respectful of the patient's wishes. Adoption of less competitive, more collaborative communication strategies might benefit not only the patient and family but also health and social care providers.

REFERENCES

Agency for Healthcare Research and Quality. (n.d.). *Root cause analysis: Background.* Retrieved from http://psnet.ahrq.gov/primer.aspx?primerID=10

Anthoine, E., Delmas, C., Coutherut, J., & Moret, L. (2014). Development and psychometric testing of a scale assessing the sharing of medical information and interprofessional communication: The CSI scale. *BMC Health Services Research, 14*, 126. Retrieved from http:www.biomedcentral.com/1472-6963/14/126

Brock, D., Abu-Rish, E., Chiu, C., Hammer, D., Wilson, S., Vorvick, L., et al. (2013). Interprofessional education in team communication: Working together to improve patient safety. *Quality and Safety in Health Care, 22*, 414–423.

Budin, W., Brewer, C., Chao, Y., & Kovner, C. (2013). Verbal abuse from nurse colleagues and work environment of early career registered nurses. *Journal of Nursing Scholarship, 45*, 308–316.

Chen, D., Green, S., & McCollum, M. (2014). Practicing standardized team communication in the anatomy laboratory. *Medical Education, 48*, 1109–1110.

Gonzalo, J., Wolpaw, D., Lehman, E., & Chuang, G. (2014). Patient-centered interprofessional collaborative care: Factors associated with bedside interprofessional rounds. *Journal of General Internal Medicine, 29*, 1040–1047.

Hagemeir, N., Hess, R., Hagen, K., & Sorah, E. (2014). Impact of an interprofessional communication course on nursing, medical, and pharmacy students' communication skill self-efficacy. *American Journal of Pharmaceutical Education, 78*(10), Article 186.

HealthIT.gov. (n.d.). *What is an electronic medical record (EMR)?* Retrieved from http://www.healthit.gov/providers-professionals/electronic-medical-records-emr

Hills, L. (2013, September/October). Overcoming the 10 most common barriers to effective team communication. *Medical Practice Management*, pp. 99–103.

Interprofessional Education Collaborative. (2016). *Core competencies for interprofessional collaborative practice: 2016 update.* Washington, DC: Author.

Interprofessional Education Collaborative Expert Panel. (2011). *Core competencies for interprofessional collaborative practice: Report of an expert panel.* Washington, DC: Interprofessional Education Collaborative.

Joint Commission. (n.d.). *Speak Up initiatives.* Retrieved from http://www.jointcommission.org/speakup.aspx

Keshet, Y., Ben-Arye, E., & Schiff, E. (2013). The use of boundary objects to enhance interprofessional collaboration: Integrating complementary medicine in a hospital setting. *Sociology of Health and Illness, 35*, 666–681.

Kolata, G. (2015, June 21). Racing the clock, saving the heart: Faster care helps death rate plunge 38% in decade. *New York Times*, pp. 1, 14–15.

Matzke, B., Houston, S., Fischer, U., & Bradshaw, M. (2014). Using a team-centered approach to evaluate effectiveness of nurse-physical communications. *Journal of Obstetric, Gynecologic & Neonatal Nursing, 43*, 684–694.

Maxwell, L., Odukoya, O., Stone, J., & Chui, M. (2014). Using a conflict conceptual framework to describe challenges to coordinated patient care from the physicians' and pharmacists' perspective. *Research in Social and Administrative Pharmacy, 10*, 824–836.

Morrison, E. (2014). Employee voice and silence. *Annual Review of Organizational Psychology and Organizational Behavior, 1*, 173–197.

Mundt, M., Gilchrist, V., Fleming, M., Zakletskaia, L., Tuan, W., & Beasley, J. (2015). Effects of primary care team social networks on quality of care and costs for patients with cardiovascular disease. *Annals of Family Medicine, 13*, 139–148.

Office of the National Coordinator for Health Information Technology. (2014). *Update on the adoption of health information technology and related efforts to facilitate the electronic use and exchange of health information.* Retrieved from http://www.healthit.gov/sites/default/files/rtc_adoption_and_exchange9302014.pdf

Patterson, P., Pfeiffer, A., Weaver, M., Krackhardt, D., Arnold, R., Yealy, D., & Lave, J. (2013). Network analysis of team communication in a busy emergency department. *BMC Health Services Research, 13,* 109–121.

Pinelli, V., Papp, K., & Gonzalo, J. (2015). Interprofessional communication patterns during patient discharge: A social network analysis. *Journal of General Internal Medicine, 30,* 1299–1306.

Roter, D., & Larson, S. (2002). The Roter Interaction Analysis System (RIAS): Utility and flexibility for analysis of medical interactions. *Patient Education and Counseling, 46,* 243–251.

Serensen, K., van Broucke, S., Fullam, J., Doyle, G., Pelikan, J., Slonska, Z., & Brand, H., for (HLS-EU) Consortium Health Literacy Project European. (2012). Health literacy and public health: A systematic review and integration of definitions and models. *BMC Public Health, 12*(1), 80. doi:10.1186/1471-2458-12-80

University of Toronto. (2008). *Advancing the interprofessional education curriculum 2009. Curriculum overview. Competency framework.* Toronto: University of Toronto, Office of Interprofessional Education.

Villasenor, J. (2014, October 3). Five things the Texas Ebola case can teach us about critical infrastructure security. *Forbes.* Retrieved from http://www.forbes.com/sites/johnvillasenor/2014/10/03/five-things-the-texas-ebola-case-can-teach-us-about-critical-infrastructure-security/

Weller, J., Boyd, M., & Cumin, D. (2014). Teams, tribes, and patient safety: Overcoming barriers to effective teamwork in healthcare. *Journal of Postgraduate Medicine, 90,* 149–154.

Whitlow, M., Drake, E., Tullmann, D., Hoke, G., & Barth, D. (2014). Bringing technology to the bedside using smartphones to improve interprofessional communication. *Computers, Informatics, Nursing, 32,* 305–311.

Windle, R., & Warren, S. (n.d.) *Communication skills.* Retrieved from http://www.directionservice.org/cadre/section4.cfm

Wittenberg-Lyles, E., Oliver, D., Kruse, R., Demiris, G., Gage, L., & Wagner, K. (2013). Family caregiver participation in hospice interdisciplinary team meetings: How does it affect the nature and content of communication? *Health Communication, 28,* 110–118.

Wizemann, T. M., and Institute of Medicine. (2011). *Health literacy implications for health care reform: Workshop summary.* Washington, DC: National Academies Press.

5

ROLES AND RESPONSIBILITIES

Teri Kennedy

Case Study: Mrs. Garcia

During her transportation to the hospital Mrs. Garcia meets a number of professionals who either do not bother to introduce themselves to her or ignore her multiple requests for someone to explain what is happening to her. The family members of Mrs. Garcia are also given little explanation of who the various professionals are and what their roles are in Mrs. Garcia's care.

This case illustrates a lack of providing the patient and family with a clear understanding of the roles and responsibilities of the health care team, and the importance of ensuring that patients and their family members understand the roles and responsibilities of each of the professionals involved in care.

INTRODUCTION

Interprofessional collaborative practice requires an understanding of the roles and responsibilities of all members of the team. As evidence supports the crucial relationship between teamwork and the quality and safety of patient care (Manser, 2009), "nowhere is the need for teamwork more relevant than in the healthcare arena" (Weiss, Tilin, & Morgan, 2014, p. 4). Practitioners must possess and be able to demonstrate essential knowledge, skills, and values to work effectively as members of health care teams. They must also be proficient in competencies involving four core domains in interprofessional collaborative team practice: values and ethics, roles and responsibilities,

53

interprofessional communication, and teamwork and team-based practice (Interprofessional Education Collaborative [IPEC], 2016). This chapter will focus on the core competency domain of roles and responsibilities.

CORE AND SUBCOMPETENCIES

Health professionals must be able to "use the knowledge of one's own role and those of other professions to appropriately assess and address the healthcare needs of patients and to promote and advance the health of populations" (IPEC, 2016, p. 10) to demonstrate competency related to roles and responsibilities for interprofessional practice. There are 10 subcompetencies related to the general IPEC competency for roles and responsibilities (see Appendix A for the full list of the RR subcompetencies).

RR1: Communicate one's roles and responsibilities clearly to patients, families, community members, and other professionals.

To use this knowledge effectively, health professionals must first be able to recognize and possess an in-depth understanding of their own role and the roles of other members of the interprofessional team. This involves the development of both professional and interprofessional competencies that demonstrate particular "knowledge, skills, and values/attitudes" (IPEC Expert Panel, 2011, p. 2). The focus for *professional competencies* is to understand the role of a health profession within a specific context of care, whereas the focus for *interprofessional competencies* is to understand roles across and between health professionals as well as with patients, families, and communities "as appropriate to improve health outcomes in specific care contexts" (IPEC Expert Panel, 2011, p. 2).

RR2: Recognize one's limitations in skills, knowledge, and abilities.

In addition to recognizing the primary roles and responsibilities of members of the interprofessional team, it is also important to recognize the boundaries circumscribed by these roles. Understanding and communicating roles and role boundaries can help the interprofessional team work together more effectively in the provision of care. See RR5 for a discussion of clues to role boundaries.

RR3: Engage diverse professionals who complement one's own professional expertise, as well as associated resources, to develop strategies to meet specific health and healthcare needs of patients and populations.

RR4: Explain the roles and responsibilities of other providers and how the team works together to provide care, promote health, and prevent disease.

Collaboration begins by taking the time to learn as much as possible about other professions (Grant, Finoccio, & California Primary Care Consortium Subcommittee on

Interdisciplinary Collaboration, 1995). Demonstrating competency in the knowledge of the role of other health professionals has been linked to successful collaborative team practice (MacDonald, Bally, Ferguson, Murray, & Fowler-Kerry, 2010) and involves specific behavioral indicators. A professional who is competent in this domain

- describes where the scope of one's own profession ends and another begins
- is open to/seeks out the contributions of other team members
- addresses misconceptions/stereotypes among team members
- respects the roles, expertise, and unique contributions of other team members
- identifies common/overlapping professional skills amongst team members
- values the enhanced benefits of the collaborative efforts of the team
- describes the different perspectives and knowledge of other professions. (MacDonald et al., 2010, p. 239)

This requires first identifying which health professions are members of a given health care team.

MEMBERS OF THE INTERPROFESSIONAL TEAM

A wide range of professionals perform a role in health care. Members of the team may vary depending on the "goals and tasks of the team" (Grant et al., 1995, p. 23), disciplines and skills required for each practice setting (p. 46), and needs of individuals and populations served. Team members may include (in alphabetical order), but are not limited to, an audiologist, counselor, dental hygienist, dentist, dietician, direct care worker, medical assistant, nurse practitioner, occupational therapist, pharmacist, physical therapist, physician (doctor of medicine or of osteopathy), physician assistant, psychiatrist, registered nurse, social worker, and speech–language pathologist. Those members considered core to the interprofessional team will vary by setting and be adjusted based on a patient's needs. To introduce the general and specific competencies related to roles and responsibilities and related concepts, this chapter will focus on the roles of members of the interprofessional team found in primary care settings.

Primary care is "the provision of integrated, accessible health care services by clinicians who are accountable for addressing a large majority of personal health care needs, developing a sustained partnership with patients, and practicing in the context of family and community" (Institute of Medicine [IOM], 1996, p. 8). It is useful to think of teams as including core members who "regularly function together on a full-time basis" or *extended* or *consulting* members who may contribute "important skills and services on an intermittent basis" (Grant et al., 1995, p. 46). Once the makeup of the core and extended team has been determined, it is important for members to learn about each other's "role expectations" (p. 46) as well as the "skills and training of other team members" (p. 50), especially during the early stages of team development or when there is a change of team membership or composition.

CORE MEMBERS OF THE PRIMARY CARE TEAM

The first and foremost member of any health care team, regardless of setting, is the patient. It is important to remember that the patient is the person who is the center and main focus of the team. *Patient-centered care* "is an approach to delivering care which advocates that patients and their relatives are located at the centre of the care-giving process" (Reeves, Lewin, Espin, & Zwarenstein, 2010, p. 9). It involves providing care that is respectful of, responsive to, and guided by individual patient preferences, needs, and values (IOM, 2001). Although this approach keeps the patient at the center of care, language matters. Referring to a person as a "patient" can relegate him or her to a single role and discourage health care professionals from viewing the person's roles and relationships holistically.

In a person-centered, participant-directed approach to care, the patient is viewed holistically and is empowered to be an active participant in his or her health and behavioral health care. Each person plays a critical role as active participant in his or her own self-care and as the source of information about the unique experience of his or her own health. People serve as "the experts in their own life" and "the best source to identify their own strengths, needs, and preferences" (National Resource Center for Participant-Directed Services, 2012, p. 1). Individuals' responsibilities include describing their perceptions of their own health; reporting changes in their health over time; sharing their responses to self-care, recommended treatments, and interventions; and discussing factors that foster or hinder their adherence to care recommendations, treatments, and interventions.

In a person-centered approach to care, the patient's family is also a key partner and member of the health care team. The family serves in a supportive role, providing social and emotional support. The family or a nonrelative may also serve a primary role as a caregiver to the person at the center of care. Taking the simple steps of identifying the family or informal caregivers, involving them in discussions about the person's care, and working with them to ensure that they understand and can demonstrate the ability to provide needed care can go a long way to support successful care and care transitions.

MEMBERS OF THE INTERPROFESSIONAL PRIMARY CARE TEAM

In addition to the person and his or her family, members of the interprofessional primary care team (in alphabetical order) typically include a counselor, medical assistant, nurse practitioner, pharmacist, physician, physician's assistant, registered nurse, and social worker. As a result of the "increasing breadth and complexity" of health care and the multifaceted and chronic care needs of people served by the health care system, extended members of the primary care team may also include a dentist, dietician, occupational therapist, pharmacist, physical therapist, and podiatrist, as well as a range of other allied health professionals (Grant et al., 1995, p. vi). Each team member has a principal role or roles and a unique educational background depending on their professional orientation. The principal role and educational background of the core and representative extended members of the primary care team are discussed in the following paragraphs (also see Table 5.1).

The role of mental health counselor is to foster "change and problem resolution" related to behavioral health and substance use disorders through a combination of traditional psychotherapy, problem-solving strategies, psychoeducation, prevention, and crisis management services. Education includes a master's degree in counseling or related mental health field, a minimum of two years post-master's supervised clinical experience, and state or national licensure (American Mental Health Counselors Association, n.d., para. 1).

A medical assistant (MA) serves as a "patient liaison . . . helping patients feel at ease" (American Association of Medical Assistants, 1996–2015, para. 4) at the primary care site and explains the instructions of the primary care provider. MAs are trained to perform both administrative and clinical duties. They obtain medical histories, prepare patients for examination, collect and prepare laboratory specimens, carry out basic laboratory tests and procedures such as suture removal and dressing changes, and explain treatment procedures. MAs graduate from a nationally accredited certificate or associate's-level medical assisting program, complete a supervised practicum, and pass a national certification exam.

The principal roles for the nurse practitioner (NP) are to conduct patient assessments; order, perform, and interpret diagnostic tests; diagnose and treat acute and chronic conditions; prescribe medications; manage the patients' overall care; provide counseling; and educate patients on "disease prevention and positive health and lifestyle choices" (American Association of Nurse Practitioners, 2012–2015, para. 5). Education includes a master's or doctoral degree, advanced clinical training, and state licensure.

The role of the pharmacist is "to achieve positive outcomes from the use of medication which improves patients' quality of life with minimum risk" (American Association of Colleges of Pharmacy, 2015, para. 3). Education includes a doctoral degree, state licensure, and examination (Bureau of Labor Statistics, 2014–2015a).

"A primary care physician is a specialist in Family Medicine, Internal Medicine or Pediatrics" who provides comprehensive first contact and continuing care that "may include chronic, preventive and acute care" (American Academy of Family Physicians, 2016) for individuals with a range of symptoms and health issues. The physician's roles include promoting and maintaining health, preventing disease, diagnosing and treating acute and chronic conditions, as well as providing patient education and counseling. Education includes a doctoral degree, internship, residency programs, national examination, and state licensure (Bureau of Labor Statistics, 2014–2015b, 2016).

The principal roles of the physician assistant are to complete medical histories; conduct physical exams; provide preventive care counseling; facilitate testing, diagnosis, and treatment of illnesses; develop treatment plans; and prescribe medications (American Academy of Physician Assistants, n.d.). Education includes three years of academic training, including the completion of medical school prerequisite courses, clinical rotations, national certification, and state licensure.

The role of the registered nurse (RN) includes health promotion, care coordination, counseling, and education. The RN completes medical histories, conducts physical exams, and administers "personalized interventions," including medications and wound

Table 5.1: Professional Roles

Team Member	Role(s)
Counselor	Fosters change and problem resolution related to behavioral health and substance use disorders through a combination of traditional psychotherapy, problem-solving strategies, psychoeducation, prevention, and crisis management services.
Family	Provides social and emotional support and caregiving.
Medical assistant	Serves as a patient liaison helping patients feel at ease in the physician's office and often explaining the physician's instructions. Obtains medical histories, prepares patients for examination, collects and prepares laboratory specimens, carries out basic laboratory tests and procedures, and explains treatment procedures.
Nurse practitioner	Conducts patient assessments; orders, performs, and interprets diagnostic tests; diagnoses and treats acute and chronic conditions; prescribes medications; manages patients' overall care; counsels and educates patients on disease prevention and positive health and lifestyle choices.
Occupational therapist	Helps people function in all of their environments, including home, work, school, and community, and addresses the physical, psychological, and cognitive aspects of their well-being through engagement in everyday activities or occupation.
Patient	Active participant in his or her own self-care and source of information about the unique experience of his or her own health.
Pharmacist	Achieves positive outcomes from the use of medication, which improves patients' quality of life with minimum risk.
Physician	Promotes and maintains health, prevents disease, diagnoses and treats acute and chronic conditions, and provides patient education and counseling.
Physician assistant	Takes medical histories, conducts physical exams, diagnoses and treats illnesses, orders and interprets tests, develops treatment plans, counsels on preventive care, and writes prescriptions.
Registered nurse	Provides health promotion, care coordination, counseling, and education; gathers health histories; conducts physical exams; and administers personalized interventions, including medications and wound care.
Social worker	Facilitates coping with life stressors, illness, and disability and promotes treatment compliance through prevention, health promotion, community referrals, care coordination, psychoeducation, wellness coaching, counseling, and support.

care (American Nurses Association [ANA], 2015b). Education includes an associate's or bachelor's degree, national examination, and state licensure (ANA, 2015a).

Last but not least, as a member of the core primary care team, the social worker facilitates coping with life stressors, illness, and disability through "interventions to deal with personal, interpersonal, and environmental barriers" (Vourlekis, Ell, & Padgett, 2001, p. 184). Principal roles include prevention, health promotion, community referrals, care coordination, wellness coaching, counseling, and support (DeBonis, n.d., slide 10). Social workers also serve as behavioral health consultants facilitating relaxation and stress reduction, pain management, cognitive interventions, and patient education (Collins, 2012). Although a master's degree, internship, examination, and state licensure are required to practice social work in primary care and integrated medical and behavioral health settings (Bureau of Labor Statistics, 2014–2015c), care coordination in the community may be facilitated by an individual with a bachelor's degree in social work.

Extended team members may include the occupational and physical therapist, as well as other allied health professionals. The occupational therapist (OT) helps individuals "function in all of their environments," including "home, work, school, [and] community" (American Occupational Therapy Association [AOTA], 2015b, para. 2). The OT focuses on the "physical, psychological, and cognitive aspects of . . . well-being through engagement [in] . . . occupation" or everyday activities (AOTA, 2015b, para. 2). Education includes a master's or doctoral degree, field experience, national certification exam, and state licensure (AOTA, 2015a).

As an extended member of the primary care team, the physical therapist (PT) works with individuals who have "conditions that limit their abilities to move and perform functional activities in their daily lives" (American Physical Therapy Association [APTA], 2015b, para. 1). The PT facilitates treatments that "promote the ability to move, reduce pain, restore function, and prevent disability" and helps to prevent "loss of mobility" through fitness and wellness programs (APTA, 2015b, para. 2). Education includes a doctoral degree and state licensure (APTA, 2015a).

RR5: Use the full scope of knowledge, skills, and abilities of professionals from health and other fields to provide care that is safe, timely, efficient, effective, and equitable.

There are a variety of sources that can help members of the health care team further define the boundaries of their professional roles and responsibilities and those of other members of the interprofessional team.

CLUES TO ROLE BOUNDARIES

As a starting point, it is important to understand *scope of practice*, or the breadth of responsibilities and practice guidelines that circumscribe the boundaries within which each professional practices. Such an understanding helps professionals ascertain role boundaries and discover how those boundaries relate to those of other members of the primary care team. Scope of practice identifies the type of patients with whom each profession works and standards that guide practice; defines the extent and limits of the health or behavioral health interventions that each profession can perform; and describes the procedures, actions, and processes that practitioners are permitted to undertake ("Scope of Practice," 2002).

Clues to determine and define scope of practice for members of the primary care team may be found in accreditation standards, professional competencies, codes of ethics, and licensure standards. Additional clues can be gathered by reviewing liability considerations and exploring practice context. Each of these sources will be addressed individually (also see Figure 5.1).

Accreditation standards of the schools or programs in which a health professions student is enrolled or from which health professionals graduate provide an initial clue to determine role boundaries related to scope of practice. Accreditation is a process by which an educational institution demonstrates that it has met specific requirements that can be formally evaluated by an official review board or organization ("Accreditation," 2003). If these requirements have been met, the educational institution is granted the ability to offer a degree that meets a set of standards for each given profession. Examples of accrediting bodies include the Liaison Committee on Medical Education, American Association of Colleges of Nursing, Commission on Collegiate Nursing Education, and Council on Social Work Education.

Professional competencies, another clue to role boundaries, differentiate an academic degree from a professional degree and establish the level of proficiency in

Figure 5.1: Scope of Practice
© Teri Kennedy, 2016, Aisling West Publishing. Used by permission.

knowledge, attitudes, and skills that must be demonstrated for students in each health discipline to graduate from an accredited professional school or program ("Professional Competence," 2009). Competencies may be exhibited through course work and simulation exercises or demonstrated through internships and clinical rotations. The competencies required for each team member can be identified by reviewing the accreditation standards that apply to each health profession or discipline. Competencies vary by profession, degree level, and specialization.

In addition to accreditation standards and professional competencies, each health profession has a code of ethics that aids in determining the boundaries of professional roles and responsibilities ("Code of Ethics," 2009). A code of ethics is a set of principles that facilitates professional decision making in choosing between right and wrong. As ethical decisions are not strictly black and white and professional practice can be fraught with ethical dilemmas, a code of ethics provides guidance when there is not a clear course of action for a given situation. Ethical guidance related to roles and responsibilities can be found under standards that guide practitioners to practice only within their areas of competence.

Licensure standards provide another clue to the boundaries of roles and responsibilities for members of the interprofessional team ("Licensure," 2003). Each profession has a set of standards that relates to professional licensure, certification, and credentials. Licensure standards exist at the state level, are regulated by state-level boards that oversee various professions, and may vary by state. Some professions have national licensure standards that apply across states in addition to specialized credentials. Examples of licensing bodies include the American Counseling Association, Federation of State Medical Boards, American Medical Association, National Council of State Boards of Nursing, Federation of State Boards of Physical Therapy, and Association of Social Work Boards.

Liability considerations provide additional insight into understanding boundaries of professional roles and responsibilities. Health professionals are guided by and practice in environments that require compliance with applicable health care laws, rules, and regulations that vary depending on the type of facility, whether a hospital, outpatient clinic, skilled nursing facility, or private practice. Liability involves legal responsibility for one's acts or omissions. Failure to meet these responsibilities can result in malpractice involving negligence or misconduct ("Liability," 2008), which includes operating outside of appropriate professional roles and responsibilities or scope of practice.

Care is not provided in a vacuum. It is always provided within a context. This practice context includes five factors: the biography and history of the person and family, culture and history of the community, health care setting, model of care delivery, and practice location. Each of these factors will be reviewed as they relate to practice context. Practice context is informed by what sociologist C. Wright Mills (1959) referred to as the *sociological imagination*, which "enables us to grasp history and biography and the relations between the two within society" (p. 6). From the perspective of person-centered care, this includes the unique biography and history of the person who is receiving care, as well as that of the person's family. Biography includes all of the biological, psychological, social, and spiritual factors related to the individual and the family, including their culture. History refers to the historical period in which that individual and family lives, including relevant historical events.

Community culture and history is another important consideration that relates to practice context. This includes socioeconomic, cultural, and historical factors. The culture and history of the community as it relates to health care may provide a clue to the presence of health disparities that may need to be considered. Understanding community culture is also important to identifying who else might be an appropriate member of the interprofessional team, such as a community health worker or *promotora*, or a folk medicine healer such as a *curandero*.

Practice context also includes the health care setting, practice site, and facility type in which patient care is provided, such as the physician's office, community clinic, or home. It is more than just the building in which care is provided. It also includes the personnel who provide care, the service delivery facilities, and the "educational and environmental facilities that work to help prevent disease" (Barker, 2003, as cited in National Association of Social Workers, 2005, p. 12).

The practice location also includes the geographic locale in which health care is being provided. The geography of an area may include long distances separating communities or geographic barriers to accessing care, such as rivers, lakes, mountains, or canyons. Within the context of health care, practice location may also include geographic areas that have been designated as health professions shortage areas or medically underserved areas (Health Resources and Services Administration, n.d.), which may be urban, suburban, or rural. Such areas may delineate certain scope of practice boundaries more broadly to meet population health needs.

Finally, practice context includes the model of care delivery, or the way in which health care is provided. The Patient Protection and Affordable Care Act of 2010 (ACA) proposed incentives to create models of care delivery that are person-centered and better coordinated by integrating health and behavioral health services. Such models include integrated primary care and patient-centered medical homes. The ACA also encouraged care delivery and payment models focusing on the social determinants of health as a means of fostering health equity and access and improving individual and population health. To be effective, such models require a clear understanding of the roles and responsibilities of each team member.

> RR6: Communicate with team members to clarify each member's responsibility in executing components of a treatment plan or public health intervention.

Professions are forged by the development of each discipline into an "independent, autonomous and self-contained area of knowledge" (Fournier, 2000, as cited in Nancarrow & Borthwick, 2005, p. 903), which is "achieved by constructing boundaries" (p. 903). Professional boundaries are not fixed but rather shift as a result of changes in need, supply and demand, tasks, disciplinary dominance, regulation, legislation, funding, and professional alliances. "The healthcare professions have never been static in terms of their own disciplinary boundaries, nor in their role or status in society" (Nancarrow & Borthwick, 2005, p. 897).

In part, professional boundaries have shifted as a result of "staffing shortages in medicine, nursing and the allied health professions" (Nancarrow & Borthwick, 2005,

p. 898). Select tasks previously performed by professionals are now the domain of health care assistants, community health workers, and even family and informal caregivers. For example, whereas nurses previously performed dressing changes for wound care, this task may now be carried out by medical assistants and family caregivers. Shifts in roles can also occur as a result of changes at the policy or regulatory level, as when the Centers for Medicare and Medicaid Services (CMS) revised a rule permitting registered dietician nutritionists to order diets in hospitals (CMS, 2015).

In some cases, professions have ceded a portion of their roles. This can occur partially as a result of supply and demand, as when orthopedic surgeons focused on roles that were "fun and well-remunerated" and relinquished the role of counseling older adults about the "prevention and treatment of osteoporosis" (Heckman, 1998, as cited in Nancarrow & Borthwick, 2005, p. 899). This shift in roles provided the opportunity for podiatrists, internists, and physicians in primary care and emergency medicine to fill the void. Changes in role boundaries resulting from shifting tasks can create tensions between disciplines, such as those between physicians and nurse practitioners resulting from the latter's expanding role of "making independent diagnoses and treatment decisions" (Wiysonge & Chopra, 2008, p. 1).

Role boundaries "are influenced by the dominance of other disciplines, regulatory and legislative frameworks and the ability of the profession to convince funders and the public to purchase their services" (Freidson, 1974, as cited in Nancarrow & Borthwick, 2005, p. 904). In addition, role boundaries can be affected by "professional alliances of particular disciplines" (Freidson, 1970, as cited in Nancarrow & Borthwick, p. 904). The next section will introduce sources that can facilitate the identification of role boundaries, provide examples of role overlap, and address ways in which members of the interprofessional team can successfully identify and navigate potential areas of role overlap.

RR7: Forge interdependent relationships with other professions within and outside of the health system to improve care and advance learning.

In reviewing the principal roles of core and extended members of the primary care team, it is apparent that there are roles that team members have in common. These roles include care coordination, which is shared by the registered nurse and social worker, or "health promotion and primary prevention needs related to behavioral change," which is shared by the nurse practitioner, physician, physician assistant, registered nurse, social worker, and public health professionals (IPEC Expert Panel, 2011, p. 5). In addition to recognizing the primary roles of key members of the interprofessional team and identifying sources that further delineate their scope of practice or boundaries of their professional roles and responsibilities, it is important to identify areas of potential role overlap. Doing so contributes to improved team communication and better health outcomes for the patient.

RR8: Engage in continuous professional and interprofessional development to enhance team performance and collaboration.

Role clarification is an interprofessional competency focused on understanding one's own role and the roles of others in an interprofessional health care context. Role clarification helps to avoid the common problems associated with inaccurate role perception and lack of communication and negotiation related to role overlap. The ability to understand one's own professional role and correctly identify the roles of team members leads to more informed contributions to the team's functioning and decision making.

Research demonstrates that teams can either cause or prevent adverse events in patient care (Manser, 2009). "Teamwork requires a shared acknowledgement of each participating member's roles and abilities. Without this . . . adverse outcomes may arise from a series of seemingly trivial errors that effective teamwork could have prevented" (Baker, Gustafson, Beaubien, Slas, & Barach, 2005, p. 14). The ability to correctly understand one another's roles and identify areas in which one's role overlaps with that of another team member leads to better communication and effectiveness in navigating one's role to complement the contributions of fellow team members. Although it is important to pursue opportunities to improve one's own professional development to maintain and expand professional competencies, it is equally important to focus on continuing education to develop and improve performance in interprofessional collaborative team care.

Learning one's own role and those of fellow interprofessional team members, checking one's assumptions about the roles of other team members directly with one's colleagues, communicating one's roles and responsibilities clearly to the team, and identifying and discussing areas of role overlap facilitates role clarification. Proactively facilitating role clarification among members of the interprofessional team supports improved team functioning, decision making, communication, and complementary team roles, which fosters improved patient care. Engaging in professional and interprofessional development opportunities fosters enhanced team performance.

WHEN ROLES OVERLAP

RR9: Use unique and complementary abilities of all members of the team to optimize health and patient care.

RR10: Describe how professionals in health and other fields can collaborate and integrate clinical care and public health interventions to optimize population health.

Members of groups, including members of interprofessional teams, assume three primary roles: task roles, socioemotional or maintenance roles, and organizational roles. As these names suggest, task roles "facilitate a project from inception to completion"; socioemotional roles "contribute to positive atmosphere of the group and foster cohesion"; and organizational roles "like leader . . . or project manager keep the group organized" (Wheelan, 2005, p. 42). Within a highly functioning team, task roles may overlap, and socioemotional and leadership roles may shift depending on situation and context. A team member's ability to navigate changes in role boundaries and role overlap is improved when boundaries are conceived as permeable membranes. "Quality health care that is accessible and cost effective requires that the boundaries between . . . stakeholders are made permeable through consistent collaboration" and involves "skills in team building, team membership, and the understanding of group dynamics" (Weiss et al., 2014, p. 4).

In primary care, it is common to find an overlap in task roles of team members, such as interacting with and educating patients or developing care plans (Grant et al., 1995). Task role overlap also applies to public health interventions addressing general health literacy or disease-specific health education. In addressing role overlap, "it is better to begin by differentiating tasks before negotiating roles" as doing so "tends to diminish issues of professional territoriality and ownership" (Grant et al., 1995, p. 47). According to organizational theory, members in learning organizations "respect each other's differing roles, experience and expertise, and value them as learning assets" (Barr, 2013, p. 6). Respecting each profession's roles and experience, and the value their expertise adds to the quality of patient care, fosters a collaborative team environment.

In addition to understanding the differing task roles played by members of the interprofessional team, it is also important to consider each team member's professional competencies and potential areas of overlap. According to Barr (1998), there are three types of professional competencies: common, complementary, and collaborative competencies (see Figure 5.2).

Common competencies are those that overlap and are "held in common between all professions" (Barr, 1998, p. 184). This overlap may be a result of role shift, such as that between physicians and nurse practitioners, or role extension, such as occurs in health professions shortage areas. Sometimes, new providers emerge to fill gaps in shortage areas, such as the use of midlevel dental providers in oral health to reduce disparities and increase access to underserved populations (Rodriguez et al., 2013).

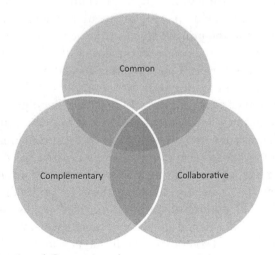

Figure 5.2: Professional Competencies

Source: Interprofessional Education Collaborative Expert Panel, 2011, *Core Competencies for Interprofessional Collaborative Practice: Report of an Expert Panel* (Washington, DC: Interprofessional Education Collaborative), Figure 4, p. 13. Used by permission.

Complementary competencies are those that "distinguish one profession and complement those which distinguish other professions" (Barr, 1998, p. 184). This may result from the identification of a useful role overlap while retaining complementary expertise, such as the useful role overlap in oral health between dentists, who "identify systemic diseases," and pediatricians, who facilitate "preventive oral care" (IPEC Expert Panel, 2011, p. 13).

Collaborative competencies are those "which every profession needs to collaborate within its own ranks, with other professions, with non-professionals, within [and] between organisations, with patients and their carers, with volunteers and with community groups" (Barr, 1998, p. 184). Roles and responsibilities is one of the four core collaborative competencies for interprofessional team practice (IPEC, 2016).

Regardless of practice setting, the roles played by each member of the interprofessional team may vary depending on "degree of contact with the patient and in level of responsibility for patient care," requiring the establishment of clear areas of responsibility to support effective team functioning and quality care (Grant et al., 1995, p. 23). Learning to effectively explain one's role facilitates clear communication with the patient, patient's family, community members, and to other members of the interprofessional team. This contributes to improved team coordination and better health outcomes for patients and populations.

COMMUNICATING ROLES

Sharing information about one's role on the interprofessional team is an important part of each team member's introduction to patients and their families. By following a few simple steps, the health professional can effectively and clearly communicate his or her role and help patients and families understand how this role relates to that of other members of the interprofessional team providing for their care. It is important to reduce the use of jargon and to provide information in a way that is both culturally grounded and sensitive to the primary language of the patient and family.

On meeting the patient, the pharmacist might say the following: "Good morning, Mrs. Garcia. My name is Angela. I am a pharmacist and a member of the team that will be providing and coordinating your care. I am here today to discuss your new medication to treat and control your diabetes and high blood pressure. We will review all of your current and new medications and talk about how you can monitor your care. Then we'll discuss some negative reactions that can sometimes occur with your new medications and what to do in case you have a negative reaction."

After reviewing this information, the pharmacist might continue by saying, "Mrs. Garcia, do you have any questions about anything we've discussed related to your new diabetes and high blood pressure medications? Here is a list of possible signs and symptoms and contact information in case you experience any adverse effects during the weekday or after hours. If you or your family has any additional questions, you can reach me by calling our office and asking for the pharmacist. Here is a business card with my name and telephone number for your convenience. Thank you for your time, Mrs. Garcia."

As can be seen from this example, communicating one's role to patients and families is as simple as sharing a polite greeting, stating one's name, introducing one's professional role on the interprofessional team, explaining the purpose of the visit, asking whether the patient or family has any questions, sharing follow-up information, and explaining how the professional can be reached by the patient and family. In the case of Mrs. Garcia, it is important to consider that her primary language is Spanish and to converse with her in a linguistically appropriate way, either by speaking to her in Spanish or arranging for a professional translation service. It is also important to provide written instructions in Spanish.

It is also important to effectively and clearly communicate one's role to other members of the interprofessional team. For example, on joining a team or meeting another member of the interprofessional team, the social worker might say, "Hello, my name is David and I am a social worker. I can support the work of our team by helping Mrs. Garcia with problem solving, resources, and coping skills related to her recent stroke and support her adherence to her new diabetes and high blood pressure medication, diet, and self-care. I can also facilitate her referral to our hospital's diabetes support group and connect her to a grandparent caregiver program in our community."

Depending on the specific circumstances and patient or family situation, the social worker might add, "I was trained to work in integrated care settings, so I can assist Mrs. Garcia through psychoeducation, counseling, and support. I know this experience has been very stressful for her. I also have specialized training in stress reduction techniques, so I can also teach Mrs. Garcia some mindfulness meditation practices to help her reduce stress."

Communicating one's role with members of the interprofessional team is as simple as sharing a polite greeting, stating one's name and profession, and describing ways in which the member can contribute to team care through his or her professional role. Depending on individual circumstances, it might also be useful to share information about specialized education, training, or certifications that may relate to the team's care of particular patients and families.

Communicating professional roles can be accomplished by following a few simple steps. Clearly explaining one's role to the patient, the patient's family, and other members of the interprofessional team contributes to improved team coordination and better health outcomes for the patient.

CLARIFYING ROLES: POSITIVE AND NEGATIVE IMPLICATIONS

Because role overlap between health professionals is a common occurrence, it is also important to clarify one's role to patients, families, and other members of the interprofessional team. This final section will focus on the importance of clarifying roles and introduce related concepts, including role perception, the knowing paradox, role diversity, variety diversity, role overlap, and role clarification on effective teamwork and patient care.

It is common to hold beliefs about how well one understands the roles of other members of the primary care team. Similarly, it is common to hold beliefs about how well other team members understand one's role. These beliefs are referred to as *role perception*. Correct role perceptions support effective teamwork and facilitate improved interprofessional communication. Health professionals who understand their own professional role and are able to correctly confirm the roles of fellow team members can make more informed contributions to the team's functioning and decision making.

Role perception can also have negative implications. Research on interprofessional teams has found that members can operate under a *knowing paradox*, or a mistaken belief that they understand the roles and responsibilities of their colleagues. If team members are confident that they understand the roles of their colleagues without confirming their understanding of these roles, it can serve as a barrier to learning more about other team members' roles and responsibilities. This can result in unrealistic role expectations (Pellatt, 2005).

Another example of the knowing paradox is the mistaken belief that an individual's roles are misunderstood by that person's colleagues. If team members believe that their colleagues do not understand their role, these members can feel misunderstood and undervalued, which can lead to a less confident or assertive role in team decision making (Pellatt, 2005).

Either of these incorrect role perceptions related to the knowing paradox can lead to ineffective teamwork and can have negative consequences on patient care. If the contributions of an individual team member are reduced as a result of the knowing paradox, it diminishes the contributions of the whole toward quality patient care. Additionally, misperceptions in roles can lead to conflict and discord between team members. Such conflict can spill over into patient care, inadvertently placing the patient at the center of the conflict and amidst the power relationships that can develop between team members as a consequence of role misperception (Pellatt, 2005).

Role diversity involves understanding the variations in roles resulting from differences among team members in professional expertise, diversity of background, or cultural characteristics. Role diversity includes two related concepts: variety diversity and disparity diversity (IPEC Expert Panel, 2011).

Variety diversity involves "categorical differences among team members" (IPEC Expert Panel, 2011, p. 20), including diversity of professional roles and expertise, demographic background, or cultural characteristics between members of an interprofessional team. Such diversity can be a benefit to effective team functioning, adding to the overall skills, perspectives, and resources available to the interprofessional team. This same diversity can result in positive and negative role stereotyping, which can have a negative impact on effective team functioning (IPEC Expert Panel, 2011).

When such stereotypes create or reinforce perceptions about the worth of a profession, it is referred to as *disparity diversity*. Such diversity can result in an erosion of mutual respect and "prevent[s] professions from taking advantage of the full scope of abilities that working together offers to improve health care" (IPEC Expert Panel, 2011, p. 20).

As previously discussed, the tendency of the roles of team members to intersect is referred to as *role overlap*. The role of each member of the primary care team can be thought of as a piece of a jigsaw puzzle. There is a natural tendency for these roles to interlock, just like the pieces of a puzzle. Role overlap can result when more than one member of the interprofessional team holds expertise in a specific area of patient care (Pellatt, 2005).

Role overlap in interprofessional teams is natural and can be beneficial to patient care and effective team functioning when team members take the time to communicate their role and clarify the roles of others. Failure to effectively communicate and clarify roles can result in confusion, leading to ineffective patient care and poor team functioning.

Being able to correctly identify areas in which one's role overlaps with that of another team member can result in information that can facilitate better communicate with and complement the contributions of one's team members. To better understand the concept of role overlap in practice, consider the following two examples.

One example of role overlap relates to professionals who may hold a common certification, such as a certified diabetes educator, "a health professional who possesses comprehensive knowledge of and experience in prediabetes, diabetes prevention, and management" (National Certification Board for Diabetes Educators [NDBDE], 2015b, para. 1). Various health professionals can qualify as a certified diabetes educator, including a clinical psychologist, registered nurse, occupational therapist, optometrist, pharmacist, physical therapist, physician, podiatrist, dietitian, dietitian nutritionist, or master's-level social worker (NCBDE, 2015a).

If two or more members of the interprofessional team hold the same certification, it is extremely important to discuss which professional will address which aspects of diabetes education and management. It is important to identify and discuss areas of role overlap with members of the primary care team. It is also important to clarify to the patient what part of his or her diabetes education and management will be addressed by each member of the team and when to contact each of these team members.

Another example of role overlap can occur when more than one professional has specialized education in behavioral health. These professionals are prepared to work with patients and families in settings that provide integrated care or specialized behavioral health care. Professionals with such a specialization may include, but are not limited to, a counselor, clinical psychologist, registered nurse, physician, or social worker. Again, if two or more members of the interprofessional team possess specialized education in behavioral health, it is extremely important to discuss which team member will address which aspects of behavioral health care for the patient and family. When introducing oneself to other members of the interprofessional team, it is important to identify this potential area of role overlap. It is also important to clarify to the patient and their family what part of the patient's behavioral health care will be addressed by which members of the team and how and when to contact each respective team member.

Interprofessional collaborative practice requires teamwork, which necessitates practice and mastery of the subcompetencies related to roles and responsibilities for collaborative practice. The following toolbox provides an opportunity to explore and practice roles and responsibilities through a case study and related activities. Understanding one's own and others' roles, as well as practicing strategies for role clarification, enhances team performance and improves the quality of patient outcomes. Remember, it takes a team to learn and effectively navigate interprofessional roles and responsibilities.

TOOLBOX

Review the following case study, then respond to the questions and complete the exercises that follow later in the chapter.

Case Study: Mrs. Louise Nygård

Mrs. Louise Nygård is an 80-year-old widowed Caucasian woman. She is accompanied by her adult daughter, Leanne, and is being seen at an integrated primary care site. She has a history of hypothyroidism, mild to moderate arthritic changes, acid reflux, hiatal hernia, glaucoma, and macular degeneration. Six months ago following an outpatient visit for a colonoscopy, she was told that she was borderline anemic. She was recently discharged home following a hospitalization for congestive heart failure, which the attending physician determined had resulted from severe anemia. She is awaiting the results of a liver biopsy that was conducted after a suspicious mass was detected through a CT scan during her hospitalization.

Louise is the daughter of Norwegian and German immigrants who settled in the Midwest. Louise, an elementary school teacher, met and married Harry, a barber, after World War II. The couple moved to a small town where Louise gave birth to a son, Ken, and daughter, Leanne. Louise gave up teaching to care for the children until both started elementary school. Her Lutheran faith was important to her. She made sure that the children regularly attended church, even though they didn't always attend as a family. Louise returned to full-time teaching, which allowed her to get home at about the same time as the children and stay home with them during the summer.

Louise was in good health throughout her childhood and young adulthood. She eventually developed hypothyroidism and acid reflux, for which she began taking medications. Harry had hypertension, and what began as social drinking during the war gradually turned into alcoholism. Louise initially enjoyed drinking socially with Harry and their mutual friends, but his drinking increasingly caused conflict between the couple. Although she dearly loved Harry, Louise began turning to work as an outlet to escape her frustrations. Son Ken pursued work out of state to get away from the family problems shortly after completing high school. Daughter Leanne moved out of the house after enrolling in college, later marrying her high school sweetheart and moving to the southwestern United States.

After Harry lost his job as a result of behaviors associated with his alcoholism, the couple moved from their small town in the Midwest to a city in the southwestern United States to be closer to Leanne. Louise longed to live in a larger community where they could blend in and people would not know about her family's issues. Louise found a full-time teaching position, but Harry was never able to hold down a job again after the move because of his continued drinking. The year that Louise was scheduled to retire, the couple decided to downsize and moved into a retirement community. Before they had unpacked from the move, Harry suffered a massive heart attack and died suddenly, leaving Louise widowed at the age of 65 and living in a new community where she did not know her neighbors.

After retirement, Louise threw herself into a variety of activities, including reading mystery novels, playing piano, and drawing, but these solitary activities did not give her the social outlets for which she yearned. She valued her independence and enjoyed driving to the grocery store, often striking up conversations with people while standing in the checkout line. She was close to Leanne but did not want to "bother" her daughter, feeling that Leanne's priorities were her husband, children, and career as a real estate agent. She visited some churches in the area but never felt the sense of connection she had felt back in the Midwest. Louise began to go to the neighborhood swimming pool and attended happy hours at the clubhouse to meet other residents in the retirement community. She struck up some acquaintances but no real friendships, choosing to maintain her privacy and keep out of neighborhood politics. She preferred instead to talk on the phone each evening with Leanne. Over time, Louise started drinking alone at home.

In her late 60s, Louise began to experience aches and pains from arthritis and started using eye drops for glaucoma. She walked less but continued to go to the swimming pool, where she did her own pool exercises. She continued to take medications for her hypothyroidism and to experience indigestion from acid reflux, eventually being diagnosed with a hiatal hernia. In her 70s, she was diagnosed with macular degeneration, which gradually led to a loss of all but her peripheral vision. As her vision deteriorated, she gradually gave up reading, piano playing, and drawing and eventually stopped driving altogether. She began complaining of lethargy, which she thought was related to her hypothyroidism. However, after a colonoscopy, her physician told her she was showing signs of borderline anemia.

Leanne began visiting Louise once a week, assisting with grocery shopping, driving her mother to doctor's appointments, setting up her medications, and helping with mail and bills. Louise accepted this help but was protective of her daughter's time and would wait for Leanne to visit before asking for assistance.

One day, Leanne found Louise lying on her bed, exhausted, and with an ashen face. She drove her to a nearby hospital, where Louise was admitted and diagnosed with congestive heart failure. The physician determined that the congestive heart failure had resulted from severe anemia. A biopsy was conducted as a CT scan revealed a suspicious mass on her liver.

After 10 days, Louise was discharged home from the hospital without services. She lives in a lower-level unit that requires her to go down a half flight of stairs. She has a bathtub but prefers to take sponge baths and uses her tub for extra storage. She has a bandage on her stomach from the biopsy that must be changed daily, and she was prescribed new medications on discharge. She was told to schedule an appointment with her primary care doctor following discharge and is awaiting the results of the liver biopsy.

Ecological Theory

Theory can provide a useful lens through which to view individuals and their families. Bronfenbrenner's (1979) ecological theory posits that human development involves individual actions, circumstances that occur within the environment, the dynamic and changing interactions between individuals and their environment, and the meaning individuals ascribe to events that occur within the context of their environment. It is a useful theory through which to view individuals and families in the context of their health and in interaction with the roles of health professionals and the health care system.

According to ecological theory, the environment is made up of a set of nested systems, similar to a set of Russian dolls (see Figure 5.3). At the center is the individual and the individual's attributes, including gender, age, health, and marital status. Next is the microsystem, which includes the family, peers, church, school, and health services (Bronfenbrenner, 1994). Moving outward is the mesosystem, which involves the relationships between microsystems, such as "home and school, school and workplace"; the exosystem, including social services, neighbors, local politics, mass media, industry, "workplace, family social networks, and neighborhood-community contexts"; and finally the macrosystem, which encompasses the attitudes and ideologies of the larger culture, including "belief systems, bodies of knowledge, material resources, customs, life-styles, opportunity structures, hazards, and life course options" (p. 40). Operating in a third dimension is the chronosystem, which involves changes or consistencies over the life course in individual and environmental characteristics, such as health, "family structure, socioeconomic status, employment, place of residence, . . . and ability in everyday life," including functional status (p. 40).

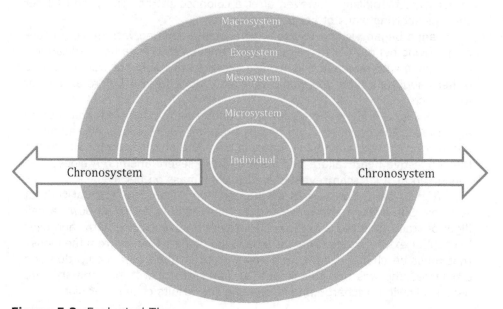

Figure 5.3: Ecological Theory

Source: Adapted from U. Bronfenbrenner (1979), *The Ecology of Human Development* (Cambridge, MA: Harvard University Press).

Applying Ecological Theory to Mrs. Nygård

Imagine that you are a health professional working in the integrated primary care site at which Mrs. Nygård and her daughter are being seen.

- Using ecological theory as a lens, describe what you know about Mrs. Nygård at each of the following six system levels:
    1. Individual (gender, age, health, marital status, etc.)
    2. Microsystem (family, peers, church, school, health services)
    3. Mesosystem (interaction between microsystems and between the microsystem and exosystem)
    4. Exosystem (social services, neighbors, local politics, mass media, and industry)
    5. Macrosystem (attitudes and ideologies of the culture)
    6. Chronosystem (changes or consistencies in health, family structure, socio-economic status, employment, residence, and functional status)

- How could this information guide the role you might play in Mrs. Nygård's care?
- Describe the role or roles you might play in her care, assuming you were one of the following core or extended members of the primary care team: counselor, medical assistant, nurse practitioner, occupational therapist, pharmacist, physical therapist, physician, physician assistant, registered nurse, or social worker.
- How might you introduce yourself to Mrs. Nygård and her daughter to communicate your role?
- How might you introduce yourself to another team member to communicate your role on the interprofessional team providing for Mrs. Nygård's care?
- How might roles overlap between these professionals?

Roles and Care Mapping

Despite attempts to develop integrated and coordinated systems of health care, services can often be experienced as fragmented and disjointed by patients and family members. Patients and family members often serve as their own care coordinators, making the connections between home, health care, and community resources. Care coordination "requires establishing a common base of practice" for members of the interprofessional team, establishing critical paths toward outcomes and goals (Schwoebel, 1998, p. 259), and determining the roles of each team member in achieving these goals. Care mapping is a useful tool that can be used to identify members of the patient and family's interprofessional team, clarify roles, determine possible areas of role overlap, and identify areas in need of care coordination and communication.

Care mapping is a family driven, person-centered process "which guides and supports the ability of families and care professionals to work together to achieve the best possible health outcomes" (Antonelli & Lind, 2012, para. 5). It provides a pictorial representation of the individual's and family's strengths and needs, within the context of "both the big picture and small details of all of the resources needed" to support the individual and family (para. 6) and helps the family and interprofessional team visually appreciate the relationship between individual and family needs (para. 7). It can also provide a unique way for health professions team members to understand their relationship to the individual and family, as well as other team members, providers, and resources.

Develop a Care Map for Mrs. Nygård

Review the care map developed by a mother to describe the complex care needs of her son (the care map is depicted in Figure 5.4).

1. Develop a care map to describe the strengths, resources, and care needs related to Mrs. Nygård's health care, social support, legal and financial needs, community resources, and information, advocacy, and leadership.
2. Identify the interprofessional team members who have a role to play in each of the areas of strength and need identified for Mrs. Nygård.
3. Specify the role of each team member you have identified.
4. Identify potential areas of role overlap. How might you address this overlap in the interest of coordinated person- and family-centered care?

Figure 5.4: Care Map

Source: Adapted from R. Antonelli & C. Lind, *Care Mapping: An Innovative Tool and Process to Support Family-Centered, Comprehensive Care Coordination* (Poster session presented at the annual Primary Care Innovation Conference of the Harvard Medical School Primary Care Center, Boston, October 2012).

REFERENCES

Accreditation. (2003). In *Miller-Keane encyclopedia and dictionary of medicine, nursing, and allied health* (7th ed.). Retrieved from http://medical-dictionary.thefreedictionary.com/accreditation

American Academy of Family Physicians. (2016). *Primary care: Definition #3—Primary care physician.* Retrieved from http://www.aafp.org/about/policies/all/primary-care.html

American Academy of Physician Assistants. (n.d.). *What is a PA?* Retrieved from https://www.aapa.org/what-is-a-pa/

American Association of Colleges of Pharmacy. (2015). *Role of a pharmacist.* Retrieved from http://www.aacp.org/resources/student/pharmacyforyou/Pages/roleofapharmacist.aspx

American Association of Medical Assistants. (1996–2015). *What is a medical assistant?* Retrieved from http://www.aama-ntl.org/medical-assisting/what-is-a-medical-assistant#.VdgUQ5fg8hQ

American Association of Nurse Practitioners. (2012–2015). *What is an NP?* Retrieved from http://www.aanp.org/all-about-nps/what-is-an-np

American Mental Health Counselors Association. (n.d.). *Facts about clinical mental health counselors.* Retrieved from http://www.amhca.org/?page=facts

American Nurses Association. (2015a). *How to become a nurse.* Retrieved from http://www.nursingworld.org/EspeciallyForYou/What-is-Nursing/Tools-You-Need/RegisteredNurseLicensing.html

American Nurses Association. (2015b). *What nurses do.* Retrieved from http://www.nursingworld.org/EspeciallyForYou/What-is-Nursing/Tools-You-Need/RNsAPNs.html

American Occupational Therapy Association. (2015a). *FAQ on OT education and career planning.* Retrieved from http://www.aota.org/Education-Careers/Considering-OT-Career/FAQs/Planning.aspx

American Occupational Therapy Association. (2015b) *Occupational therapy: Improving function while controlling costs.* Retrieved from http://www.aota.org/about-occupational-therapy/professionals.aspx

American Physical Therapy Association. (2015a). *Physical therapist (PT) education overview.* Retrieved from http://www.apta.org/PTEducation/Overview/

American Physical Therapy Association. (2015b). *Role of a physical therapist.* Retrieved from http://www.apta.org/PTCareers/RoleofaPT/

Antonelli, R., & Lind, C. (2012, October). *Care mapping: An innovative tool and process to support family-centered, comprehensive care coordination.* Poster session presented at the annual Primary Care Innovation Conference of the Harvard Medical School Primary Care Center, Boston. Retrieved from http://www.childrenshospital.org/care-coordination-curriculum/care-mapping

Baker, D. P., Gustafson, S., Beaubien, J. M., Salas, E., & Barach, P. (2005, April). *Medical teamwork and patient safety: The evidence-based relation* (AHRQ Publication No. 05-0053). Retrieved from http://www.ahrq.gov/qual/medteam/

Barr, H. (1998). Competent to collaborate: Towards a competency-based model for interprofessional education. *Journal of Interprofessional Care, 12,* 181–187.

Barr, H. (2013). Toward a theoretical framework for interprofessional education. *Journal of Interprofessional Care, 27,* 4–9.

Bronfenbrenner, U. (1979). *The ecology of human development.* Cambridge, MA: Harvard University Press.

Bronfenbrenner, U. (1994). Ecological models of human development. In T. N. Postleth-waite & T. Husen (Eds.), *International encyclopedia of education,* Vol. 3 (2nd ed.). Oxford, United Kingdom: Elsevier.

Bureau of Labor Statistics. (2014–2015a). *Occupational outlook handbook: Pharmacists.* Retrieved from http://www.bls.gov/ooh/healthcare/pharmacists.htm

Bureau of Labor Statistics. (2014–2015b). *Occupational outlook handbook: Physicians: Summary.* Retrieved from http://www.bls.gov/ooh/healthcare/physicians-and-surgeons.htm

Bureau of Labor Statistics. (2014–2015c). *Occupational outlook handbook: Social workers.* Retrieved from http://www.bls.gov/ooh/community-and-social-service/mobile/social-workers.htm

Bureau of Labor Statistics. (2016). *Occupational outlook handbook: Physicians and surgeons: How to become a physician or surgeon.* Retrieved from http://www.bls.gov/ooh/healthcare/physicians-and-surgeons.htm#tab-4

Centers for Medicare and Medicaid Services. (2015, May 12). *Federal register: Food and dietetic services.* Executive Order 13563, 482.28(b). Retrieved from https://www.federalregister.gov/articles/2014/05/12/2014-10687/medicare-and-medicaid-programs-regulatory-provisions-to-promote-program-efficiency-transparency-and#citation-1

Code of ethics. (2009). In *Mosby's medical dictionary* (8th ed.). Retrieved from http://medical-dictionary.thefreedictionary.com/code+of+ethics

Collins, S. (2012, May 23). Social work and primary care: A natural collaboration [Webinar]. Retrieved from http://socialworkers.org/ce/online/Resources/20125814415231_May%2023%202012%20Webinar%20Slides.pdf

DeBonis, J. A. (n.d.). The role of social work in integrated care. Module 2 [Webinar]. Retrieved from http://www.cswe.org/CentersInitiatives/DataStatistics/58020/62695.aspx

Grant, R. W., Finocchio, L. J., & California Primary Care Consortium Subcommittee on Interdisciplinary Collaboration. (1995, January). *Interdisciplinary collaborative teams in primary care: A module curriculum and resource guide.* San Francisco: Pew Health Professions Commission.

Health Resources and Services Administration. (n.d.). *Shortage designation: Health professional shortage areas & medically underserved areas/populations.* Retrieved from http://www.hrsa.gov/shortage/

Institute of Medicine. (1996). *Primary care: America's health in a new era.* Washington, DC: National Academies Press.

Institute of Medicine. (2001). *Crossing the quality chasm: A new health system for the 21st century.* Retrieved from http://www.nap.edu/catalog/10027.html

Interprofessional Education Collaborative. (2016). *Core competencies for interprofessional collaborative practice: 2016 update.* Washington, DC: Interprofessional Education Collaborative.

Interprofessional Education Collaborative Expert Panel. (2011). *Core competencies for interprofessional practice: Report of an expert panel.* Washington, DC: Interprofessional Education Collaborative.

Liability. (2008). In *West's encyclopedia of American law* (2nd ed.). Retrieved from http://legal-dictionary.thefreedictionary.com/liability

Licensure. (2003). In *Miller-Keane encyclopedia and dictionary of medicine, nursing, and allied health.* Retrieved from http://medical-dictionary.thefreedictionary.com/licensure

MacDonald, M. B., Bally, J. M., Ferguson, L. M., Murray, B. L., & Fowler-Kerry, S. E. (2010). Knowledge of the professional role of others: A key interprofessional competency. *Nurse Education in Practice, 10,* 238–242.

Manser, T. (2009). Teamwork and patient safety in dynamic domains of healthcare: A review of the literature. *Acta Anaesthesiologica Scandinavica, 53,* 143–151.

Mills, C. W. (1959). *The sociological imagination.* New York: Oxford University Press.

Nancarrow, S. A., & Borthwick, A. M. (2005). Dynamic professional boundaries in the healthcare workforce. *Sociology of Health & Illness, 27,* 897–919.

National Association of Social Workers. (2005). *NASW standards for social work practice in health care settings.* Washington, DC: Author.

National Certification Board for Diabetes Educators. (2015a). *Discipline requirements.* Retrieved from http://www.ncbde.org/certification_info/discipline-requirement/

National Certification Board for Diabetes Educators. (2015b). *What is a certified diabetes educator?* Retrieved from http://www.ncbde.org/certification_info/what-is-a-cde/

National Resource Center for Participant-Directed Services. (2012). *Person-centered training resource guide for options counselors.* Retrieved from http://nrcpds.adobeconnect.com/p48tlbhmohu/

Pellatt, G. C. (2005). Perceptions of interprofessional roles within the spinal cord injury rehabilitation team. *International Journal of Therapy and Rehabilitation, 12,* 143–150.

Professional competence. (2009). In *Medical dictionary.* Retrieved from http://medical-dictionary.thefreedictionary.com/professional+competence

Reeves, S., Lewin, S., Espin, S., & Zwarenstein, M. (2010, September). *Interprofessional teamwork for health and social care.* Retrieved from https://www.researchgate.net/publication/273794153_Interprofessional_Teamwork_in_Health_and_Social_Care

Rodriguez, T. E., Galka, A. L., Lacy, E. S., Pellegrini, A. D., Sweier, D. G., & Romito, L. M. (2013). Can midlevel dental providers be a benefit to the American public? *Journal of Health Care for the Poor and Underserved, 24,* 890–904.

Schwoebel, A. (1998). Care mapping: A common sense approach. *Indian Journal of Pediatrics, 65,* 257–264.

Scope of practice. (2002). In *McGraw-Hill concise dictionary of modern medicine.* Retrieved from http://medical-dictionary.thefreedictionary.com/scope+of+practice

Vourlekis, B. S., Ell, K., & Padgett, D. (2001). Educating social workers for health care's brave new world. *Journal of Social Work Education, 37,* 177–191.

Weiss, D., Tilin, F., & Morgan, M. (2014). *The interprofessional health care team: Leadership and development.* Burlington, MA: Jones & Bartlett Learning.

Wheelan, S. A. (2005). *Group process: A developmental perspective* (2nd ed.). Needham Heights, MA: Allyn & Bacon.

Wiysonge, C. S., & Chopra, M. (2008, August). *Do nurse practitioners working in primary care provide equivalent care to doctors? A SUPPORT summary of a systematic review.* Retrieved from http://apps.who.int/rhl/effective_practice_and_organizing_care/SUPPORT_Task_shifiting.pdf

6

TEAMS AND TEAMWORK

Carmen Morano

Case Study: Mrs. Garcia

After a few days in the hospital being treated and monitored after an ischemic stroke, Maria Garcia, her daughter, Tania Jacquez, and son-in-law, Miguel Jacquez, meet with Mrs. Garcia's health care team to discuss her discharge planning. Both Tania and Miguel are employed full time; consequently, in addition to working part time at the local church cafeteria, Maria assumes a primary caregiving role for her grandchildren. The team is familiar with Mrs. Garcia, considers her to be noncompliant, and has already decided she needs to go to inpatient rehabilitation. Maria and her daughter feel strongly that now that she has been stabilized and her medications adjusted during her three days in the neurology step-down unit, she is ready to be discharged home, with home care.

   The agenda of the team is to have Mrs. Garcia placed in the hospital-owned rehabilitation unit. The initial discharge plan does not reflect the wishes of the Garcia family. This is the social worker's first team meeting, and she is uncertain of how the team functions. She has information to contribute, but the team has not asked her and appears to have already determined a plan of care. Finally, she cannot hold back. The social worker interrupts the meeting and angrily states that she does not agree with the plan.

This chapter focuses on how statements made by the team reflect their prior memberships and how their membership (that is, interactions) with Mrs. Garcia will affect their capacity to explore the factors contributing to her repeated visits to the emergency department. This chapter highlights poor team development, a lack of professional skills, and a complete lack of awareness and disregard for the wishes of the Garcia family.

INTRODUCTION

The final core competency domain, teams and teamwork, is described as follows: "Apply relationship-building values and the principles of team dynamics to perform effectively in different team roles to plan and deliver patient/population-centered care that is safe, timely, efficient, effective, and equitable" (Interprofessional Education Collaborative [IPEC], 2016, p. 14). The teamwork behaviors included in this domain are "(a) cooperating in the patient-centered delivery of care; (b) coordinating care with other health professionals so that gaps, redundancies, and errors are avoided; and (c) collaborating with others through shared problem solving and shared decision making, especially in circumstances of uncertainty" (IPEC Expert Panel, 2011, p. 24). Cooperating, coordinating, and collaborating within a patient-centered framework are complex processes that require knowledge, skills, and behaviors that are further illuminated in the 11 subcompetencies linked to this domain (see Appendix A for the full list).

In their review of the literature, Reeves, Lewin, Espin, and Zwarenstein (2010) identified five common elements that occur in highly functioning teams: shared identity; clear roles, tasks, and goals; interdependence; integration; and shared responsibility. Woodfield and Kennie (2008) also developed six core elements of a highly functioning team. According to them, such teams (1) clarify areas of decision making and time management, (2) develop team working and collective agenda setting, (3) establish team behaviors and team roles, (4) consider location and resources, (5) focus on collective performance management related to top performing teams (subsumed in this is developing explicit evaluation techniques), and (6) foster team development (Woodfield & Kennie, 2008).

It is important to note that although common elements of teamwork have been identified and teamwork and collaboration are frequently mentioned as competencies within most (if not all) health disciplines, there is little discussion as to what preparation students in the health professions should receive to work collaboratively on an interprofessional team (IPT) (Oandasan et al., 2006). With little or no specific curricular content on team development and teamwork, most student learning is left to on-the-job training that is supervised by field instructors, proctors, or mentors (who themselves are not adequately trained in interprofessional practice) in settings that do not necessarily adhere to interprofessional practice (Advisory Committee on Interdisciplinary, Community-Based Linkages, 2014). Some disciplines, such as business organizational management (Dyer, Dyer, & Dyer, 2013; Hellriegel & Slocum, 2011), social work, and psychology, do have specific curricular content on team or group leadership development that is combined with field practicums.

Social work programs offer different methods of practice, such as practice with individuals or families, community organizing, administration and management, and group work (Council on Social Work Education, 2015). Even when a social work program does not offer group work as a specific method, all social work programs include curriculum or a specific course in group work. However, even though social workers are frequently the only members of the team with both didactic and practical group work skills, the traditional role of social workers on interdisciplinary teams is usually limited to attending to the psychosocial needs of patients. Given that social workers are one of the few health care professionals offered curricular content on group development, the social worker could help facilitate early team-building training exercises that are critical to a team's functioning. Perhaps the utilization of the knowledge and skills of a social worker could help to increase the likelihood of developing a highly effective interprofessional team.

In addition to on-the-job training, almost everyone, including potential members of the IPT, has had some prior experience participating on a team. Those prior experiences, positive and negative, will influence the individual's current participation on the IPT. As illustrated in Figure 6.1, the highly functioning interprofessional health care team requires each member to maintain personal and professional values, ethics, roles, and responsibilities while integrating those of their colleagues to develop a higher order of critical thinking, attitudes, and behaviors.

Achieving this higher order of interprofessional values, ethics, roles, and responsibilities requires a level of shared trust that can develop only with open and honest communication. It should not be surprising that mastery in this domain is contingent on an outcome of achieving competency in each of the other core competencies. No fewer than six of the 11 TT competencies and skills are articulated in the other three domains. For example, values and ethics are referred to in subcompetencies TT2 and TT4; roles and responsibilities are referred to in TT5 and TT11, and interpersonal communication is referred to in TT3 and TT6.

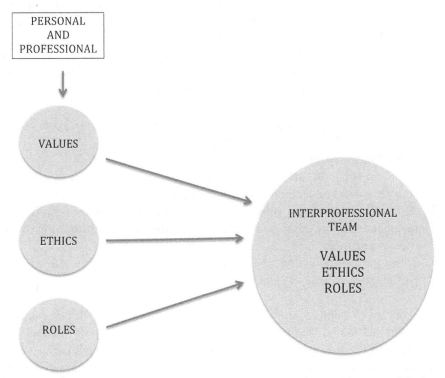

Figure 6.1: Integrating Personal and Professional Values, Ethics, and Roles

BECOMING A MEMBER OF THE TEAM

It has been argued that interprofessional teams and teamwork and groups and group work are not interchangeable concepts (Reeves et al., 2010). I maintain that there are key concepts from group and group work development that have clear implications for understanding functional and dysfunctional IPTs. Teamwork in health care can be understood and explained as a specific type of group experience, frequently labeled a "task-focused group" (Bruce, 1980; Grigsby, 2006; Katzenbach & Smith, 1993). In some of the early work on teamwork, Katzenbach and Smith (1993) defined teamwork as, "a small group of people with complementary skills committed to a common purpose and set of performance goals" (p. 21). Uniting to form a common purpose requires individual members of the team to develop a level of trust in their colleagues, an understanding of each member's role, and the capacity to communicate personal and professional values. Understanding how an individual's prior experiences either facilitate or restrict current membership on the team is important to the overall development and functioning of the team.

The membership perspective provides a framework to understand or explain why individuals vary in their approach and capacity to being a contributing member of the IPT. The membership perspective posits that individuals are a composite of all the memberships they have experienced throughout their life (Falck, 1988). Memberships represent those interactions between individuals, as well as those between the individual and larger systems, such as service delivery agencies. Falck posited that memberships in both the present (seen) and in the past (unseen) influence the individual's capacity for becoming fully engaged in a new membership, in this case the interprofessional team. The membership exercise I developed has been used to help members of the IP team to understand how their colleagues' prior team experiences and memberships might influence their current participation. Steps 1 through 4 of this exercise can be just as effective when completed individually as a self-awareness exercise:

1. Take time to think back to prior memberships or roles of being part of a team.
2. Select five of these team memberships.
3. What thoughts and feelings does this memory evoke?
4. On a scale of 1–10, with 10 = *extremely positive* and 1 = *extremely negative*, rate your thoughts and feelings about being on team.
5. After reflecting on your prior membership, you can break into dyads with the members of the team and take turns presenting and then listening to 1–3 of these experiences.
6. Following the discussion, use the same scale to indicate your thoughts about participation in your current (or future) health care team.

The concept of membership becomes even more relevant as health care engages in a person-centered model of care. Just as with professionals, the past memberships of the patient with the various medical systems will affect the patient's current capacity to become a member of the health care team. This is reflected in comments made by staff upon learning that Mrs. Garcia is in the emergency department. The nurse states:

"Yep, our frequent flyer has finally landed. Wasn't she just here about a month ago? Just once I'd like for some of these people to follow our discharge instructions. Is that really asking so much?" The doctor's response suggests she never explored the importance of Mrs. Garcia to the overall function of the family: "I gave her a plan. I really went over it with her, but all she talked about was getting back to her grandkids." If a patient's prior memberships with the health care system held the physician as the omnipotent leader of the team, the patient can feel powerless to challenge or even ask simple questions of the physician. All members of the highly functioning team in a patient-centered model of care should strive to have a level of awareness or mindfulness (Epstein, 1999) about both their own experiences with power, privilege, and oppression and, most important, the experiences of their colleagues and patients.

Another important concept that we can draw from the membership perspective is *conditional accessibility*. This states that all memberships come with conditions or expectations. If or when those conditions (expectations) are not met, there is a risk of losing that membership on that team. The failure of the team to provide the new social worker with some understanding of how the team functions almost resulted in her not contributing vital information about the wishes of the family. Similarly, the patient who does not know the norms of the team might hold back on important information about the reasons behind their expressed desires. The case of the Garcia family illustrates not only poor skills among the professionals themselves but also a complete lack of awareness and disregard of the wishes of the Garcia family.

THEORETICAL FRAMEWORKS FOR TEAM AND TEAMWORK

There are a number of theoretical underpinnings, typologies (categories), and frameworks that can be found throughout the literature. Although a detailed discussion of each is beyond the scope of this text, Reeves and colleagues (2010) present a more thorough discussion that is worthy of review. In their review they present three types of group or team: nominal, convenient, and committed (Bruce, 1980), and another framework with five types of teams: the working group, pseudo-teams, potential teams, real teams, and high-performance teams (Katzenbach & Smith, 1993). Reeves and colleagues (2010) offer a range of typologies, from the broadest, networking followed by coordination and collaboration, with teamwork representing the most focused type of team. Their contingency approach that includes shared team identity, clear roles and goals, interdependence, integration, and a shared responsibility reflect a description of five types of teams that are consistent with the types of teams I have encountered in my own work.

In their review of relevant social sciences, theoretical frameworks have particular relevance to health care teams. As illustrated in Table 6.1, Reeves and colleagues (2010) organized theories into micro, mid-range, and grand theories. This organization highlights the importance of including theories that "help to illuminate all the different elements of teamwork," including the relational, processual, organizational, and contextual components (p. 79).

Systems theory (von Bertalanffy, 1968) and systems-ecological theory (Bronfenbrenner, 1979) provide theoretical frameworks to understand team processes and functioning

Table 6.1: Social Science Theories That Aid Better Understanding of Interprofessional Teamwork

Factor	Theoretical Approach	Type	Teamwork Focus
Relational	Psychodynamic perspectives (Bion, 1961; Marris, 1968; Menzies, 1970)	Micro	Unconscious processes related to team function
	Social psychological perspectives (Brown, 1999; Tajifel & Turner, 1986)	Micro	Social identity and conflict
	Interactionism (Goffman, 1963; Strauss, 1978)	Micro	Team interactions
Processual	Activity theory (Engeström, 1999)	Mid-range	Completion of team tasks and activities
Organizational	Institutional influence (DiMaggio & Powell, 1983)	Mid-range	Influence of institutions on team relations and team performance
Contextual	Professionalization (Freidson, 1970)	Mid-range	Closure between professions
	Discourse theory (Foucault, 1972)	Grand	Wider influences of social power on interprofessional teamwork
	Surveillance theory (Foucault, 1972)	Grand	

Source: Cited in S. Reeves, S. Lewin, S. Espin, & M. Zwarenstein (2010), *Interprofessional Teamwork for Health and Social Care* (Oxford, United Kingdom: Wiley-Blackwell). Reprinted with permission.

on the microsystem, mesosystem, exosystem, and macrosystem. These frameworks posit that all parts of the systems are connected, from the micro individual to macro cultural attitudes and ideologies. A change in one part of a system affects all other parts. The flow of information between system boundaries is relevant to all health disciplines. The application of systems knowledge to the micro level (such as at the cellular level for medicine) is different than the knowledge required to understand the macro level of patients and their families.

TEAMS AND TEAMWORK SUBCOMPETENCIES

TT1: Describe the process of team development and the roles and practices of effective teams.

Describing the process of team development and the roles and practices of effective teams actually represents three different competency skills. The skill to describe the process of team development and the various roles associated with team functioning requires a theoretical understanding of team or group processes, especially if the description is to go beyond that of passive observation. Chapter 5 provides an excellent review for understanding the different professional roles and responsibilities associated with the different disciplines; therefore, this chapter focuses on the process roles associated with high-functioning teams. Roles such as facilitator, compromiser, summarizer, time-keeper, and documentarian are vitally important to team functioning. Understanding the nature of these roles and how these process roles intersect with the professional roles of colleagues requires an added level of knowledge and skills, especially if the principles of patient-centered interprofessional practice are a team's priority. Unlike the professional role of the nurse or social worker, which will remain constant, the introduction of each new patient and each new situation will require the process roles assumed by the members of the team to change. For example, if the presenting situation is one that involves complex medical complications, the nurse or physician might be better suited to be the team facilitator of the discussion. If the situation is complicated by complex psychosocial issues, the social worker might be better suited to be the team facilitator.

To describe the process of team development, individual members would benefit from understanding the stages of development that all groups experience. Although the health care team is a unique, highly specialized task group, the basic stages of group or team development should not be ignored. Team development mirrors the process or stages of group development as articulated by Tuckman in 1965. Unfortunately, the pace of health care in many settings seldom allows structured time for the team to work through the coming together of a team (forming), establishing the expectations of how the team will interact or conduct its work (norming), the vying for attention or leadership (storming), and the ultimate goal of carrying out its work as an IP team (performing) stages of team development (Tuckman, 1965; Yalom & Leazcs, 2005). It is unrealistic to think that a team will go from forming to performing without experiencing the norming and storming. Thus, it is important to have the skills to take advantage of situations that provide an opportunity to accomplish the tasks of norming and the inevitable storming. As illustrated in the case of Mrs. Garcia, the failure of the team to introduce the new social worker to the members of the team (forming) and provide her with some understanding of how the team operates (norming) resulted in a break-down in communication and a general failure in the initial discharge plan (performing) presented to Mrs. Garcia. The team failed to provide the family with any information about the team process and norms, let alone make any attempt to help the Garcia family to think they had any role in the meeting other than to listen to the "experts."

TT2: Develop consensus on the ethical principles to guide all aspects of team work.

Developing a consensus on ethical principles to guide care would not appear to be problematic for health care professionals. Doing no harm, obtaining informed consent, and maintaining patient or person autonomy are common principles adhered to by all the health professions. Yet in the context of person-centered care, achieving this competency can be one of the most challenging. It was quickly apparent that not all team members perceived the autonomy of Mrs. Garcia and her family in the same way in their first plan of care.

The application of these principles can and will vary, especially if there is a commitment to person-centered care. The cultural, economic, religious, organizational, and individual ethics of all those involved must be considered in order to arrive at a consensus. Chapters 3 and 4 provide a more complete discussion and a solid foundation for achieving this competency.

TT3: Engage health and other professionals in shared patient-centered and population-focused problem-solving.

As evidenced in the Garcia case, although the team initially appeared to be engaged in problem solving, there was no voice given to the patient's values. Shared patient-centered problem solving requires a level of trust between provider and patient that is not always easy to achieve for either party. Previous roles (memberships) that providers have had with patients, especially those perceived as incapable of managing their own care, as well as patients who have had experiences with professionals who have not acknowledged their needs, will affect patient-centered collaboration and problem solving. Understanding how these previous memberships can intersect with motivation, capacity, and opportunity (Ripple, 1964) is critical to developing trust in a patient-centered problem-solving process.

Patient-centered problem solving also requires a clear understanding of the various roles and responsibilities of each member of the interprofessional team. Understanding the roles and responsibilities of the team is easier when the team has worked together over a period of time, but this is not always the case in health care. Traditional delivery of health care has fostered the role of observer or learner when patients or family members are included in team case conferencing. Although there is growing recognition of the importance of including patients as members of the health care team, the degree to which the patient's voice is included in the problem-solving process varies greatly. Achieving person- or patient-centered practice and participant direction requires a level of trust and communication from both the providers and the patient. The roles and responsibilities of all members of the team, including the patient and family member, must be clearly understood. Although a detailed discussion on the philosophical and practical application of "person-centered' and "participant-direction" is beyond the scope of this text, a number of resources and training materials can be found on Boston College's National Resource Center for Participant-Directed Services Web site.

Life course theory is also helpful to understanding how the cumulative life experiences of individuals can affect both motivation and capacity to engage in a patient-centered approach to problem solving. Life course theory posits that social and political events throughout the individual's life can have an impact on individuals and cohorts of individuals. As such, life course realities, such as racism, ageism, sexism, gendered stereotyping, discrimination, and cumulative advantage and disadvantage, can affect perceived power and privilege among members of the team. The hierarchical model of health care has traditionally positioned the physician as the most powerful and privileged member of the team, followed perhaps by nurses, physical and occupational therapists, social workers, and finally the patient. Patient-centered problem solving inherently requires a realignment of this traditional model to one that positions and prepares the patient to not only be at the center of the IP team, but to have a clear voice to express their priorities and wishes.

> TT4: Integrate the knowledge and experience of health and other professions to inform health and care decisions, while respecting patient and community values and priorities/preferences for care.

Integrating the knowledge and experience of other professions requires individuals to balance their personal disciplinary experiences of delivering care with the experiences of their colleagues and, most important, the patient. The person-centered approach requires an awareness of and respect for the individual's perspective of self and family, as well as the individual's perception of community values and priorities or preferences for care. Encouraging honest communication can foster a relationship where patients feel safe to disclose when they are not following or understanding the care recommendations or feel concerned about their role in the care plan. In writing about end-of-life care in his book *Being Mortal*, Atul Gawande states the importance of asking four key questions that are at the root of person-centered care: "What is your understanding of the situation and its potential outcomes? What are your fears and what are your hopes? What are the trade-offs you are willing to make and not willing to make? Lastly, what is the course of action that bests serves this understanding?" (Gawande, 2014, p. 259).

In the case of the Garcia family, the team cannot determine that discharging Mrs. Garcia home is a reasonable option until she and her family answer the aforementioned questions. Preparing the family to monitor Mrs. Garcia's progress and symptoms consistently and communicate any changes to the provider is a complex but necessary process. The team must first clearly communicate the requirements of a safe discharge home and confirm that the family is willing to accept the trade-offs associated with the identified care needs.

> TT5: Apply leadership practices that support collaborative practice and team effectiveness.

The roles associated with a highly functioning team should be situation dependent. Like other teamwork roles, the leadership role must be flexible and shared among members as the situation changes. Both choice theory (Glasser, 2010) and emotional intelligence are used to understand what qualities of team leadership result in improved team functioning (Goleman, Boyatzis, & McKee, 2002). Emotional intelligence (EI) requires an awareness of the individual's needs and, just as important, an awareness of the needs of others. Interprofessional teamwork occurs when the individual needs and wants of all members of the team become unified into an interprofessional plan of care (Goleman et al., 2002). The leaders who use EI to bring about positive attitudes and behaviors are noted by Goleman and colleagues to be the "primal" leaders.

TT6: Engage self and others to constructively manage disagreements about values, roles, goals, and actions that arise among health and other professionals and with patients, families, and community members.

The skill to engage self and others requires a reflective and reflexive engagement with individuals' perceptions and understanding of any situation (see TT9). The disagreements that emerge during this process are best understood as opportunities to further clarify a position, value, or rationale of individual members. In addition to clarifying values and managing communication (discussed in Chapters 3 and 4, respectively), understanding the emotional connection that individuals have to an idea or position is critical to managing any disagreement. The EI approach suggests that recognizing, understanding, and discussing the emotional needs of both individual members and the larger needs of the team will result in better team functioning.

TT7: Share accountability with other professions, patients, and communities for outcomes relevant to prevention and health care.

Shared accountability for outcomes relevant to prevention and care rests on recognizing the micro-, macro-, and mesosystems associated with quality patient-centered care. The interaction and linkages between the individual, providers, and the medical and community-based social systems of care, and, most important, the provider and the community, are best understood within an ecological systems framework (Bronfenbrenner, 1979). Accountability for outcomes also rests on a diligent identification of the strengths, weaknesses, and interaction of multiple systems contributing to both the prevention and capacity for self-care.

In addition to understanding roles and responsibilities of different team members, sharing accountability requires a recognition of how individual experiences occurring during their life influence their interactions with others, especially doctors and others in the health care profession who traditionally have been perceived to be in a position of power. The team's lack of awareness about the wishes of the family is not uncommon, especially with patients and families who have not been included in the decision-making process throughout their life course.

TT8: Reflect on individual and team performance for individual, as well as team, performance improvement.

TT9: Use process improvement to increase effectiveness of interprofessional teamwork and team-based services, programs, and policies.

TT10: Use available evidence to inform effective teamwork and team-based practices.

One challenge to reflecting and evaluating team performance is that all evaluation has to be understood from multiple perspectives. Consider the case of Mrs. Garcia. Although team members thought they had performed admirably, in the eyes of Mrs. Garcia and her family, their efforts failed. Any reflection on a team's performance can be influenced by the evaluator's position and the focus of the evaluation. For example, the perspective from administration on how the team responds to administrative priorities is different than the perspective of the team members on how the team functions. Similarly, the perspective of team members on how the team is functioning might be very different from the perspective of the patient. Consequently, the team might be evaluated negatively by administration when a discharge is delayed because of inadequate community-based care; however, if that one-day delay prevents a costly return to the emergency room or rehospitalization of the patient, then the evaluation by administration could be significantly more favorable.

The challenges of evaluating effective teamwork practice, as well as interprofessional education and training programs, are well documented (Barr, 2005; Gillan, Lovrics, Halpern, Wiljer, D., & Harnett, 2011; Reeves et al., 2008). Among the recommendations of the recent Institute of Medicine (IOM) (2015) report were the need to better align IPE and interprofessional practice and greater use of theoretically based models of IPE and linking IPE with patient level outcomes. It is noteworthy that in most of the published literature addressing some of the challenges there was little, if any, mention of including the voice of patients. Using a social justice lens, the available evidence can be limited to the evidence that is deemed worthy by a select few for consideration. The inevitable privileging of certain voices at the cost of other voices can be a threat to patient-centered models of care. The voices of patients and family members should be a key consideration as health care moves in the direction of providing patient-centered care. To date, the voices of patients and family members have been limited to a telephone survey focusing on patient satisfaction after care is provided, but not on the role or interactions with the interprofessional team.

TT11. Perform effectively on teams and in different team roles in a variety of settings.

Following the discussion provided earlier in this chapter, the competence to perform in a variety of roles associated with effective teamwork is best mastered if the roles related to team functioning (leader, timekeeper, documentarian, facilitator, and so on) are distinguished from the roles related to patient care (nurse, social worker, physician, and so on). Regular debriefing of team members' performance facilitating the functioning of the team must occur within the context of the presenting situation. Recognizing that different situations might demand members to assume unfamiliar roles, the debriefing process should be framed as an opportunity for learning. This requires a level of trust among the members of the team so that the opportunity to learn is not sabotaged by overly critical discussion.

STRATEGIES TO DEVELOP COMPETENCY

Pre-Certificate

In addition to the strategies presented in Part 3 of this book, there are a growing number of opportunities for developing competence in team and teamwork. Given the overcrowded curriculum that many disciplines face, enhancing existing curriculum with content, also known as curriculum infusion, is one approach worthy of consideration. However, infusing interprofessional content into an already overcrowded curriculum requires a systemic commitment to interprofessional learning by administration and faculty across multiple disciplines. There are a number of curricular infusion tools that were developed by the Gero-Ed Center and are available online (http://www.cswe.org/CentersInitiatives/GeroEdCenter.aspx). Although they were developed for infusing content on aging, the lessons learned from their efforts translate nicely to infusing interprofessional content into existing curriculum.

In addition to infusing content into existing curriculum (and in the absence of an interprofessional pre-certificate program such as those outlined in Part 3, with multiple disciplines learning together), there are a growing number of models that provide interprofessional learning opportunities for students. The Geriatric Assessment Interdisciplinary Team is a voluntary program that provides a two-day elective in interprofessional practice for University System of Maryland students through the Eastern Shore and Western Maryland Area Health Education Centers via grant funding to the Geriatrics and Gerontology Education and Research Program. Northeastern University also offers interdisciplinary certificates in a range of subjects, including preparing students to serve infants and toddlers with disabilities or who are at risk for developmental delays, as well as certificates in aging that focus on the health care needs of older adults (http://www.northeastern.edu/bouve/about/iprep/).

Post-Certificate Strategies for Practicing Providers

There are a number of group exercises available that can be used to facilitate a process through the forming, norming, storming, and performing stages (Yalom & Leazcs, 2005) of team development. It is important to think about which theoretical framework best applies to the context, strengths, and goals of the team. For example, a strategy for developing the team in the emergency department might include a time-limited fast-paced activity, whereas an oncology team might benefit from a strategy that requires reflection and sharing of personal information. The growing number of team training and education programs in health care that have been developed in the past decade is noteworthy. That number is even larger when taking into account team-building training programs in areas such as mental health and child protection, as well as in other disciplines, such as organizational management, liberal arts, and education. Combinations of didactic lecture, experiential exercises, simulation experiences, and supervised experiences with patients are common to most, if not all, educational training curricula.

In addition to established training programs such as TeamSTEPPS (http://teamstepps.ahrq.gov/about-2cl_3.htm) and Interprofessional Team Capstone (Brock et al., 2013), as discussed in chapter 4, the following strategies can be used to develop competence in effective teamwork. I have used the membership exercise in interprofessional training programs I have facilitated to provide a foundation for interprofessional relationships that result in effective teamwork. As team members learn about prior memberships or roles and the conditions of accessibility associated with those roles, especially their professional roles, the their level of trust and intimacy with their colleagues will ultimately improve.

Bayley, Wallace, Spurgeon, Barwell, and Mazelan (2007) described an evaluation of the Teambuilding Program, a two-day training program for health care professionals. The program included content on viewing professionals' perspectives and expectations of the roles, functions, tasks, and responsibilities of team members. The participants then developed the team norms and values as expressed in behavioral terms. The training program concluded with an experiential problem-solving exercise. Although they found short-term gains in perceptions of the team, the effects were not necessarily enduring.

The Teams of Interprofessional Staff Project (TIPS) used three two-day face-to-face sessions that were delivered over an eight-month period using a mixed method approach to evaluate the impact of interprofessional team development for five teams (Bajnok, Puddester, MacDonald, Archibald, & Kuhl, 2012). This training program included a focus on team functioning, team member satisfaction, the ability to work effectively both individually and as a team, and patient well-being. Among the noteworthy findings from this study were the importance of institutional support for interprofessional teams, a perceived benefit of the knowledge and tools provided during the training, and, for some participants, an improvement in patient care (Bajnok et al., 2012).

A five-session interprofessional training model that took place over a two-year period was conducted by Cashman, Reidy, Cody, and Lemay (2004). Content focused on team characteristics, collaborative problem solving, and communication. Using the System for the Multiple Level Observation of Groups (Bales & Cohen, 1979), the researchers analyzed changes in a team over time. The dimensions originally identified by Bales and Cohen include dominant versus submissive, friendly versus unfriendly, and acceptance versus nonacceptance of task orientation of established authority. Prior to participating in the intervention, individual team members were asked to respond to a series of 26 questions that probed values that each team member ascribed to the current teams. Though the training program produced positive effects, findings indicated that better approaches to reducing team turnover are needed to ensure that interdisciplinary teams grow. It is noteworthy that results from follow-up interviews with participants indicated that a number of factors, such as micro-, macro-, and meso-level challenges, resulted in a diminishing of the training outcomes.

Achieving competency in the teams and teamwork domain is a complex and challenging process. As previously discussed in the introduction to this book, there is a paucity of empirical data about interprofessional education and training (IOM, 2015). That said, developing theoretically informed models of training that establish evaluation strategies during the design phase of programs is a critical next step in the evolution of interprofessional education and practice (IOM, 2015).

REFERENCES

Advisory Committee on Interdisciplinary, Community-Based Linkages. (2014, October). *Transforming interprofessional health education and practice: Moving learners from the campus to the community to improve population health* (13th annual report). Retrieved from http://www.hrsa.gov/advisorycommittees/bhpradvisory/acicbl/Reports/thirteenthreport.pdf

Bajnok, I., Puddester, D., MacDonald, C. J., Archibald, D., & Kuhl, D. (2012). Building positive relationships in healthcare: Evaluation of the Teams of Interprofessional Staff interprofessional education program. *Contemporary Nursing, 42*(1), 76–89.

Bales, R. F., & Cohen, S.P. (1979). *SYMLOG: A systematic multiple level observation of groups.* New York: Free Press.

Barr, H. (2005). Evaluation, evidence and effectiveness. *Journal of Interprofessional Care, 19,* 535–536.

Bayley, J. E., Wallace, L. M., Spurgeon, P., Barwell, F., & Mazelan, P. (2007). Teamworking in healthcare: Longitudinal evaluation of a teambuilding intervention. *Learning in Health and Social Care, 6,* 187–201.

Brock, D., Abu-Rish, E., Chiu, C., Hammer, D., Wilson, S., Vorvick, L., et al. (2013). Interprofessional education in team communication: Working together to improve patient safety. *Quality and Safety in Health Care, 22,* 414–423.

Bronfenbrenner, U. (1979). *The ecology of human development: Experiments by nature and design.* Cambridge, MA: Harvard University Press.

Bruce, N. (1980). *Teamwork for prevention.* Chichester, United Kingdom: Wiley.

Cashman, S. B., Reidy, P., Cody, K., & Lemay, C. A. (2004). Developing and measuring progress toward collaborative, integrated, interdisciplinary health care teams. *Journal of Interprofessional Care, 18,* 183–196.

Council on Social Work Education. (2015). *Educational policy and accreditation standards.* Retrieved from http://www.cswe.org/File.aspx?id=81660

DiMaggio, P., & Powell, W. (1983). The iron cage revisited: Institutional isomorphism and collective rationality in organizational fields. *American Sociological Review, 48,* 147–160.

Dyer, W. G., Jr., Dyer, J. H., & Dyer, W. (2013). *Team building: Proven strategies for improving team performance* (5th ed.). San Francisco: Wiley.

Epstein, R. M. (1999). Mindful practice. *JAMA, 282,* 833–839.

Falck, H. (1988). *Social work: The membership perspective.* New York: Springer.

Gawande, A. (2014). *Being mortal: Medicine and what matters in the end.* New York: Macmillan.

Gillan, C., Lovrics, E., Halpern, E., Wiljer, D., & Harnett, N. (2011). The evaluation of learner outcomes on interprofessional continuing education: A literature review and an analysis of survey instruments. *Medical Teacher, 33,* e461–e470.

Glasser, W. (2010). Choice theory: A new psychology of personal freedom. New York: HarperCollins.

Goffman, E. (1963). *The presentation of self in everyday life.* New York: Penguin Press.

Goleman, D., Boyatzis, R., & McKee, A. (2002). *The new leaders: Transforming the art of leadership into the science of results.* London: Time Warner Books.

Grigsby, R. K. (2006, July–August). Are you really a team player? *Academic Physician and Scientist,* pp. 4–5.

Hellriegel, D., & Slocum, J. W. (2011). *Organizational behavior.* Mason, OH: South-Western.

Institute of Medicine. (2015). *Measuring the impact of interprofessional education on collaborative practice and patient outcomes.* Washington, DC: National Academies Press.

Interprofessional Education Collaborative. (2016). *Core competencies for interprofessional collaborative practice: 2016 update.* Washington, DC: Author.

Interprofessional Education Collaborative Expert Panel. (2011). *Core competencies for interprofessional collaborative practice: Report of an expert panel.* Washington, DC: Interprofessional Education Collaborative.

Katzenbach, J., & Smith, D. (1993). *The wisdom of teams: Creating the high-performance organization.* Boston: Harvard Business School Press.

Oandasan, I., Baker, G. R., Barker, K., Bosco, C., D'Amour, D., Jones, L., et al. (2006). *Teamwork in healthcare: Promoting effective teamwork in healthcare in Canada.* Ottawa: Canadian Health Services Research Foundation.

Reeves, S., Lewin, S., Espin, S., & Zwarenstein, M. (2010). *Interprofessional teamwork for health and social care.* Oxford, United Kingdom: Wiley-Blackwell.

Reeves, S., Zwarenstein, M., Goldman, J., Barr, H., Freeth, D., Hammick. M., & Koppel, I. (2008). Interprofessional education: Effects on professional practice and health care outcomes. *Cochrane Database Systemic Review, 1,* CD002213.

Ripple, L. (1964). *Motivation, capacity, and opportunity.* Chicago: University of Chicago Press.

Tajifel, H., & Turner, J. (1986). The social identity theory of inter-group behavior. In S. Worchel & L. Austin (Eds.), *Psychology of intergroup relations* (pp. 1–24). Chicago: Nelson-Hall.

Tuckman, B. (1965). Developmental sequence in small groups. *Psychological Bulletin, 63,* 384–399.

von Bertalanffy, L. (1968). *General system theory: Essays on its foundation and development* (Rev. ed.). New York: George Braziller.

Woodfield, S., & Kennie, T. (2008). 'Teamwork' or 'working as a team'? The theory and practice of top team working in the UK higher education. *Higher Education Quarterly, 62,* 397–415. doi:10.1111/j.1468-2273.2008.00399.x

Yalom, I. D., & Leazcs, M. (2005). *Theory and practice of group psychodynamics* (5th ed.). Cambridge, MA: Basic Books.

Part 3

INTERPROFESSIONAL EDUCATION PROGRAMS IN THE UNITED STATES

7

UNIVERSITY OF KENTUCKY

James C. Norton

The University of Kentucky (UK) was established 150 years ago and is the flagship institution for higher education in the state. A land-grant university, it is a Carnegie Research Intensive institution and acknowledged also as an engaged institution by the Carnegie Foundation. It is nationally ranked in a number of areas. Its academic health center was founded in the early 1960s and now includes six health professions colleges. It has a number of distinctions. The Markey Cancer Center is the state's only National Cancer Institute Designated Cancer Center. UK's Center for Clinical and Translational Science joined the ranks of federally funded centers in 2011, receiving a Clinical and Translational Science Award from the National Institutes of Health. Its College of Pharmacy is consistently listed among the top 10 in the nation, and the College of Medicine was recognized for its commitment to social justice in 2010. UK HealthCare was identified as a rising star in terms of quality by the University Health Systems Consortium in 2013.

Interest in interdisciplinary education (IPE) has been long-standing at UK, but activity has increased significantly in recent years and taken on a more formal structure. In 2010, the Center for Interprofessional Health Education, Research and Practice (now the Center for Interprofessional Health Education) was established. This process will be described in detail later. The center reports to the provost and is governed by a board of directors made up of the deans of the involved colleges. It is chaired by one of the board's members named by the provost, with advice from the board. The center's director is also named by the provost with advice from the board and works closely on a day-to-day basis with the board chair.

In terms of the organizational structure relevant to IPE, UK is one of the few institutions in the country with all six health professions' colleges located on the main campus of the university in close proximity to one another. The colleges serve the disciplines of dentistry, health sciences, medicine, nursing, pharmacy, and public health. The

College of Health Sciences, originally called the College of Allied Health Professions, offers a number of programs organized in two large departments. The Department of Rehabilitation Sciences offers programs in athletic training, communication sciences and disorders, physical therapy, and a rehabilitation sciences doctoral program. The Department of Clinical Sciences offers programs in clinical and reproductive sciences, clinical nutrition, medical laboratory science, physician assistant studies, human health sciences, and clinical leadership and management.

In terms of the geography, the Colleges of Dentistry, Health Sciences, Medicine, Nursing, and Pharmacy are contiguous and, for the most part, connected to one another and to UK HealthCare's Kentucky Clinical and Chandler Hospital by hallways and covered bridges. The College of Public Health, though not connected to the academic health center, is a short walk away. The Colleges of Communications and Information and of Social Work, both of which have been actively involved in the efforts, are within reasonable walking distance. This proximity greatly helped the developmental efforts in that people could attend meetings with relative ease, and perhaps even more important, many of those involved in the effort encountered one another in the normal course of their clinical and academic work. Such chance encounters offer opportunities for quick discussions and exchange of ideas, making the work of committees more efficient and contributing to the sense of collegiality that is so important when embarking on an initiative such as this.

Although UK has the advantages described above, there also are structural barriers that are fairly typical of academic health centers. Academic and clinical collaboration has occasionally occurred, but the colleges function largely autonomously, with their respective deans reporting to the provost. They are also, to a degree, competitive with one another in matters of funding. Because they are autonomous as regards their curricula, class scheduling, beyond having to follow the university's calendar, is done as the colleges see fit and without regard to the scheduling of the other colleges. The exception to this has to do with classroom access. Though each college has control over certain classrooms, a much larger number of rooms are scheduled centrally. Historically, the colleges have also managed clinical training autonomously. The bulk of clinical training for medicine and dentistry is done within the UK HealthCare system, while for other colleges and programs, clinical sites outside UK are primarily used. As will be described later, one of the earliest successes of the emerging IPE initiative was an effort led by the Area Health Education Center (AHEC) Program in 2008 to get clinical rotations across the programs at UK, the University of Louisville, and the private University of Pikeville's osteopathic college on a common calendar of four-week blocks. Until this was done, clinical rotation schedules differed substantially across disciplines.

A final structural reality about UK is worth mentioning in this context. It has not, in fact, been a barrier but could be at some point. It concerns the relationship between the clinical enterprise (UK HealthCare) and the academic programs. The enterprise is led by the executive vice president for health affairs, Dr. Michael Karpf, who reports directly to the president and is responsible for ensuring the success, financial and otherwise, of UK's large and complex health care delivery system. All of the academic programs, in contrast, report through their deans to the provost, who, in turn, reports to the president. This administrative structure was implemented some years ago by then president Lee Todd, replacing the chancellor system. In that system, there was a chancellor for the medical center to whom both the clinical enterprise and the health professions academic programs reported. Because the clinical enterprise serves as the primary clinical training site for many of the academic programs, there is potentially an advantage, in the context of developing IPE, in having a single individual overseeing both the clinical enterprise and the academic programs. For example, there might be identified a clinical service particularly well suited to serve as a teaching site for IPE but one whose leadership does not have a particular interest in training multiple professional students. In such a situation, there could be a conflict between the academic programs and the clinical program in question. Resolution of such a conflict is potentially more easily achieved in a system in which the conflicted parties report to the same leader. To be clear, this has not been a problem at UK, where the enterprise has been exceedingly supportive of IPE and the center, both financially and philosophically. Still, the administrative structure offers some potential vulnerabilities should the leadership change.

HISTORY OF IPE AT UK

At UK, there is some history of explicitly interprofessional training, much of it associated with the AHEC Program. There are, however, examples that predate the establishment of AHEC nationally or at UK. As early as the 1960s, the Kentucky January Program placed health professions students of many disciplines in communities during the winter break to diagnose community health issues and work on solutions. This occurred under the leadership of then dean of the College of Allied Health Professions (now the College of Health Sciences) Dr. Joe Hamburg. Later, the program was postponed to May, and it persisted into the 1990s, when it was abandoned because of a decline in participation outside the disciplines within the college.

Once in place, AHEC became an early champion of IPE at UK. In 2004, for example, the AHEC Program convened the directors of clinical courses that included AHEC rotations to discuss formally introducing IPE during such rotations. AHEC-sponsored meetings of these course directors were an annual event at that time, and IPE was a theme chosen for one such meeting. National experts, including Barbara Brandt, Maria C. Clay, Pamela Mitchell, and Joe Florence, were brought in to a retreat setting for this event and there was much enthusiasm for IPE expressed. Translation of that enthusiasm into substantive curricular change, however, was not widespread, though some innovations were attempted. For example, a member of the community faculty from the College of Pharmacy, Dr. Tom Houchens, worked with then AHEC Program associate director Jim Ballard to introduce interprofessional shadowing during community-based rotations for pharmacy students, the goal being to provide the student with an in-depth understanding of the work of other health professionals. More recently, there have been examples of colleges and programs identifying opportunities for IPE in simulation settings as well as at clinical training sites. Activities like these provided some historical context and gave faculty members who contributed to the process of creating a contemporary IPE culture at UK firsthand experience.

Finally, in terms of history, it is also worth noting that interprofessional practice has long been part of the UK HealthCare culture. Though it is more evident in some clinical services than in others, interprofessional practice has historically been espoused as a core value. As an interest in IPE was developing in the academic programs, it became clear that there were a number of highly effective clinical services that were interprofessional in their philosophy and function. These programs offered a sort of role modeling for faculty working to create IPE experiences for their students. Examples included the trauma service, cystic fibrosis clinic, and physical medicine and rehabilitation services associated with Cardinal Hill Hospital and the Markey Cancer Center's program of comprehensive, interprofessional care for cancer patients, among many others.

IDENTIFICATION OF FACULTY AND CREATION OF THE WORKING GROUP

To a great extent, the IPE faculty champions who emerged during the period roughly from 2000 to the present were self-selected. However, it was also essential that such individuals have the support of their deans. As work in IPE began in earnest around 2008, three of the deans played particularly critical roles: Drs. Jay Perman, Jane Kirshling, and Sharon Turner.

Jay Perman was dean of the College of Medicine from 2004 to 2010. As a pediatric gastroenterologist, Dr. Perman had engaged in interprofessional practice all of his professional career and was thus a key champion and role model for IPE at UK. His counterpart in the College of Nursing at that time was Jane Kirshling, doctor of nursing science. She also was keenly interested in IPE, promoting it among her faculty and supporting early efforts at curricular reform. The relatively rapid development of IPE infrastructure at UK owes a very great deal to these two deans; their departure within a year of one another was a loss to UK and to the IPE effort then under way. Dr. Perman became president at the University of Maryland's Professional Campus in Baltimore, and Dr. Kirshling followed him there shortly thereafter, recruited in part to lead IPE at that institution. Dr. Sharon Turner, dean of the College of Dentistry, also was instrumental in a number of ways. First, she was a strong advocate for IPE generally and for ensuring that dentistry was at the table and fully engaged. Also, much of the funding that supported the center came indirectly from the College of Dentistry through its practice plan.

In addition to these three leaders, Dr. Tim Tracy, dean of the College of Pharmacy, was an early and articulate supporter of IPE. Dr. Lori Gonzalez, who was dean of the College of Health Sciences during this developmental phase, ultimately became the first chair of the board of directors once a formal center was established. Dr. Tracy followed her in leading the board and provided guidance to the center's first director, Dr. Andrea Pfeifle, first in his role as board chair and subsequently as interim provost. Once a permanent provost was named, Dr. Tracy returned to the college and continued to guide the IPE effort and to chair the board. More recently, he was named provost after the brief tenure of his predecessor, and because the center resides in the provost's office, he continues to play a critical role. Dr. Janie Heath replaced Dr. Kirshling as dean of the College of Nursing. IPE was very high on her list of priorities. She currently chairs the board.

In terms of programs and faculty involved, all the health professions colleges and programs were initially engaged in the effort, as were the Colleges of Social Work, Law, and Communication and Information. Over time, the College of Public Health became less involved. The initial commitment with the College of Law was never very strong and dissipated over time, ending formally in 2015. More recently, the College of Public Health has reengaged and is a full partner at present. A sizeable number of people were involved in the working group and the subgroups that spun off from it. Identifying all of them here would take up a great deal of space. As we discuss the particular initiatives that led to our current status, though, key individuals will be named.

In the context of identifying faculty, it is worth reiterating that UK has had, for many years, a very strong AHEC Program. By definition, AHECs are at least multidisciplinary in their focus, if not explicitly interprofessional. Dr. Pfeifle was well connected with the AHEC Program through years of collaboration in community-based education. At that time, I led the AHEC Program. I also had an interest in IPE, as did Carlos Marin, who followed my tenure in leading the AHEC Program. Given these shared interests, Dr. Pfeifle wisely reached out to AHEC to assist in convening interested faculty members in exploring how to initiate an explicit IPE focus among our health professions colleges and programs.

When embarking on an initiative like this, the question of faculty compensation quickly arises. The issue of inclusion of IPE in the job expectations for the faculty involved was handled differently in different colleges. Both the College of Health Sciences and the College of Nursing identified IPE activities explicitly in the distribution of effort documents for the faculty members involved. Health Sciences, in fact, has at times brought in and paid adjunct faculty to cover faculty needs in IPE. In other colleges, contributions to IPE efforts were subsumed under the faculty members' general teaching responsibilities. Once it was established, the center supported faculty development activities for interested faculty by providing support for travel to professional meetings and funding accredited continuing education offerings through the UK continuing education program, UKHealthCare CECentral. It did not and does not, however, provide salary support.

TIMELINE OF KEY EVENTS

In describing the timeline and milestones, we will follow the path that led to the creation of the center and follow its evolution from founding to current status. In a general way, it is safe to say that the formal creation of the center followed the initiation of IPE efforts, rather than generating them. Dr. Pfeifle was working diligently with a great many partners in IPE efforts during the period when the proposal for the center was being written and during the period of review by various university bodies. From its inception, the center has been preoccupied with developing and implementing a core curriculum. These processes will be described below as each curricular element is described.

The following is a timeline of selected significant events:

- Working group formed (2008)
- AHEC subgroup clinical rotation schedule launched (2008)
- Deans' Interprofessional Honors Colloquium (DIHC) designed (2008)
- DIHC implemented (2009)
- Center established (2010)
- Common Reading Experience initiated (2011)
- Interprofessional Collaboration and Team Work Skills 1 (iCATS1) designed (2012)
- Elevator speech written and delivered (2012)
- iCATS1 implemented. (2013)
- Interprofessional Collaboration and Team Work Skills 2 (iCATS2) designed (2013)
- iCATS1 revised (2013)
- iCATS1 revision implemented (2014)
- iCATS2 abandoned (2014)
- Holsinger Committee Report delivered (2014)
- Holsinger Committee Report adopted (2015)
- iCATS1 revised (2015)
- Authentic Clinical IPE defined (2015)
- Center renamed (2015)

Looking over this timeline, several items should be highlighted in terms of the early developmental steps taken to make IPE a reality at UK. As mentioned before, the working group was initiated by Dr. Perman around 2008 and chaired by Dr. Pfeifle. It functioned in one form or another from then until 2014 but over time spun off a number of other committees and met less frequently. In the beginning, however, it was the source of several early IPE efforts.

AHEC Subgroup Clinical Rotation Schedule Launched (2008)

The first such effort was the reformation of the clinical rotation schedule mentioned above that synchronized to a significant degree the calendars of the clinical training programs. This was pursued for two reasons. First, it removed or greatly lessened the problem of regional AHECs and their community faculty having to cope with programs trying to place students from one program on a rotation scheduled to start on a date that fell in the middle of a rotation from another program. Second, having students arrive and leave more or less at the same time would be very helpful, if not absolutely necessary, to developing IPE experiences in clinical rotation settings. Once the schedule change was effected, a subcommittee of the working group was formed to design such a rotation. Generally, this schedule change has worked out quite well, but developing it required a considerable amount of time and negotiation. The process exemplifies a major challenge the IPE initiative had to face, that is, trying to coordinate calendars across colleges and programs to find times for students to be together. To date, this has been only partially solved (as will be described in subsequent sections of the chapter).

DIHC Designed (2008), Implemented (2009)

The DIHC also grew out of discussions in the working group. We had been struggling to find a time in the preclinical curriculum when all involved colleges and programs could free up students to participate with defining a curricular element that would be of value to them. At some point in this ongoing debate, a consensus emerged that we needed to stop talking and do something, anything that was both relevant and possible. The DIHC idea fit this bill very well for several reasons. First, because it did not involve all the students, the logistics were potentially more manageable. Second, because it would focus on a select group of motivated students, the possibility of success was high. Third, the structure we developed seemed relevant to IPE and of interest both to faculty members and to students. It will be described in detail shortly.

Center Established (2010)

Certainly a major timeline event was the establishment of the Center for Interprofessional Health Education, Research and Practice (CIHERP) in 2010. Led by Dr. Pfeifle, with assistance from the associate director, Jim Ballard, the center was given a very broad charge. Here are the mission and vision statements as approved by its board of directors at that time:

> MISSION: Promote teamwork and excellence in patient and community-centered care through interprofessional education, research, and practice.

> VISION: The University of Kentucky Center for Interprofessional HealthCare Education, Research, and Practice will lead U.S. universities and academic medical centers in developing, validating, and promoting interprofessional education and care models that improve patient and population health.

These statements reflect a very ambitious agenda for a center that consisted essentially of two part-time staff members and a large number of more or less voluntary faculty members.

Once established, the center's mode of operation continued to rely on the working group as the core, with several other committees developed to address particular elements of the mission. Specifically, a faculty development committee was formed to design programs to prepare faculty members for IPE. In addition, a practice committee was formed to explore how the center could have an impact on the mode of practice within UK HealthCare, and a research committee was charged with facilitating research on team-based care and IPE. The faculty development committee had and continues to have a significant impact. It designed innovative face-to-face training for faculty involved in Interprofessional Collaboration and Team Work Skills 1 (iCATS1), our first attempt at a course to reach all students, and produced online modules that are continuing education accredited and available to any interested person worldwide, around the clock. Conversely, neither the practice committee nor the research committee was particularly productive. In part, this was due to the fact that the curricular efforts consumed virtually all the center's limited resources.

The center's sole foray into clinical research was a 2013 Nexus Grant, funded by the National Center, which supported the examination of transitions of care from acute to rehabilitation settings. Scholarly work in IPE itself has been a consistent and successful aspect of center work, but it was not driven to any significant degree by the research committee. One thing the committee did accomplish, however, is worth noting. As there was a clear intent to publish and present findings, it was necessary to have Institutional Review Board (IRB) approval in order to study IPE. The committee made the wise decision to submit a request for global IRB approval for use of the center's evaluation instruments in educational research. Once this was achieved, it was not necessary again to go to the IRB when new studies were initiated. The primary work product generated by the practice committee was a list of potential IPE educational venues within UK HealthCare. This was a useful exercise but not one likely to affect enterprise practice in a significant way.

Common Reading Experience Initiated (2011)

In 2011, another IPE innovation, the Common Reading Experience, was launched. The idea was developed by Dr. Penni Black of the College of Pharmacy, brought to the working group, and developed by a subcommittee. The idea here was that students from the participating colleges and programs would be assigned a book to read during the summer and would then meet for a discussion of the book in facilitated small groups at the beginning of the fall semester. The assigned books dealt with a health topic (thus making them of interest to health professions students) and raised issues relevant to IPE. Two book used were *The Immortal Life of Henrietta Lacks* by Rebecca Skloot (2011) and *The Spirit Catches You and You Fall Down* by Anne Fadiman (1998). The Colleges of Dentistry, Health Sciences, Medicine, Nursing, Pharmacy, and Public Health were involved. The activity was elective for students in the College of Public Health and required for all others. The groups had from 10 to 15 members and were facilitated by faculty, sometimes assisted by a student who had done the activity the year before. As will be described later, this element became part of iCATS1.

Holsinger Committee Report Delivered (2014), Adopted (2015)

Moving to the end of the timeline, we find another watershed: the report of the Holsinger Committee in 2014. The center had been in existence for approximately four years at that time, and then provost Dr. Christine Riordan charged a committee with reviewing the center's performance. Such reviews are customary. The committee charge also included evaluating IPE more generally within the educational programs of the health and related professions. At the time the committee was doing its work, three major curricular elements were in place: DIHC, Interprofessional Teamwork and Global Health (ITGH), and iCATS1. Another, Interprofessional Collaboration and Teamwork 2 (iCATS2), was about to be launched. DIHC had been running successfully since 2008, and iCATS1 was in its second year, following a very substantial revision. The modular components of iCATS2 had been developed over the preceding two years through a grant from the Macy Foundation and in collaboration with several other academic health centers. All of these curricular elements will be described in detail in the following section. However, some of the recommendations made by the committee and ultimately adopted by the board and the provost will be described here as they provide a picture of some fundamental changes in the center's philosophy and the goals it is expected to accomplish that were a product of the committee's work.

The members of Dr. Holsinger's committee were faculty leaders from the involved colleges and programs. By the time the committee completed its work, the director of the center, Dr. Andrea Pfeifle, had left UK to lead IPE efforts at Indiana University. I was asked to serve as interim director and also became part of the committee. Fundamentally, it was felt that the charge to the center at the time of its creation was too broad to be meaningfully addressed by so small an operation. Also, in the interim, other institutional changes were made to address the research and practice aspects of the original mission statement. In 2013, the UK Center for Health Systems Research was established at UK, led by Dr. Mark Williams. It has a sizeable staff and extramural funding in the millions of dollars. Clearly, any assistance UK HealthCare might need in improving its practice environment in terms of interprofessional team-based care could be provided by this center. Similarly, empirical research on such practice falls clearly within its scope. Conversely, CIHERP has played a critical role as the catalyst for educational innovation in IPE. The core recommendation of the Holsinger Committee, then, was to focus center efforts on the development, deployment, and evaluation of IPE. What research the center pursues should be addressing pedagogy, not practice.

OVERVIEW OF THE CENTER AND IPE CURRICULUM

Administration and Staffing

At present, the center has a staff of four individuals, three of whom are full-time, one half-time. The role of director is to be filled by a senior faculty member with knowledge and experience in IPE. He or she is committed half-time to the center and is assisted by an associate director with particular expertise in evaluation but also substantial knowledge and experience in health professions education. The associate director is full-time, as are two additional staff members, one designated as program coordinator and the other as educational specialist. Although their roles overlap significantly, the program coordinator has more administrative functions than does the educational specialist. The latter primarily provides technical support of faculty members in curriculum development. Business processes are supported by staff in the provost's office, and some assistance with meeting scheduling is provided through the AHEC office via contract. As described earlier, the center is governed by a board of directors, consisting of the deans of the involved colleges. This group provides strategic direction but is not involved in day-to-day management. The center reports through the chair of the board to the provost, and contact with the chair is frequent and involves substantial operational guidance. Funding for the center comes equally from UK HealthCare and the provost.

The center's activities are guided by the Academic Leadership Committee, which consists of the academic deans or their representatives from all of the participating colleges. Input is also provided by the Student Advisory Committee, whose members are appointed by the director, with input from academic leadership. Generally, the committee is composed of students who have participated in the DIHC or Leadership Legacy. The work of the center is done primarily by the faculty development committee and a collection of course committees that manage each of the curricular elements with which the center is involved. Center staff members provide support to all of these groups. Finally, the center has developed a Fellows Program, which honors individuals who have distinguished themselves as leaders in IPE. There is a broadly prescribed set of expectations for contribution to center activities and scholarly productivity that lead to granting of fellow status. Individuals may self-nominate or be nominated by others using a form provided by the center. Nominations are evaluated by academic leadership and recommended for appointment to the board of directors, which makes the final determination.

Curriculum

The center fully manages two curricular elements, collaborates with others in the management of other curricular elements, fully manages several co-curricular elements, and collaborates in the management of several other such activities. Co-curricular activities contribute to the education of students and others in IPE but are not credit-granting activities for all participants. Curricular elements are those involving college credits.

Curricular Elements

DIHC

The DIHC was the first formal curricular IPE element developed and implemented during the period before establishment of the center at UK. It was launched in 2009 and grew out of discussions in the working group. In creating it, many of the issues that would challenge all our IPE efforts (such as scheduling, credit granting, and course listing) arose and had to be addressed.

The DIHC is a one-semester course designed to provide students with a seminar-based forum within which to explore the characteristics and implications of interprofessional practice. It is offered twice during the academic year and is built around a cross-cutting health care challenge that is chosen annually by the course committee. The primary course objective is that students understand, appreciate, and value interprofessional collaboration among their colleagues in addressing the health and well-being of patients and populations. The course goal stated in the syllabus reads, "Students will work in interprofessional teams to consider ways to promote positive, holistic health outcomes for individuals and communities." This goal remains constant across the various thematic topics around which the course has been built over the years. This course also addresses the following specific core competencies for interprofessional collaborative care, taken from the 2011 report from the Interprofessional Education Collaborative (IPEC) (IPEC Expert Panel, 2011):

VE1: Place the interests of patients and populations at the center of interprofessional health care delivery.

VE4: Respect the unique cultures, values, roles, responsibilities, and expertise of other health professions.

RR3: Engage diverse healthcare professionals who complement one's own professional expertise, as well as associated resources, to develop strategies to meet specific patient care needs.

RR4: Explain the roles and responsibilities of other care providers and how the team works together to provide care.

CC1: Choose effective communication tools and techniques, including information systems and communication technologies, to facilitate discussions and interactions that enhance team function.

CC4: Listen actively, and encourage ideas and opinions of other team members.

CC5: Give timely, sensitive, instructive feedback to others about their performance on the team, responding respectfully as a team member to feedback from others.

CC7: Recognize how one's own uniqueness, including experience level, expertise, culture, power, and hierarchy within the healthcare team, contributes to effective communication, conflict resolution, and positive interprofessional working relationships.

CC8: Communicate consistently the importance of teamwork in patient-centered and community-focused care.

TT3: Engage other health professionals—appropriate to the specific care situation—in shared patient-centered problem-solving.

TT8: Reflect on individual and team performance for individual, as well as team, performance improvement.

The Colleges of Dentistry, Health Sciences, Medicine, Nursing, Pharmacy, Public Health, and Social Work regularly participate in the DIHC. In the College of Health Sciences, the physical therapy program has been consistently involved. Similarly, kinesiology and counseling psychology students from the College of Education and students from the College of Communication and Information have occasionally participated. I am currently one of the course codirectors, as well as being director of the center and holding a faculty appointment in the College of Medicine. My codirector is Dr. Pat Burkhardt, a professor and associate dean in the College of Nursing. There are identified faculty members from the participating colleges or programs who, together, form the course committee. All members serve as preceptors for the small groups, and they also function as the college or program contacts for the students participating. For simplicity, I will use the word "programs," realizing that, in some cases, colleges are the administrative unit involved.

The DIHC includes five Friday afternoon seminars at which a 40- to 50-minute presentation by a content expert is followed by facilitated small group work. All classes are scheduled from 2 to 5 p.m. To maintain a balance of representation across the disciplines and keep the class a manageable size for the kinds of activities involved, DIHC enrollment for any given semester does not exceed 40 students. Thus, each program can enroll usually four to eight students. If one participating program does not fill its limit, its seats may become available for other programs. The course generally provides one credit hour, though some programs may elect to add additional requirements to justify granting more credit hours. The program contacts manage this process, which does not affect or alter the common experience of the one-credit-hour course.

Small group work is the heart of the DIHC, and the groups are structured to include students from as many participating programs as possible. They are led by a faculty facilitator from one of the participating programs. There is an expectation that such facilitators will be provided by all participating programs in a manner roughly proportional to the number of students from the program enrolled. The small group meetings begin with a structured activity led by the facilitator, then move on to an open format, during which students work together on a project. The sessions begin with some discussion of the presentation they just have heard, then move on to the structured activities.

Session 1: The course begins with an introduction to the course and of all group members and preceptors.

Session 2: A Day in My Life. Students are expected to come to class prepared to spend three to four minutes helping others in the group understand what it is like to walk for a day in their shoes. Students are encouraged to discuss why they chose their future profession, what path they took to get there (education, culture), and some of the opportunities they expect to find particularly exciting after graduation.

Session 3: Interprofessional Shadowing. The students are asked to come to class prepared to discuss one or two "lessons learned" from their interprofessional shadowing experience. Interprofessional shadowing is one of the most highly rated elements of this very highly rated course. It involves all students spending three hours shadowing a provider from a discipline other than their own. They select the experience from a menu of options on a first-come, first-served basis, though dental students have priority for evening and weekend options because of their highly structured clinical responsibilities. The objectives for this experience are that the students will be able to

1. Describe the community or clinical health care setting in terms of the services provided, the types of clients or patients served, and the most frequent health problems encountered in that setting.
2. Describe the different types of community or clinical health care providers in the setting. What are their roles and scope of practice?
3. Describe the different types of community or clinical health care providers outside the setting with whom professionals in the setting work to provide care for clients or patients. This could include referral patterns, consultation relationships, and community resources, for example.
4. Given what they observed, describe an optimal interprofessional practice for the clients or patients served in this practice.

These objectives inform students' "lessons learned" discussion. As noted, this is an extremely popular element of the DIHC. We consistently hear from students during the evaluation debriefing at the end of the course that they wish they had the opportunity to shadow a second provider. We are working to make that an option.

Session 4: Lessons Learned from the Team. As part of the course, students complete an 18-item self- and peer evaluation of team competencies. This is turned in to the center for scoring and feedback, and the students receive a form that shows their self-rating, anonymous ratings from their peers, and summary data. This methodology originated at the Medical University of South Carolina and was modified for use at UK. Factor analytic study of the instrument identified the following themes: contributes to achieving group tasks, maintains positive group communication, and maintains a positive attitude. Examples of items on the scale for each of these factors are offered below:

Achieves Group Tasks

1. Initiates (proposes tasks, goals, or actions, defines group problems, suggests a procedure); during the small group discussion in this session, they share what they feel they have learned from the team experience, with an emphasis on how they think it might affect their practices going forward.
2. Demonstrates accountability (takes responsibility for contributing, completes tasks; assumes roles of facilitator, recorder, and timekeeper; supports team decisions).

Maintains Positive Group Communication

Communication gatekeeper (helps others to participate, keeps communication channels open, keeps people from dominating conversation).

1. Resolves conflict (helps people explore their differences, agrees on common points, reconciles disagreements, relieves tension in group, admits own errors).

Maintains a Positive Attitude

1. Appreciates the value of team decisions and a positive regard for teamwork.
2. Invites feedback and thoughts about improving team effectiveness.

Items are rated on a 5-point scale anchored by *never* and *consistently*. The activity during the session is generally limited to work on the project.

The final two sessions of the DIHC consist of presentations by each team of their project. These projects are a collaborative effort and are intended actively to engage students in problem-solving and exploratory experiences. Each team project identifies and addresses one aspect of the health problem that is the theme during the year students are enrolled. The team then plans and executes a project that addresses the interprofessional collaborative practice implications of that aspect. In the academic year 2014–2015, for example, the theme was transitions of care. Examples of potential projects for this topic included collaborative transition strategies, ethical issues that arise in care transitions, effective treatment of individuals as they transfer from one care context to another, and how the issue of transitions of care could be addressed in art, theater, or literature. Examples of potential projects include creating an educational module for student, professional, or community groups that describe transitions of care challenges; producing a review of the literature on the topic; or compiling a review of films that contribute to or address issues of care transitions. A team might create and act out a transition situation that illustrates challenges teams might encounter and solutions teams might implement. Students are encouraged to be creative in identifying problems and suggesting solutions. We ask them to think broadly in terms of the nature of their project, but consideration of how interprofessional teams can contribute to solutions is essential.

Each team's work on the project is facilitated by a preceptor. As noted, the process starts at the first small group meeting, and preceptors generally stay for the whole session. Thereafter, however, it is up to the team to decide whether they want or need the preceptor's involvement in planning the project. Most of the planning is done in the small group meetings after the structured activity is complete, so preceptors often leave at that point. The teams always set up a method for communication, either using the course Blackboard Shell or an alternative of their choosing and frequently meet outside regular class hours to work on the project. A preliminary plan for the project is submitted to the center by each group between the first and second class meeting. Over the years, students have been remarkably creative in these projects. We have had video productions and one-act plays written and performed, as well as more conventional didactic presentations. Teams have created informational procedures addressing the needs of particular populations, such as high school students or persons with limited health literacy. The presentation sessions are attended by all DIHC faculty members as well as the deans or their representatives and other invitees.

Designing the Course

The DIHC was created in 2008 by a very dedicated and enthusiastic subgroup of the working group. The faculty members involved seemed to thoroughly enjoy the process.

It was led by Drs. Burkhardt, Pfeifle, and Norton, with significant input from faculty representing all of the programs involved. The general outline of a semester-long small-group structure built around a particular health issue emerged fairly quickly, as did a commitment to the idea that there should be some work product produced by the teams of students as the capstone of the experience. It was also early agreed that this should be an honors experience, reserved for students identified by their deans as being, first, academically strong and able to take on an additional course beyond the normal curriculum of their program and, second, particularly suited to and interested in teamwork and interprofessional collaboration. We were setting ourselves up for success in choosing to work initially with only the best students. This turned out to be a wise decision, given the complexities subsequently encountered when developing curricula for a broader audience. It was important, as we were launching IPE at UK, that our initial efforts be well received so that there would be a degree of positive buzz about IPE in the colleges and programs. DIHC certainly did that, but it was not implemented without some challenges. The first of these was scheduling.

Scheduling

The first issue that had to be addressed was finding a time for the group to meet. The amount of effort expended on this was frankly appalling, and I expect a similar story can be told about any institution that is striving to bring students from different academic programs together face to face. Every proposed time was inevitably deemed by one program or another to be impossible. We finally settled on Friday afternoon from 2 to 5 p.m. as the best option, but even then, some programs can have students available for DIHC only one of the two semesters. I would make the personal observation that no time is actually impossible and that the ultimate solution to this problem must reside with an authority higher than programs or deans. If the chief academic officer at an academic institution decides that it is important and necessary to ensure that there are time slots kept open for IPE experiences, programs will quite suddenly discover that what seemed impossible is actually quite possible. However, until such a decision is reached at the highest administrative level, IPE initiatives will struggle and, in some cases, founder because they cannot find a meeting time on which all interested programs can agree.

Course Listing

A second issue that was discussed and debated for quite a while was how best to structure the course as regards its academic status and home. One possibility, of course, would be to house it in an IPE center that was able to offer courses for academic credit. This is easier said than done as the governing and administrative regulations around the granting of academic credit are rigid and complex. At the time we were working on the DIHC, although talk of establishing a center had begun, no such center then existed, and the thought of creating one that could grant academic credit was a daunting prospect. Furthermore, it could be argued that there is not a great advantage in having a center with that capability. A better way might be to find ways to embed such courses into the existing course structure of the programs involved. That could happen in one of two ways. First, it might be possible to modify an existing course and add DIHC to it. Alternatively, each program could create a new course with the specifications of the DIHC and offer it within the program. What happened with DIHC was the latter. Because the course was selective, it could not easily be added to a required course. Therefore, it is generally listed as a newly created elective or as a special topics or independent study type of existing elective. In the case of the College of Medicine, for example, it was created as a new elective in the Department of Psychiatry, because I have a faculty appointment there. This method has worked quite well, and we see no reason to alter it.

Course Credit and Grading

As mentioned earlier, the activity was designed to meet the requirements for one credit hour as described in the university's academic policies. For some colleges, however, this created a problem as they either did not offer one-credit electives, or they felt that students would not be incentivized to participate unless more credits were offered. The solution to this was quite simple. Colleges or programs wishing to do so could add, for their students, some additional requirements to meet the university's expectations for a two-credit course, but ensuring this add-on in no way compromised the core expectations. Programs also vary in their grading practices. For many programs, the course is pass/fail, while others assign letter grades. This does not seem to have a differential effect on the degree of student engagement, and again, it is working well.

Interprofessional Collaboration and Teamwork Skills 1 (iCATS1)

iCATS1 was our first course designed to bring all students together in one required curricular element. This had been the charge of the center's board of directors, but such inclusiveness has been only partly achieved. In the first two years the course was offered, there were many programs that did not participate. The first year the course was offered, the participating disciplines were dentistry, medicine, nursing, physical therapy, and communication sciences and disorders. The pharmacy and physician assistant programs joined the second year. The course was offered as an elective for medical students. As iCATS1 enters its third iteration, though, more programs are joining, and the College of Medicine is now fully engaged.

Current Structure

As presently structured, iCATS1 runs for the whole academic year with 90-minute meetings in September and April, 75-minute meetings in November and March, and 60-minute meetings in October and February. The September, November, March, and April meetings involve all students meeting at a time set by the course directors for reasons that will be made clear shortly. The other two meetings are small group activities done at a time chosen by consensus for each group. iCATS1 is a required element in another preexisting course in nearly all colleges and programs. In the College of Medicine, for example, it is part of the first year of a two-year sequence called Introduction to Clinical Medicine.

The September and April meetings make a sort of bookend pair to the course and are large convocations with all students present. The April session kicks off the course and includes several elements. First, a patient describes how team-based care, or the lack of it, affected his or her health outcome. Second, there are short presentations by faculty and former students, explaining the rationale for the course, that is, why IPE is important and why we begin the process very early in the professional education process. Third, the structure and requirements of the course are briefly reviewed. All of this takes approximately 50 minutes. It is followed by the first meeting of the small groups at which two objectives are achieved. First, the students meet one another and share why they chose the profession they are pursuing. Second, the group determines its meeting time for the October and February meetings. Group membership has been prearranged by the center to balance professions across groups as much as possible. Furthermore, there is a Canvas Course Shell to facilitate group interaction and tracking.

The April meeting is a second convocation of the entire group. At this meeting, students meet in small groups with other students from their program that are facilitated by faculty from their program. The purpose of these focus groups is to debrief and provide feedback. It is an opportunity for students to reflect with their peers on what they learned about working with students from other disciplines. The formal course evaluation also is completed at the closing session of iCATS1.

At the one-hour October and February meetings, the student groups view video presentations of clinical cases discussed by groups of experienced clinicians. The two cases are crafted such that all of the health professions of all the involved students play a part in at least one of them. Each of the cases leads to a 75-minute simulation experience using standardized patients. It occurs the following month. The simulation in the fall addresses transitions of care, the simulation in the spring, and error disclosure.

The simulation sessions, which involve over 70 student groups, are a logistical challenge. The sessions begin with all students and preceptors convening for an orientation. They then proceed to assigned rooms where the standardized patients are waiting. The students are divided into two groups of five and spend 10 minutes discussing how they will do the simulation, for example, who will start, who will address what issue, and so on. The first group then spends 15 minutes doing the simulation with the other group observing. A five-minute debriefing follows, and then the second group does the simulation, observed by the first. A final debriefing includes the standardized patient giving feedback. The standardized patients are instructed to convey different attitudes in the two instances. For example, the patient is accepting of what happened and conveys a forgiving attitude in the first error disclosure simulation, whereas in the second, he or she is angry and litigious. The simulation experience is very highly rated by both students and faculty.

A total of 680 students overall participated in the program, with the largest representation from the schools of medicine, nursing, and pharmacy. All students are in their first year of professional school when they take iCATS1. In the case of physician assistant studies, however, they are in the second half of their first year when iCATS1 begins because they are admitted in the fall. Half of the nursing students are in a similar situation as that college admits students in both spring and fall semesters.

History

Looking back at the initial development and delivery of iCATS1, it is possible to identify problems that may have contributed to a less than optimal first-year offering, a fundamental one being that we may have tried to do too much. In an effort to be inclusive of all colleges and programs, content development was pursued by a great many people organized into committees. These design teams worked more or less independently in putting together content based on an overall structure of the course that had been prescribed by academic leaders from the programs and designed to address specific IPE competencies. Another committee, the implementation team, was charged with translating the work of the design teams into a practical delivery strategy using the structure prescribed. The result was a very ambitious and complicated course.

There were not overall course objectives for the first iteration of iCATS1. Rather, for each of the sessions, there were specific learning objectives that reflected the intent of the design team that put that session together. For example, TeamSTEPPS (a federal government evidence-based program developed to improve safety within health care settings) was one of the topics that covered two sessions. The objectives for these sessions were as follows:

1. Describe the importance of clear individual and interpersonal communication to high-quality health care team performance.
2. Demonstrate beginning proficiency in the use of structured communication techniques.

Although the overall evaluation of the first iteration was not very good, the one element that was well received was the second simulation. In the first simulation, most students watched while a few students were actively involved, whereas in the second, all students actively performed the simulation. The second simulation was the most highly rated element in iCATS1 for that year, and the second iteration would yield a similar result.

For the second iteration, a modified iCATS1 was developed by a smaller group consisting primarily of the academic leadership with representation from the design and implementation teams. A decision was made to substantially reduce the amount of prework required and to attempt to focus more on the team-building experience and less on content. To achieve this, we reduced the number of sessions to six and made them longer in duration to ensure sufficient time for building team relationships. To create more of a sense of continuity, the course was built around an evolving case.

Course objectives for the entire experience were developed, and it was expected that students at the conclusion of the experience would be able to

1. Use plain language to describe the roles and responsibilities of their respective team members to others (that is, patients).

2. Discuss values and ethics that support interprofessional collaborative practice.
3. Use selected structured communication techniques in one or more simulations to facilitate collaborative care.
4. Participate in interprofessional teams and reflect on specific behaviors in themselves and other team members that enhance collaboration and teamwork.

Student and faculty evaluations of the second iteration were better than for the first, but there remained many opportunities for improvement. First, students remained unclear as to why they were being trained in teamwork skills. That is, the underlying rationale for interprofessional practice had not been adequately explained. Second, the longitudinal case seemed contrived to include every possible profession and, given the long hiatus between meetings, did not function as intended to provide continuity during the course. Finally, given their level of training, students felt ill prepared to explain the role of their profession to their peers. As in the preceding year, however, the simulation experience that concluded the small-group sessions was very well received.

As previously described, in the third, current version of iCATS1, session length has been reduced to one hour for the case discussion sessions and 75 minutes for the simulations. Only the opening and closing convocations last an hour and a half. Prework also has been reduced to readings that translate very directly to what will be done in the session. For example, an overview of team communication precedes the first case session where team communication will be observed and discussed. Similarly, information on error disclosure precedes the second simulation, which is an error disclosure exercise. In earlier versions of iCATS1, the readings were more extensive and touched on many interesting and important topics but may not have immediately related to action in the session in all cases.

Scheduling

As iCATS1 involves so many programs and is generally a required element, the scheduling challenges were even greater than in DIHC. I will reiterate the point made earlier that the ultimate solution to this problem is a determination at the highest level that some modest but specific time periods in the academic calendars of all health professions and related colleges will be carved out and held exclusively for IPE curricular elements. For now, though, the model of evening times for the parts of the course that involve all students and group flexibility for the small-group meetings that was implemented in the first iteration of iCATS1 persists.

Course Listing

As noted earlier, in almost all cases, iCATS1 is part of another course for the colleges and programs involved. There is thus no formally separate course listing or registration for it, though it does function as a quasi-separate course, managed by the center, with its own Canvas Shell and course materials. It is important that students understand how iCATS1 fits into the course in which it is embedded as, in some cases, this has not been made sufficiently clear. We are working with the programs to correct this.

Course Credit and Grading

Grades are assigned by the facilitators in the Canvas Course Shell. The disposition of these grades, however, is dependent on the course director for the particular course in each program that includes iCATS1 as a course requirement.

To summarize, iCATS1 has been a complicated journey for the center and for the programs involved. It is a work in progress, as are all academic courses, and there is always room for improvement. That said, we are convinced that a required, universal, or near universal IPE experience early in the education of health and related professions students is important for building a culture of IPE at an institution and preparing students for IPE as an essential element in their education.

Interprofessional Teamwork in Global Health

Interprofessional Teamwork in Global Health (ITGH) is a course for a select group of learners from all health professions colleges and residencies as well as some other undergraduates. The idea for it came from the assistant provost for global health, who wanted to make an existing international service activity more academic in character. The Shoulder-to-Shoulder Ecuador Health Brigade is a one-week experience in which students work firsthand alongside faculty, medical professionals, and local Ecuadorian staff in the Centro Médico Hombro a Hombro clinic. The program is open to undergraduate and graduate students from all academic disciplines, and academic credit is provided. ITGH prepares the learners to work effectively as an interprofessional team to promote positive, holistic health outcomes both for individuals and for communities. To support this course, the center manages logistics for the six meetings of its eight groups. Academic management of the course resides with the teaching faculty. The course occurs during the spring semester, with the Ecuador experience scheduled for the summer break.

Interprofessional Shadowing (NUR-540)

Participants in NUR-540, a required course in the College of Nursing, must complete three hours of interprofessional shadowing. Shadowing is part of DIHC, so the center has some experience in managing the process. Accordingly, we provide support to the College of Nursing by assisting in the recruitment of preceptors and in ensuring that students have appropriate observer status. There is a substantial regulatory framework that must be addressed when introducing learners into clinical environments, and a distinction is made between students and observers. Only the former can interact with and participate in the care of patients. Students who are shadowing cease to be "students" and become "observers." Center staff assist the students in NUR-540 in obtaining their observer badges and help with the orientation to this specific role. The center also assists in the actual scheduling and placement of students.

IPE Modular Repository

The repository is a growing collection of educational resources supporting IPE. It is maintained by the center, making materials available to UK and other interested faculty. The initial contents of the repository were two modules created by the South Eastern

Consortium for IPE, a group of academic health centers led by UK and funded through a grant from the Macy Foundation. Modules on patient safety and transitions of care were created through a collaborative process and currently are available to any interested faculty member at any time worldwide through the center's Web site. These modules can form the core of an interprofessional course offered asynchronously to groups of dispersed students during clinical rotations, or they can be used to supplement an existing course. On an ongoing basis, the center facilitates the creation, validation, implementation, and dissemination of IPE modules in face-to-face, online, and blended formats at the rate of approximately two modules each year. This is done by center staff in collaboration with interested faculty, with staff time allocated to assist in the creation of modules and subsequently to provide support for implementation. That support takes two forms. First, there is desk-side faculty development in the use of the learning management systems in which the modules reside. Second, there is consultation available on optimizing teaching techniques in use of the modules to ensure effective use of these curricular elements.

Authentic Clinical IPE

One of the major recommendations of the Holsinger Committee was to abandon efforts toward creating a second-year required course for all health professions and related students and focus instead on identifying opportunities to integrate IPE into existing clinical experiences. During 2013, work was done by a consortium of academic health centers to create IPE teaching materials that could be used when students were unable to meet face to face. At UK, the vision was that these materials would form the basis for iCATS2. Funding from the Macy Foundation made possible this work, and two modules were created, one focused on transitions of care and a second on patient safety. They were piloted successfully with student volunteers and were tentatively to be rolled out in the 2014–2015 academic year. For a variety of reasons, a decision was reached to put that on hold, at least until the second semester. As the Holsinger Committee began its work, discussion of iCATS2 assumed a prominent position. A decision had to be made regarding whether to pursue it as initially planned. Although the modules that had been developed were judged to be of considerable value, the committee quickly came to the conclusion that the iCATS2 course structure seemed contrived and cumbersome. It envisioned creating virtual interprofessional teams at a time in the students' education when real teams would be all around them at the clinical sites in which they were training. Accordingly, the committee recommended abandoning iCATS2 as originally conceived and directed the center to work as a catalyst for the creation of what it termed Authentic Clinical IPE, that is, using existing clinical courses as the site for ensuring that IPE competencies are taught and evaluated.

At UK, we are just beginning this endeavor. It is being informed in part by the work of the practice committee mentioned earlier, through which practice environments within UK HealthCare that use team-based care were identified. The center is convening groups of faculty members to look at these sites and explore ways IPE competencies can be integrated into the clinical teaching going on there. We are also working to identify existing instances of IPE involving our various colleges and programs. For example, the Internal Medicine Third Year Clerkship has for some time conducted patient-specific medication review sessions involving pharmacy students doing their acute care rotation, as well as medical students and residents in both medicine and pharmacy. This is exemplary IPE and has been so identified by the College of Pharmacy but not by the College of Medicine. Facilitating such identification and evaluation for the College of Medicine is a role for the center. The center also is developing a data set on IPE experiences that will track student participation in a manner that should serve the various colleges and programs well in documenting their compliance with the increasingly specific expectations regarding IPE among the accrediting bodies.

Co-Curricular Elements

Leadership Legacy

This semester-long experience complements the formal curriculum by providing participants with a series of cohort-based activities in retreats, workshops, service, and mentoring relationships to enhance interprofessional leadership skills and professionalism. Examples of activities in Leadership Legacy include creation of a service learning project and a mock legislative hearing. The latter involves the students in teams of eight identifying a health-relevant issue on which legislative action might be pursued. They work together to prepare a presentation advocating their position to a legislative committee. A mock hearing is then arranged at the state capitol in cooperation with the Kentucky Legislative Research Commission. In the spring of 2015, we were fortunate to have state senator and former governor Julian Carroll, former state senator and current circuit judge Ernesto Scorsone, and two additional individuals with experience in lobbying serving on the panel.

Interprofessional Lunch and Learn

This student-led extracurricular colloquium provides students with an understanding of how professionals can work collaboratively in interprofessional teams to improve health outcomes for patients and communities. The center provides meals and manages logistics for monthly meetings and also assists student leaders in identifying speakers.

CONMIGO Interprofessional Interest Group

The name of the program, which means "with me" in Spanish, was chosen by the students. This student-led extracurricular colloquium provides students with the opportunity to understand the barriers facing Latino communities in accessing health care and to discuss methods of overcoming those barriers. The center provides meals and manages logistics for monthly meetings and also assists student leaders in identifying speakers.

EVALUATION STRATEGIES

From its inception, evaluation has been taken very seriously by our center. Dr. Pfeifle is a firm believer in the importance of tracking outcomes, and she charged associate director Jim Ballard with leading this effort. He continues in this role to good effect today.

Tools

The tools we have generally used to evaluate intervention outcomes include one that is used widely and others with more limited utilization. The Heineman Attitudes toward Health Care Teams Scale (ATHCTS) is a valid and reliable tool to evaluate team training programs and was designed to measure the attitudes of team members from different professions (Heinemann, Schmitt, Farrel, & Brallier, 1999). We use it pre- and postintervention to track changes in attitudes toward interprofessional team care. The ATHCTS consists of two subscales: Quality of Care/Process (14 items) and Physician Centrality (6 items). The Quality of Care/Process subscale measures team members' perceptions of the quality of care and the quality of teamwork that can occur in a patient care context as a result of interprofessional team care. The Physician Centrality subscale measures team members' attitudes toward physicians' authority in teams and their control over patient information.

The Team Understanding Scale is used in conjunction with the ATHCTS and was developed at UK. It includes demographics (student ID, gender, program, ethnicity, graduation year, past IPE participation) and assesses participants' self-reported knowledge of the educational requirements of other professions and knowledge of the scope of practice for other professions.

Self/Peer Assessment of Team was developed jointly by staff at UK and the Medical University of South Carolina. This instrument is primarily designed to help students reflect on their own team skills and on those of others within their teams. It is designed to be a behavioral inventory of team skills recognized (for self) or observed (team members) scored on a 0-to-4 scale anchored by 0 (*behaviors not observed*) and 4 (*behaviors consistently observed*).

Findings

In terms of student attitudes, with great consistency, we find pre- to postexperience movement in the direction expected. That is, after completing a center IPE activity, students generally have a more positive attitude toward team-based care than they had before doing the activity.

Evaluations of activities have ranged widely from extremely positive for DIHC to neutral to negative for the first iteration of iCATS1. We have used this feedback to alter and improve experiences viewed negatively and have seen positive movement in the evaluations for iCATS1 with the second iteration.

SUSTAINABILITY

At present, the long-term viability of the center seems assured. The funding streams from UK HealthCare and the Office of the Provost are recurring. To date, there has been a good return on investment in that the center has been very productive but not very expensive to maintain. Productivity has been demonstrated in terms of number of students touched by center curricular and co-curricular offerings, by the evaluations of those offerings in terms of both process and outcomes, and by significant scholarly work on IPE that the center has facilitated. There were eight abstracts from UK involving center staff members accepted for presentation at Collaborating across Borders 5th Conference in 2015.

In terms of strategies pursued to ensure sustainability, the most fundamental one was making the case to leadership that IPE is an essential part of health and related professions education and that having a center to catalyze such pedagogy is a wise thing for an academic health center to do. It is valuable for centers such as ours to pursue grants, but such efforts must be clearly seen as opportunities to do specific things.

LESSONS LEARNED

To be frank, I am not sure that any of the lessons learned are at all surprising. It might be better put that we have had many expectations confirmed. In the case of UK, most of the people most intimately involved in this effort were fairly senior and sophisticated educators who did not embark on this with any illusion that it would be easy to do. That said, it may still be useful to run through what emerged during the process in the hope that others might benefit from our experience. Much of this has been touched upon in the description of the creation of the curricular elements already presented, so this may be something of a reprise of points made earlier. I will go through factors we found to be critically important and discuss each of them briefly.

Developing a Rationale

Making changes in curricula inevitably meets resistance for a variety of reasons, both valid and questionable. In the first place, it is almost always easier to keep doing what you are doing than to do something else. That sort of inertia is universal in academia—it is probably universal, period. The students are graduating, they are getting jobs, why change? Instituting systematic IPE experiences into a traditional, silo structure requires pretty significant changes in faculty behavior; to make that happen, a compelling rationale must be offered. In the case of IPE, this is not difficult to do as there is a growing literature demonstrating the outcome advantages of team-based versus silo-based care. Political and health economic factors also are relevant here. The Patient Protection and Affordable Care Act clearly envisions both outcomes-based reimbursement and team-based approaches to care. What is necessary, though, is to find ways to disseminate information like this to the faculty. Faculty members may be conservative and resistant to change, but they are not immune to evidence. Accordingly, one of the things we did was to look for opportunities to discuss IPE in a scholarly way in settings like departmental grand rounds. In retrospect, we could have done more of this, so perhaps a suggestion for institutions interested in pursuing IPE would be to find opportunities to get the evidence supporting it in front of faculty. The question then becomes, who best to do that?

Faculty Champions

At every institution, there are faculty members who are particularly highly respected by their peers. At UK, we were very fortunate to have all of the deans committed, at least in principal, to the notion that IPE should be part of our educational program. Without the support of the deans, nothing is likely to happen. The support of the deans by itself, however, is not sufficient. There is often a degree of mistrust of administration among faculty members. It is critically important that there be rank-and-file champions identified, nurtured, and engaged in the effort early in the process. During the semester before we were to launch iCATS1, we created what we termed "the elevator speech." This was an approximately ten-minute presentation with accompanying PowerPoint slides that could be delivered by anyone. We then worked to get on the agenda of faculty meetings in the various involved programs to let the faculty know what was afoot and how they might be involved. In this process, an effort was made to have the presenters be persons who would be viewed as credible by the faculty to whom they were speaking, that is, faculty champions.

Course Logistics

Talented, committed faculty can do a terrific job designing innovative courses and exciting experiences to deliver IPE. They cannot, however, alter the academic calendar, nor can they create rooms for small group meetings or invent faculty preceptors to be in those rooms when the students are there. These three logistical needs, time, space, and people, must be addressed early and often in developing and implementing IPE.

At UK, we certainly anticipated the fact that scheduling courses that cut across colleges and programs would not be easy. We also knew that there are physical limitations in our (and most other institutions') facilities as regards small-group learning space availability. What we perhaps did not anticipate was the magnitude of these challenges and the amount of staff time and energy that would have to be expended on an ongoing basis to address them.

As regards the calendar, I described above the effort expended through the AHEC Program to synchronize the clinical rotation calendar and the success that was achieved. On the preclinical side, though, we have not had as much success. Our Friday afternoon schedule for DIHC functions reasonably well but works during only one of the two semesters for College of Pharmacy and the other semester for the Physical Therapy Program. For iCATS1, scheduling has been a nightmare of daunting proportions. Because nearly all students participate, a large number of programs with completely unsynchronized calendars are involved. This has necessitated evening scheduling for events that involve all students meeting at the same time. For the iCATS1 small groups, we leave it up to the groups and their preceptors to work out a time. When these sessions were 90 minutes, the only realistic option was an evening meeting, as a morning session would have to begin at 6:30 to avoid running into an 8:00 class. The only other possibility is to meet on weekends, an option that seems to appeal to no one. Currently, these sessions are one hour, offering more flexibility in scheduling.

Finally, there is the need for faculty. As you design curricular elements, it is not difficult to be quite specific as to what faculty resources will be required. Conversely, what may be very difficult is actually finding those faculty resources. Here the support of the deans and program directors is essential, but even having that in general terms may not be sufficient. To effectively address this issue, you must translate such support for the idea of IPE into job-specific allocations of faculty effort, using whatever metric is customary at your particular institution. As you work on curriculum design, you simultaneously look both at the faculty resources the design will require and the realistic availability of faculty to do the work. Although small groups of five might be your ideal, groups of five require precisely twice as many faculty hours as do groups of 10. Given this precious resource, you want to be sure the relative benefit is proportional to the cost. Will students really benefit twice as much from the five-person model as compared with being in groups of 10? Could groups of 10 episodically break into two groups of five for some experiences, with the preceptor moving back and forth between them? Questions like these should be continuously considered as you husband faculty resources.

Facilitating IPE Research

Our decision to seek a global IRB for use of the center's evaluation instruments in educational research was a very good one. It has allowed us to study virtually all our educational interventions, with the possibility of scholarly presentations always there. Certainly the primary purpose in evaluating curricular elements it to improve them, but a side benefit of the process at UK is providing faculty members with the possibility to generate scholarly work that enhances their reputations and potential for promotion. In an academic environment, this is not a small matter and has had the effect of incentivizing faculty participation in the center's educational efforts.

Keeping the End in Mind

Certainly, the ultimate aim of IPE is improved patient outcomes and better community health. That aim, however, is many steps removed from an IPE course delivered in the first semester of a pharmacy student's academic program. It is important, therefore, to have a clearly articulated set of interim objectives the IPE program is meant to achieve and to assess the attainment of those objectives continuously. At UK, we have identified a number of these interim objectives and assess them on an ongoing basis. One of them concerns the attitudes students have toward team-based care. We assess these attitudes early in the student's career and periodically thereafter as IPE elements are encountered. Another example of an interim objective is attainment of the core competencies for interprofessional collaborative care, taken from the 2011 report from the IPEC (IPEC Expert Panel, 2011). For all of our IPE activities, improvement in one or more of these competencies is an expected outcome and is assessed. Finally, all of the major accrediting bodies relevant to health professions education include interprofessional competencies as expected outcomes of their training programs. Accordingly, there is an expectation that IPE is included in the curriculum in an identifiable way. To this end, the center maintains a central database that provides documentation of the IPE experiences of students in each of the colleges and programs in a manner that is helpful to them in completing self-study documents and in preparing for site visits. We consider this objective achieved when a college or program undergoes reaccreditation and is not cited for failing to provide IPE.

REFERENCES

Fadiman, A. (1998). *The spirit catches you and you fall down: A Hmong child, her American doctors, and the collision of two cultures.* New York: Farrar, Straus and Giroux.

Heinemann, G. D., Schmitt, M. H., Farrel, M. H., & Brallier, S. A. (1999). Development of an Attitudes towards Health Care Team Scale. *Evaluation & the Health Professions, 22,* 123–142.

Interprofessional Education Collaborative Expert Panel. (2011). *Core competencies for interprofessional collaborative practice: Report of an expert panel.* Washington, DC: Interprofessional Education Collaborative.

Skloot, R. (2011). *The immortal life of Henrietta Lacks.* New York: Broadway Books.

8

THE UNIVERSITY OF MARYLAND AT BALTIMORE

Kelley Macmillan and Deborah Rejent

In early 2011, the associate dean from the MSW program at the University of Maryland at Baltimore (UMB) and the coordinator of the MSW program at the off-campus site in Shady Grove, Maryland, a regional higher education center, began meeting with instructors from the Shady Grove campus to develop an interprofessional education (IPE) course. In addition to social work, the other disciplines involved were nursing (undergraduate level) and pharmacy (doctoral level) at UMB and the undergraduate respiratory therapy program located in Salisbury, Maryland, which also offered courses at the Shady Grove campus. Over a period of two years, faculty from these programs expressed a commitment toward IPE, which was a topic often discussed at many university levels. Although our various home campuses each had initiatives regarding IPE, large committees on the campuses had not reached decisions about how to actually offer courses across schools and departments.

Previously, the faculty on the Shady Grove campus had offered a Geriatric Imperative course jointly offered by nursing and pharmacy for two semesters. These faculty members wanted to offer a course that provided students with an opportunity to develop interprofessional teamwork skills during patient simulation exercises. The Shady Grove social work coordinator had been involved in the Geriatric Imperative course and was supporting the School of Social Work to become engaged in this new IPE course offering. The faculty involved agreed to move forward and begin developing an IPE course at the Shady Grove site to serve as a pilot for our home campuses.

Most of the faculty were in contact with each other by virtue of either having a primary work assignment at Shady Grove, thereby getting to know each other in that capacity, or by attending a monthly planning committee with representatives from all nine campuses of the University of Maryland system, which had programs at Shady Grove. An informal in-person meeting to discuss interests was scheduled and a decision was made to focus on critical care settings, as each of our professions had established roles in health settings. There were many other logistics and issues to consider before we could offer the course, such as methods of opening the course to students in many universities and programs, managing registration, navigating workload issues for faculty, and getting approval to offer a new course.

In March 2011, the University of Maryland Shady Grove curriculum committee approved a course titled Interprofessional Approaches to the Critically Ill Patient, to be offered in the fall of 2011. The plan was for faculty from nursing, pharmacy, respiratory care, and social work to coteach this course, which would be offered to students from these four respective professional disciplines. The faculty from these disciplines on the Shady Grove campus offered an IPE event in the spring of 2011 to encourage interest among the student body for the fall IPE course offering. The associate dean for the MSW program agreed to add the IPE critical care course as a new offering in the fall of 2011.

Each school has different procedures for approving new courses. The School of Social Work's policy is that a new course can be offered as a special topics course for up to two times before going through a full curriculum review to become a permanent course in the MSW program. The MSW curriculum committee approved the special topics course on the Shady Grove campus. After this course was offered twice, it was approved to be an advanced clinical elective in the MSW program.

The associate dean for the MSW program attended several meetings with the Shady Grove faculty planning on teaching the IPE course that fall to finalize the syllabus and course curriculum and content. Two other social work faculty members were invited to participate in the planning and teaching; in the end, three social work faculty agreed to coteach the course the first year. During the first year of the course offering, these three social work faculty members divided the teaching responsibility among them, each one committing to attend the class on specific days during the fall semester. Beginning with the second and subsequent years, only one core faculty member from social work cotaught the Interprofessional Approaches to the Critically Ill Patient course.

The social work, nursing, and pharmacy faculty are members of the University of Maryland system, and the respiratory therapy faculty member is a member of the Salisbury University system. Even though one faculty member was teaching primary content on a particular day, all four faculty disciplines were present in the classroom and added to the discussion. This discussion was sometimes very specific to the faculty member's profession. At other times, it was directed to general concepts and ideas that cut across the professions. When a faculty member was absent, the faculty member identified and enlisted a faculty member from her or his professional discipline to be present in the class. The current four core faculty members have worked together as a team over four years and developed the mutual respect, communication, and teamwork that served as model for the students and was consistent with course objectives regarding teamwork.

SPECIFIC ELEMENTS OF THE CURRICULUM

The course content includes

- lectures and assigned readings
- five quizzes based on the readings (25 percent of the grade)
- two nonmedical team-building exercises
- five simulation exercises that include SimMan 3G and actors
- five individual postsimulation reflection papers (5 percent)
- five graded team SOAP notes (25 percent) based on the five simulation exercises
- five graded team SOAP notes (25 percent) based on five written cases
- one group paper (10 percent)
- one group presentation (10 percent) based on the group paper.

The SimMan 3G, an advanced patient simulator, is a life-size mannequin that can be programmed to exhibit physiological and neurological symptoms. The technology includes the ability to have a person controlling the simulator speak through a microphone that is audible to students. The mannequin is also connected to heart, respiration, blood pressure, and oxygen saturation monitors. The five simulation exercises with SimMan 3G are in labs that are equipped as treatment rooms; the lab rooms also permit audiovisual recording for the students to view their simulation at a later time.

Syllabus

There is one syllabus for the course. This syllabus has to meet discipline-specific requirements. To accomplish these goals, there is a section of the syllabus that addresses overall requirements, a course overview, course objectives, assignments, and grading of assignments. There is also a section on course policies and requirements that are specific to each discipline, such as academic integrity and conduct, enrollment, student outcomes, and grading scales.

The overall course objectives are as follows:

1. Identify and develop or enhance the strengths of participating members of the interprofessional team in the care of critically ill patients.
2. Critically evaluate evidence-based physical or medical, psychosocial, and ethical treatment of the critically ill.
3. Assess and prioritize the physical or medical, psychosocial, and ethical needs of critically ill patients during hospitalization.
4. Collect and analyze pertinent patient information to develop patient-specific physical or medical, psychosocial, and ethical interventions and monitoring plans for critically ill patients.
5. Interpret pharmacokinetic, pharmacodynamic, and hemodynamic monitoring and subsequent response to significant changes in the critically ill patient.

6. Demonstrate interprofessional team communication and the influence of the interprofessional team professional expertise on outcomes within a critically ill setting by using simulation technology and case examples.

The implicit social work curriculum is focused on the expectation that social workers will act as patient and family advocates; assess current and future psychosocial needs and interventions, including discharge needs; and function as full members of the team. Social work performance outcomes include (a) demonstrated support of the patient and family; (b) engagement with other team members during simulations; (c) documentation of psychosocial elements in the subjective, objective, assessment, and plan components of the team SOAP note and address short-term and long-term goals; and (d) submission of social work postsimulation reflections, including commentary on hierarchy, professional status, communication among team members, the social work student's role on the team, the student's contribution to teamwork and the SOAP note, and how he or she manages conflict with other team members and the team as a whole. The group oral presentation and group paper also demonstrate social work involvement.

The evaluation of the social workers' performance is provided during team and class debriefing sessions and on their written assignments. The debriefing sessions are not graded, and the written assignments receive a group grade. Although the postsimulation reflections are not graded, the social work faculty member reviews them and provides feedback and comments. These forms of feedback are indicative of what occurs in the professional workplace. Both the team and individual team members receive feedback and are asked to reflect on their performance.

These core competencies, performance measures, and skills are consistent with the 2008 Council on Social Work Education (CSWE) educational policy and accreditation standards (CSWE, 2008). The corresponding CSWE Core Competencies are "identify as a professional social worker and conduct oneself accordingly" (2.1.1), "apply knowledge of the human behavior and social environment" (2.1.7), and "engage, assess, intervene, and evaluate with individuals, families, organizations and communities" (2.1.10).

Class Structure

The course curriculum was initially developed over a six-month period by the faculty coteaching the class to identify the course objectives, reading requirements, exercises, learning aids, and student evaluation methods. Prior to the beginning of each subsequent semester (after the first semester the class was offered), the faculty met to review content, exercises, and the course outline for delivery of content.

Students from all four professional disciplines are divided into four groups or teams. The team composition is dependent on the mix of students who register. At times, there were several nursing and pharmacy students on a team, and there were also teams without a social worker or respiratory therapist. The first two class sessions of the semester are structured for students to participate in team-building exercises in preparation for the more advanced critical care simulations and written cases. The first class is an introduction to the structure for lectures, class exercises and simulations, graded assignments, and the Core Competencies for Interprofessional Collaborative

Practice outlined by the Interprofessional Educational Collaborative (IPEC, 2011). During this first class session, students are involved in a team-building exercise with other classmates from their team assignment.

Students attend classes weekly over a 16-week semester, and course content focuses primarily on critical care of adults in an emergency room and intensive care unit setting. There are nine lectures covering critical medical conditions related to the renal, cardiovascular, neurologic, and respiratory systems and one special-topic lecture. The classroom is equipped to transmit and receive audio and visual content by using distance-learning technology because, at times, faculty present their lecture from the Baltimore location. The students can see the faculty member conducting the lecture and any presentation slides used for the lecture by the faculty member. The faculty member in Baltimore can view the classroom from the front, facilitating discussion and questions. The course curriculum (including adjustments and revisions from one year to the next) is discussed in detail in the following sections.

Course Outline

During the first three years the class was taught, faculty used an ungraded team-building exercise wherein students on each team had to recall the "safe" squares to step on to reach the other side of a square. The square was made up of four rows consisting of four blocks each; each block was secured to the floor with tape. Some blocks were "safe" and others were "toxic." A student stepped onto the first block in the first row. If it was toxic, a buzzer sounded. A second student on the team then stepped on a block in the first row (ideally remembering and avoiding the toxic block); if the block was safe, the student stepped on another block; the student could step to the right or the left or move up one row. Diagonal steps were not permitted. Team members were not permitted to talk to each other during the team trial. Teams were timed to determine which team could advance to the top of the square (the fourth row) in the shortest period of time. The other teams were not in the game trial area during other teams' trial.

The faculty recognized that this block exercise was not a good team-building exercise because it focused on the observation and memory skills of each team member and not communication and role delineation. In the fourth year, the faculty introduced a new team-building exercise called the "Marshmallow Challenge" (http://www.tomwujec .com/design-projects/marshmallow-challenge/). The task of each team was to build the tallest free-standing tower by using 20 sticks of dry spaghetti, a yard of tape, a yard of string, and a marshmallow that had to be placed on the top of the tower. The teams all started at the same time and had 18 minutes to complete the exercise. The exercise provided the teams with opportunities to strategize or plan their approach to building the tower, such as identifying the tasks to build the tower, determining whether and what roles needed to be assigned to accomplish the task, and using communication skills in all of these steps and processes.

The second class session includes another team-building exercise, which includes introducing the students to SimMan 3G. Students who had never participated in a simulation exercise before were assigned to watch a SimMan 3G tutorial video before the class. The first simulation was not a critical care situation so that the team could develop and clarify communication and role patterns during a low-stress simulation. The case for the simulation was a routine discharge planning meeting with SimMan 3G and an actor playing the role of his mother. The purpose of the role-play was to identify what environmental factors triggered the young man's asthma attack, provide education on discharge medications and precautions, demonstrate respiratory treatments, and address financial concerns regarding purchase of the medications.

In the third year of the class, we included a lecture on advance directives and legal considerations, which was taught by a faculty member from the University of Maryland School of Law. This new lecture was added to the third class session in response to student feedback at the end of year two. Students requested the content because they had limited knowledge regarding advance directives. They felt that the information would be helpful during the simulation exercises and the written cases. Several case simulations involve end-of-life decisions and withdrawal of life-sustaining measures, providing students with content that they could apply to the case.

Simulation Exercises

Prior to beginning all simulations, students were provided with a written brief summary of the case, including patient demographics (SimMan 3G was always the patient), family member demographics (the family member was always played by an actor), and patient condition upon admission, including all vital signs, known laboratory results, and any physical and psychosocial history available. Students were given two to three minutes to discuss their intervention plan before they went into the treatment room to meet the patient (SimMan 3G) and family. After each simulation, the students participated in a short debriefing session with a faculty member who observed the group simulation.

After all teams have participated in a simulation, the entire class debriefs with all faculty. This class debriefing session provides an opportunity for students to learn from each other. Because the focus of the class is about team building, team work, and communication, the students are asked to comment on "what went well" and "how will the team perform differently or better" in the future. The faculty provide feedback that points out how the teams performed well (such as communication among themselves and with the patient and family), role performance that was not confined to a specific professional role (for example, a pharmacy student providing an empathic response to the patient or family), and improvements in team functioning.

Written Cases

The second learning exercise is in the form of a written case analysis. The first written case analysis occurs at the fourth class meeting. There is a lecture that provides content related to the case to be analyzed by team; the students turn in a team SOAP note the following week. The written case is passed out to the students after the lecture, and they have 30 minutes to discuss the case and develop an intervention plan. The case is then discussed with the whole class. In this exercise, there is an emphasis on what each professional provides in the form of assessment, intervention, and care planning.

Students are permitted to use the whole class discussion content for the write-up of the case for the written SOAP note assignment.

Assignments

The reading materials for each class session consisted of articles that students could download from their library Web site. The readings were relevant to the lecture and the case for the week. Students were also required to complete five quizzes covering the five physical systems (renal, cardiovascular, neurological, respiratory, and one special topic) before the beginning of the class when the quiz was due. The quiz questions were specifically related to the readings and were constructed so that any student, regardless of discipline and knowledge of the disease process, could answer the questions on the basis of the readings. The five quizzes were worth 25 percent of the grade for the class.

One week after a simulation or a written case, student groups turn in one SOAP note. The acronym SOAP stands for Subjective, Objective, Assessment, and Plan. Writing a SOAP note is reviewed in the second class session. *Subjective* material is the information that the patient reports concerning symptoms, treatments, and medical history. Examples include the history of the current illness, family and social history, patient reports of medications, and any self-reported allergies. *Objective* information includes vital signs, results from a physical examination, lab and other testing results, and other verifiable data. *Assessment* refers to the interpretation or analysis of data from the Subjective and Objective sections. It can include whether disease or other related problems exist. *Plan* refers to the team's interprofessional strategy to address the patient issues. The plan could include referrals for more testing or evaluation, clinical monitoring and follow-up, patient and family education, and discharge counseling. The plan needs to address the immediate conditions and also consider interventions for the next level of care.

Grading of the SOAP note is based on how thoroughly the team considers the patient's strengths, needs, goals, and interests from each discipline's perspective. The SOAP notes are complex because some professions are not familiar with them. Additionally, the note must reflect an interprofessional practice perspective and include all of the patient's symptoms and conditions. In the last year, the faculty decided to introduce SOAP notes progressively. For the first few SOAP note submissions, the teams only had to record Subjective and Objective components of the notes. Students would later add the Assessment and Plan components. We learned that students struggled with this written assignment requirement. Our goal was to provide feedback in smaller doses that supported student learning.

Course Evaluation

During the last course session, students complete a course evaluation. The evaluation questions were specific to students' professional discipline, preventing a composite course evaluation. Although individual faculty members reviewed these course evaluations, results were not collated. However, when planning the course, the faculty decided to collect other course evaluation metrics. A voluntary survey was adapted from the

TeamSTEPPS survey by the core faculty teaching the course (Agency for Healthcare Research and Quality, 2014a, 2014b). The survey, consisting of 28 questions, was modified for an academic setting and included space for comments. TeamSTEPPS is a model of team cooperation that promotes safety, quality, team effectiveness, and efficiency for patient outcomes (Agency for Healthcare Research and Quality, n.d.). The survey development is discussed in detail in an article by Clark, Congdon, Macmillan, Gonzales, and Guerra (2015).

The faculty received institutional review board approval to collect the survey metrics during the first and last class sessions over three semesters. The increase in the perceived understanding of the scope of practice of other disciplines from the beginning to the end of class was substantial (from 24.4 percent to 60 percent strongly agreed or agreed). Appreciation for the complexities related to working on an interprofessional team also increased significantly, from 66.7 percent to 81 percent (Clark et al., 2015). On the basis of these findings, the faculty concluded that offering the class is beneficial despite any barriers and challenges it presents.

IMPLEMENTATION CHALLENGES

Faculty Assignments

The assignment of responsibilities for faculty was never a challenge. Faculty met frequently to plan the curriculum and course topics in the first year. During this planning phase, faculty members chose the topics they would teach; the faculty members' expertise was a key factor in their choice. As noted earlier, content was added in subsequent years. However, the additions were based on availability of a faculty member to cover the content. The more significant challenge was how to handle identifying a faculty replacement when a faculty member left the university. This is discussed in a later section.

Student Registration

An ongoing challenge from the social work perspective was recruitment of social work students. The course was offered on a day when students were at their field placements. Students who enrolled in the course included part-time students who were not in the field when the course was taught and students who negotiated with their field placement supervisor to leave the placement early and make up the time on another day.

Beginning with the fifth year the course was taught, the course was classified as a clinical course and was a valuable elective course. Although the course was originally an elective, the course classification did not meet concentration and specialization requirements. However, in year five, social work enrollment continued to be low; only two students enrolled.

Students from each professional discipline enrolled in the class through their respective schools; this registration procedure worked without difficulty. However, creating a single learning management system (LMS) site for students and faculty in the class was challenging because students enrolled in their own respective discipline or school. A further complication was that the respiratory students were not part of the University of

Maryland system. The instructional media staff in the School of Pharmacy took the lead in overcoming this challenge. They successfully created an LMS site and then "enrolled" students and faculty into the class. This did cause some confusion for the social work students, who were used to accessing Blackboard through the School of Social Work. There was an LMS site created, but it was never populated with information. The social work faculty member easily resolved social work students' concern with an e-mail before the first class session advising students about the joint LMS.

Classroom Coordination for Clinical Simulation

In the first and second years, it was challenging to coordinate the classroom and faculty for simulation exercises. The simulation exercises were conducted in a large learning laboratory instead of a simulation lab area. This required faculty to bring all of the simulation equipment (mannequin, monitors, etc.) to the lab, set the equipment up before class, and then return the equipment after class. Because the class ended at 6 p.m., this required more coordination to unlock storage areas. In year three, the simulation exercises were conducted in a simulation lab area; this was a better learning environment as it also allowed the simulation exercise for each student group to be videotaped.

A second challenge in these first two years was the coordination of faculty to manage the simulation equipment and exercise. This coordination involved scheduling a faculty member as well as the equipment. By year three, the course schedule consisted of the same clinical conditions for the five simulations, and faculty availability was no longer an issue.

Organizational Structure

The course was successfully implemented on one of the university's satellite campuses and not the main campus, where the majority of the clinical instruction occurred. On both campuses, the professional disciplines all had a different academic calendar. This made it challenging to bring four or more disciplines together for the course. Students mentioned the absence of medical students each year when the IPE faculty conducted an overall course debriefing. Though medical students did not attend any classes on the satellite campus, it was easier both structurally and pragmatically to offer the course on the satellite campus. Also, the course requirements for the medical students reduced the likelihood that they could participate in the class, even if it was offered on the main campus.

Program Sustainability

In its first four years, the course did not face significant challenges related to sustainability. The challenge in the fifth year occurred when the social work faculty member left the School of Social Work at the university. When the course was initially offered, there were three social work faculty members to share responsibility for teaching and attending class each week. At the end of the first academic year, one faculty member retired and another faculty member left the school to establish a new MSW program.

The remaining faculty member had the support of the administration to continue including this course in his teaching load. In year three, school administration began to question whether the faculty member could continue to include the course as part of his teaching load. The primary reason was the historic low enrollment of social work students; two or three social work students enrolled each time the course was offered despite efforts to promote the class. As noted earlier, the day and the time the class was offered conflicted with students' field placement days.

Planning for a social work faculty member replacement was challenging because the few faculty members with the clinical experience to take over the course were already committed. Because the school began to offer a full-time complement of MSW program courses on the same campus where the IPE course was taught, faculty resources were already committed, and there were no other faculty on the main campus to teach the course in year five. A stopgap plan was for one social work faculty member to participate in a few classes as time permitted. The fate of social work faculty presence in the course through the entire semester in year six is still unknown at this time.

LESSONS LEARNED: HOW DID THE UNIVERSITY STRUCTURE FACILITATE OR CHALLENGE IPE?

Teaching this course required the faculty to be reflective and open to feedback from students. Faculty members as a group had their own process to annually review the course in preparation for the next year. In addition, the faculty were responsive to the need to make modest adjustments when issues arose during the semester. These modest adjustments were typical for any course: how to handle situations when a student did not complete an individual course assignment, how to handle an absence of a student and the potential impact on the team during a simulation exercise, and how to handle grading of assignments.

Occasionally, a student did not complete a reflection or a quiz in a timely manner. The reflections were graded either pass or fail, and the intention was to have the students process their experience for self-growth. It was rare that a student did not submit his or her reflection on the date it was due, and if so, late submissions were allowed without penalty. If a student did not submit a quiz on time, faculty evaluated whether the student was failing to be responsible or had a technical issue with the LMS. If the student failed to manage his or her time, the faculty could penalize the student. Technical issues did not lead to a penalty. Neither of these situations occurred with any frequency.

The faculty had to discuss in more detail how to grade assignments. In the first year, faculty started the year by sharing responsibility for grading assignments for a specific simulation exercise or written case. The faculty were committed to sharing the workload, and this was the basis for our initial decision. What became apparent was that each faculty member graded differently; some faculty members were more lenient than others. The dilemma created for students was a lack of consistent feedback enabling them to improve on subsequent assignments. This was most evident for the 10 SOAP notes due during the semester. The faculty goal was for students to improve the SOAP notes.

There were four SOAP notes to grade each week (one from each team). One faculty member stepped up to be the primary grader. This faculty member then shared the graded SOAP notes with another faculty member. If there was a significant issue identified, then the two faculty members conferred and made a joint decision regarding the grade. This system worked well. Students received feedback from all disciplines and there was consistency in grading.

One challenging issue regarding assignments was that some students were more focused on the grade of the SOAP note than on learning and teamwork. They made changes to the SOAP note assignments without consulting or gaining the consensus of the team. Faculty members began to recognize when this was occurring. The faculty met as a team with the students to emphasize that their written work needed to reflect the input of all team members.

In relation to changes in course content or methods of instruction, the faculty team, as a result of their teamwork, recognized areas for improvement. Fundamentally, the faculty teaching team worked together very well and was also committed to student learning and creating a cutting-edge course. Although examples of changes in content and methods have been discussed throughout this chapter, they merit further review.

The first student team-building exercise was changed in year four to better prepare students to function as a team. The new team exercise, the "spaghetti exercise," engaged the students to communicate a plan, identify tasks and persons responsible for the task, and work toward a challenging goal. Ironically, the first time the spaghetti exercise was used, several of the faculty formed a team also. Their tower was the tallest and withstood the "test" of endurance and structural integrity. This in some measure illustrated how this faculty team had grown and developed over time.

In year four, the SOAP note requirement was adjusted so that students learned progressively how to write the SOAP note. As some disciplines do not use SOAP notes, there was a need for teaching and feedback to assist students to master and accomplish the assignment as a team. The grading of the SOAP note was constructed so that the number of points increased over time. The change in how these notes were written appeared to meet the expected outcome: well-written team SOAP notes.

One modification not previously discussed was the methods by which teams received feedback about their team simulation exercise. In the first few years, all faculty observed the teams in the same room where the simulation was occurring, and then all faculty provided feedback immediately at the end of the team's simulation. This method was changed so that faculty observed the team simulation via video and audio transmission in another area of the lab. After the simulation, the team met with one faculty member for a short debriefing session. Feedback was given only after the team evaluated their teamwork. In all years, the faculty provided feedback and observations to the entire class after all teams had finished the simulation.

Another key change regarding simulations was the use of actors playing the role of family members. Historically, faculty recruited staff and students not enrolled in the class to play these parts. In the fourth year, we began to use a modified standardized patient model. The standardized patient took the role of a family member (SimMan 3G was still used). Because the standardized patient was trained for this role and worked from a script, the model provided consistency. Additionally, the standardized patient gave all teams feedback about his or her experience when we met for the full class debriefing.

Finally, reading assignments for the course changed in year three to include more literature regarding psychosocial elements of care and intervention. Although the course was intended for team building and teamwork, initially the required readings focused almost exclusively on medical conditions and subsequent treatment. The additional readings included topics on autonomy, interprofessional team development, and working with patients in renal units and in geriatrics. In addition to these modifications to the syllabus, a guest lecturer on advanced directives and guardianships provided readings for her lecture.

In summary, the faculty teaching the course were reflective regarding content and classroom methods of instruction so that the course improved from year to year. Additionally, faculty listened to feedback from students in a class wrap-up at the end of each term. Finally, the course delivery was improved by the faculty's consistency and the overall curriculum constituency.

REFERENCES

Agency for Healthcare Research and Quality. (2014a). *TeamSTEPPS: Teamwork attitudes questionnaire (T-TAQ)*. Retrieved from http://www.ahrq.gov/teamstepps/instructor/reference/teamattitude.html

Agency for Healthcare Research and Quality. (2014b). *TeamSTEPPS: Teamwork perceptions questionnaire (T-TPQ)*. Retrieved from http://www.ahrq.gov/teamstepps/instructor/reference/teampercept.html

Agency for Healthcare Research and Quality. (n.d.). *TeamSTEPPS: National implementation*. Retrieved from http://teamstepps.ahrq.gov/

Clark, K., Congdon, H. B., Macmillan, K., Gonzales, J. P., & Guerra, A. (2015). Changes in perceptions and attitudes of healthcare profession students pre and post academic course experience of team-based care for the critically ill. *Journal of Professional Nursing, 31*, 330–339.

Council on Social Work Education. (2008). *Educational policy and accreditation standards*. Retrieved from http://www.cswe.org/File.aspx?id=41861

Interprofessional Education Collaborative Expert Panel. (2011). *Core competencies for interprofessional collaborative practice: Report of an expert panel*. Retrieved from https://www.aamc.org/download/186750/data/

9

ARIZONA STATE UNIVERSITY

Robin P. Bonifas

Interprofessional education at Arizona State University (ASU) occurs in collaboration with the University of Arizona (U of A) Phoenix campus and the Northern Arizona University (NAU) Phoenix campus. It includes the following disciplines: nursing, social work, nutrition (ASU), medicine, pharmacy (U of A), the physician assistant program, physical therapy, and occupational therapy (NAU). A new partnership with A. T. Stills University will bring dental students into the mix.

ACADEMIC ENVIRONMENT

Institutional Structure

The Macy Project, an interprofessional graduate curriculum development and implementation initiative funded by two sequential grants from the Josiah Macy Jr. Foundation since 2010, is a key motivator of ASU-initiated interprofessional activities and emphasizes preparation for collaborative practice in primary care settings. The Macy Project includes faculty representatives from ASU (nursing and social work) and U of A (medicine and pharmacy) with educational efforts focused on the four disciplines. Interprofessional learning opportunities develop in two ways: the Macy Project organizes opportunities as a whole based on students' overall interprofessional learning needs, and individual Macy team members organize and participate in opportunities apart from the Macy Project on the basis of the interprofessional learning needs of students in their specific disciplines. The individual efforts of Macy team members are termed "ripples," representing the broad influence the Macy Project is able to achieve through the extended-reach efforts of individual faculty members. An example of a Macy Project team interprofessional learning opportunity is a monthly student gathering, which brings together students from nursing, social work, medicine, and pharmacy to intro-duce them to key topics related to interprofessional practice and to foster in-person interaction that applies the new skills and knowledge. These events are developed, coordinated, marketed, and evaluated under the auspices of the Macy Project whereby team members in all four disciplines agree on the topics to be presented. An example of an interprofessional learning opportunity sponsored by individual Macy team members is Building Consensus in Interprofessional Teams, a two-hour in-person event that pairs medical and social work students to negotiate complex scenarios that can arise in prac-tice. This opportunity was developed by two Macy Project team members in conjunction with non-Macy colleagues and was coordinated, marketed, and evaluated separately from Macy-related activities. It came about through medical students' requests to work more closely with social work students and through social work students' need for practice collaborating in host settings where social work perspectives are underrepresented.

Early Interprofessional Activities

An initial interprofessional seminar was held during the fall semester of 2010. Devel-oped collaboratively between faculty at ASU and U of A, the activity involved five disci-plines: nursing, social work, nutrition, medicine, and pharmacy. Students participated in a three-hour interactive seminar with the following learning objectives:

1. Appreciate the contribution that each discipline or profession makes to the optimal outcomes of health care.
2. Discuss the different stereotypes of the health care professions and professionals.
3. Recognize the impact of personality types on stereotypes, communication styles, and decision making.
4. Explore the influences of diversity in group dynamics and problem solving.
5. Develop effective strategies for health care professionals to work together as a team.

Prior to the interprofessional session, students completed a public access version of the Myers-Briggs Personality Indicator (see http://www.humanmetrics.com/cgi-win/JTypes2.asp; Myers & McCaulley, 1998) to determine their personality type and read material describing the characteristics of their type, which included strengths and chal-lenges typically encountered in team settings. During the session, students were exposed to didactic content emphasizing advanced understanding of the Myers-Briggs personality types and how personality influences practice in health care organizations. Following the Myers-Briggs presentation, they participated in small-group breakout sessions with student representatives from each discipline and either a faculty or community practice facilitator. The facilitator guided students through a brief overview of the roles of each profession and then collaborative discussion of a complex clinical case. The following discussion questions were used:

1. What are the priorities of care?
2. What are the opportunities for collaborations with other disciplines?

3. What resources do you need to access for the optimal outcome of care for this patient?
4. Discuss how the personality of patients, family members, and health care workers may have an impact on the care of patients.

The seminar concluded with brief student presentations highlighting key results of their small-group work and areas of influential learning regarding interprofessional collaboration and the role of personality styles in team practice. Key evaluative outcomes from this project were based on questions used by the Gerontology Interdisciplinary Team Training Program (Hyer, Heinemann, & Fulmer, 2002) and assessed changes in students' values and attitudes toward interprofessional team work and gains in their understanding of colleagues' roles and training requirements.

Identification of Interprofessional Education (IPE) Faculty

Identification of IPE faculty at ASU began with the deans or directors of various programs, who were recruited by Dr. Gerri Lamb from the College of Nursing and Health Innovation, the principal investigator of the Josiah Macy Jr. Foundation grants. Nursing, medicine, and pharmacy were the original disciplines involved, with social work joining shortly thereafter, when the team recognized the value of adding a psychosocial perspective. The deans and directors then identified appropriate faculty members within their department to assume a more hands-on role in curriculum development. For example, Dr. Phil Scheinder, dean of U of A's College of Pharmacy, invited Dr. Carolyn Bae, who had expressed interest in interprofessional education, to join the Macy Project; Dr. Steven Anderson, director of the ASU School of Social Work, invited me to participate in the Macy Project because of my background in medical social work and my early involvement in IPE through the interprofessional seminar described above. From there, original team members identified and recruited like-minded colleagues to join Macy Project or Task Force activities. Dr. Teri Kennedy joined the Macy Project after expressing an interest to Dr. Lamb and added event planning skills and sustainability knowledge to the group's expertise. Similarly, Dr. Liz Harrell was added to the team because of her knowledge of student-run free health clinics, involvement with ASU's developing clinic, Student Health Outreach for Wellness (SHOW), and ability to extend the Macy Project's reach to a wide range of interprofessional students involved in SHOW.

In 2013, Dr. Gerri Lamb also extended IPE planning beyond the Macy Project to an IPE workgroup that met regularly to identify and plan interprofessional connections across the curriculum. Faculty associates with practice responsibilities in the community were included in the work group to solidify the integration of education and practice; leadership from each of the allied health programs was also included to form a strong foundation of administrative support. Faculty in undergraduate and graduate nursing, pharmacy, medicine, and social work programs were represented and typically invited to participate on the basis of specific areas of expertise that could advance the group's goals. For example, Kay Jarrell, clinical associate professor in the College of Nursing and Health Innovation, had provided mentorship and training to undergraduate nursing students in community nursing practice for several years and was added to the team because of her expertise in community service delivery and public health, an area conducive to IPE. The IPE workgroup now includes 40 members, with three subcommittees responsible for visibility of collaborative efforts through Web site development, faculty development, and interprofessional simulation.

Faculty Support

Originally, no formal faculty support was provided other than administrative blessing to participate in IPE planning activities and administrative buy-in to incorporate interprofessional learning opportunities into curricular programs across the disciplines. However, as interest in IPE grew, several faculty members were funded by the College of Nursing and Health Innovation to attend interprofessional training events, such as the Interprofessional Education Collaborative (IPEC) Faculty Development Institute and the Josiah Macy Jr. Foundation Annual Meeting. After curriculum implementation funding was received from the Josiah Macy Jr. Foundation in 2013, many core members of the Macy Project team received summary salary and support to attend interprofessional conferences, including Collaborating across Borders IV and All Together Better Health VII.

DEVELOPMENTAL PROCESS OF THE PROGRAM

Key Faculty

There are numerous faculty champions involved in IPE at ASU; those who work most closely with the School of Social Work include Beatrice Kastenbaum, Brenda Morris, Gerri Lamb, Kay Jarrell, Liz Harrell, Pauline Komnenich, Ruth Brooks, Teri Kennedy, Tina Shepard, and myself. Carolyn Bae and Lisa Hines from the U of A College of Pharmacy, Michele Lundy from the U of A College of Medicine, and Pamela Thompson from ASU's College of Health Solutions also played significant roles.

Milestones

Important milestones in ASU's IPE program include the receipt of two grants from the Josiah Macy Jr. Foundation, which supported concentrated curriculum planning, curriculum implementation, and the creation of vital community partnerships. Led by principal investigator Dr. Gerri Lamb of the College of Nursing and Health Innovation, the first Macy grant was received in 2010 to foster initial curriculum planning. The original team, composed of faculty members from ASU's College of Nursing and School of Social Work and U of A's College of Medicine and College of Pharmacy, developed a pilot curriculum for interprofessional primary care practice that was tested and refined with a small group of students from the four disciplines to identify points of strength and challenges for future implementation. The second Macy grant, received in 2013, built on this foundation to expand the curriculum to clinical partner sites in the community and incorporate a longitudinal evaluation plan. Two clinical partner sites serve as settings for interprofessional practice–focused field internships and clinical rotations: Woodmark Health Center and Southwest Health Outreach. (Agency names are fictitious for confidentiality.)

OVERVIEW OF CURRICULUM AND PROGRAM FEATURES

Curriculum Development Process

The Macy Project interprofessional curriculum was developed over two years via a series of planning meetings involving representation from each of the four included disciplines (nursing, medicine, social work, and pharmacy). The goal of early meetings was to identify two-year segments across the curriculum where students' learning needs most closely overlapped and where integration of interprofessional content would be the best fit. Within this "golden window," depicted in Table 9.1, faculty deemed students to be progressing at similar levels of professional development and clinical competencies and to be most ready to learn and value teamwork for its contributions to positive client outcomes.

After determining where in the curriculum students' learning needs were most aligned, the planning team then focused on identifying interprofessional curricular content that would best prepare students for collaborative practice in delivering quality, patient-centered primary care. Three primary learning objectives were identified:

1. Orientation to IPE: The learner will be able to discuss the goals of interprofessional education and begin formation of an interprofessional team to enable improved quality and access to care at a decreased cost in primary care.
2. Interprofessional quality improvement: The learner will be able to analyze data or concepts for an interprofessional team to improve quality outcomes for patients and families in primary care.
3. Group decision making in primary care: The learner will be able to perform within an interprofessional team to improve quality outcomes for patients and families in the primary care setting.

To enable students to achieve these learning objectives, the curriculum was designed based on the 16 IPEC competency statements (IPEC Expert Panel, 2011). The statements, as updated in 2016 (IPEC, 2016), are presented in Appendix A and discussed in more detail in chapters 3 through 6. Although joint classroom experiences were originally envisioned, it was most feasible to incorporate online learning materials, brief face-to-face learning sessions, and internship-based interprofessional coaching into existing curricula.

In addition to IPE focused on student learning, faculty development is a critical component of ASU's program. Coordinated by the Macy Project, a series of faculty development workshops has helped prepare faculty, field instructors, and clinical preceptors for teaching interprofessionally. A series of online learning modules is under

Table 9.1: The Golden Window

Profession	Summer 1	Fall 1	Spring 1	Summer 2	Fall 2	Spring 2
Medicine, starts year 2		Basic Science, Organ System		Clerkship	Clerkship	Clerkship
Doctor of Nursing Practice, starts year 1	Pharmacotherapeutics	Acute Care	Chronic Care	Outcomes	Evidence-Based Practice	Best Practices
Pharmacy, starts year 3		Pharmacotherapeutics			Practice Experience	
MSW, starts year 1		Foundational—Micro	Foundational—Macro		Concentration in Health/Mental Health	

development that will further support faculty training in this area (see the Sustainability section of this chapter for more details on the modules).

Curriculum Overview

The Macy Project Interprofessional Curriculum includes three integrated strategies: online learning resource "education bursts," case-based "Student Gatherings," and practice site team meetings led by interprofessional faculty coaches.

The *interprofessional education bursts* highlight applied content for collaborative practice and are sent via e-mail every two weeks to a wide range of health professions students. Information is designed to be brief (requiring less than 15 minutes of students' time) and focuses on advancing interprofessional knowledge. Students completing internships or clinical rotations in the Macy clinical partner sites discussed below (termed *Macy Scholars*), student volunteers at SHOW, and social work students specializing in health/behavioral health or completing an internship in a health setting receive the bursts. Example topics and associated content from the past year are listed in Table 9.2.

Table 9.2: Example Online Interprofessional Learning Bursts

Topic	Content
Collaboration	YouTube video (2:21 minutes) focused on interprofessional team process skills that achieve common goals in health care.
Role clarification	YouTube video (2:53 minutes) focused on understanding one's own role and the roles of others in an interprofessional health care context.
Roles of health care professionals	Short videos and written briefs that offer an overview of a number of health care professions and a general understanding of their roles and responsibilities. Information is presented about what each profession does, the education professionals receive, and where they might work.
Interprofessional collaboration	A brief online module (10 minutes) that introduces a common understanding and language for collaborative practice to support development of improved collaboration within health care teams.
Mutual support in teams	Two videos from TeamSTEPPS demonstrating poor examples followed by good examples of mutual support in teams.
Teamwork	These two videos are examples of how the same situation was handled in a primary care office when a staff member called in sick. In the first situation, the plan of care is not concrete or well communicated. In the second video, there are good team processes to effectively work through the situation.

The student gatherings bring students and coaches together for interactive, case-based activities that address overarching themes to support learning and skill development across internship settings. Example topics include "Preparing for interprofessional practice in integrated care settings," "Practice-based learning: How you can add value to healthcare transformation," and "Facilitating person-centered care through interprofessional practice." All gatherings incorporate a didactic component followed by an interactive activity. For example, during the gathering focused on integrated care, a panel of community experts shared their experiences in diverse settings, including the policy arena, and either explained how collaboration occurred in their organizations or how policy changes could better foster effective interprofessional practice. After a brief question-and-answer period, students worked in small groups to consider integrated health and behavioral health needs present in a case study client and how working together might facilitate positive outcomes. Macy Scholars are invited to participate in the student gatherings along with other students who would benefit from learning more about the team aspects of care delivery. For example, all social work students in the health/behavioral health specialization are invited to attend.

The faculty coach meetings integrate interprofessional experiences into primary care settings where students' collaborative contacts may be limited; patient-centered discussion emphasizes building team skills for using a whole-person perspective to effectively identify and address patients' needs. Coach meetings are held monthly; during the 2014–2015 academic year, a student-led capstone project introduced a new model for team-based practice and sharing of caseload responsibilities through a patient panel, which will be incorporated into future coaching sessions. Given the confidential nature of patient discussions, only students specifically based at the internship site participate in the coaching sessions.

Social Work Interprofessional Curriculum

The MSW program has been the primary focus for incorporating interprofessional content at ASU. Learning materials and experiences are integrated into two required courses in the health/behavioral health practice specialization, which students take during their concentration (second) year of the MSW program: Social Work Practice in Health/Behavioral Health Settings in the fall and Advanced Social Work Practice in Health Settings in the spring. In the fall, students select one interprofessional event to attend from a menu of options and write a brief reflective paper about their experience. Example interprofessional events are depicted in Table 9.3. The paper addresses the five questions listed below:

1. Briefly describe the activities that took place and the other health professionals that were present.
2. What did you learn about the roles and responsibilities of other health professionals?
3. What was the role of social work in the health situation addressed by the event?
4. What insights did you gain regarding the strengths and challenges of working with other health professionals?

Table 9.3: Learning Activities Menu

Activity	Description	Sponsor
Interprofessional Journal Club Case Study Discussion	Students from nursing, social work, and physical therapy meet for guided discussion of discipline-specific and interprofessional care needs for a complex geriatric case.	ASU & NAU
Team Arizona Interprofessional Healthcare Summit	An interprofessional community panel will explain the roles of eight health care disciplines; students then meet in small interprofessional groups to discuss roles and responsibilities related to a complex case study and develop a collaborative treatment plan.	ASU, U of A, & NAU
Bertha Strong Stroke Simulation	On their own, students review the patient's medical chart and view a 25-minute video depicting a partial interprofessional assessment of Ms. Strong, a 67-year old woman who has had a stroke; students then meet in interprofessional teams to determine next steps in the plan of care.	ASU
Interprofessional Emergency Preparedness	Students will work in interprofessional teams to practice effectively responding to a natural disaster situation.	U of A
Interprofessional Case Competition	Students will work online in interprofessional teams for about six weeks to develop a treatment plan based on a case study. Students then competitively present their treatment plans at a formal event, and the team with the best plan wins a cash prize.	ATS
Online interprofessional discussion group regarding unfolding family case study	Graduate nursing and social work students work in small teams to respond to the health and behavioral health needs of a multigenerational family. There are four learning modules and associated online discussions over the course of the semester.	ASU
St. Luke's Home Interprofessional Clinics	Monthly clinics provide student health care teams with an opportunity to build vital interprofessional skills. Clinic topics vary by month.	U of A

Notes: ASU = Arizona State University; NAU = Northern Arizona University; U of A = University of Arizona.

5. Describe one thing you learned from the interprofessional online learning bursts assigned in class so far that can guide your ability to work effectively with other professions to ensure positive client outcomes.

In addition, students complete seven interprofessional learning bursts, view and discuss brief videos depicting effective and ineffective team member behaviors and team processes, and complete four readings related to social workers as members of inter-professional teams. The videos are from the John A. Hartford Foundation's Geriatric Interdisciplinary Team Training program and feature interprofessional team members collaborating in gerontological care situations (available at http://elearning.hartfordign .org/login/index.php; login is required). The four readings are by Bronstein (2003); Graham and Barter (1999); Oliver (2013); and Parker-Oliver and Peck (2006).

In the spring, students in Advanced Social Work Practice in Health Settings com-plete an additional seven interprofessional learning bursts, select a different interpro-fessional event to attend from a menu of options, and write a similar brief reflective paper about the experience. They also participate in an interprofessional Objective Structured Clinical Exam (OSCE) with students in the Doctor of Nursing Practice (DNP) program. The OSCE scenario begins with a 30-minute nurse assessment of a standardized patient, followed by a warm handoff to the MSW student regarding any identified psychosocial needs. A 30-minute social work assessment with the standardized patient follows; the scenario concludes with a documentation period to record results of the social work assessment and the recommended course of action. MSW students are not evaluated on their performance as in a traditional OSCE but receive feedback on their interprofessional collaborative skills and psychosocial assessment to support professional growth.

Social work students also have opportunity to enroll in a one-credit elective, Inter-professional Healthcare Practice, that meets over a series of five two-hour Saturday sessions. Although students across the health disciplines have been invited to enroll, students are primarily from nursing and social work. Course content is organized around the four overarching IPEC competencies (IPEC Expert Panel, 2011)—values and ethics, role and responsibilities, interprofessional communication, and teams and teamwork—and emphasizes practical skill building. In the classroom, students participate in a series of role-play interactions involving modified standardized patients, by which I mean standardized patients who are not actually actors but students and colleagues with a dramatic flair and who are rapidly trained to portray a specific client. During these role-plays, students practice working collaboratively to discuss long-term care planning with an older woman who is having difficulty living alone independently and also to engage a family struggling with achieving consensus regarding treatment planning for a child with chronic illness and developmental disability. The highlight of the course is a visit to a nearby senior housing community, where student teams partner with ten-ants to practice collaborative assessment; students jointly spend one hour with their assigned tenant completing a brief medication review, discussing the tenant's concerns about his or her medications, and then conversing about topics of interest as identified by the tenant. The collaborative assessment session is followed by a debriefing and a small party to thank tenants for their participation.

Throughout the course, students participate in an online unfolding case study that features health challenges that can arise across the lifespan and that can benefit from a collaborative interprofessional approach. Developed by Dr. Kara Mangold as her capstone project for the DNP degree, the case study focuses on a multigenerational family; its five members are presented in the following multigenerational case study.

Kathy (Mother)

Divorced mother (Kathy), age 62, working full time as a human resources professional for a banking system. In good health for age. Had herniated disk 10 years ago that was successfully treated with surgery and physical therapy. Tries to avoid any strenuous activities and heavy lifting in order to avoid further problems. Has hypothyroidism and has been stable on medications for the last 30 years.

Mike (Kathy's Son)

Son (Mike), age 35, with Down syndrome and a history of seizure disorder. Recently diagnosed with high blood pressure and high cholesterol, for which he has been started on medications. Lives with mother, works 20 hours a week at a local grocery store bagging items and helping with customer carryout. Cannot drive but is able to walk the three blocks to and from work when weather is good.

Lindsey (Kathy's Daughter) and Tess (Kathy's Granddaughter)

Daughter (Lindsey), age 40. Divorced, shares custody of 12-year-old daughter (Tess) with ex-husband. Tess has asthma, with more frequent exacerbations in the last six months, since moving to Phoenix from Prescott. Lindsey works full time as a receptionist for a local insurance agent. Lindsey has missed quite a bit of work at her job and Tess has missed quite a few days of school since the asthma has become worse. Lindsey and Tess are on AHCCCS (Arizona Health Care Cost Containment System). Lindsey is worried about finances and had to borrow money last month from her grandmother (Barbara) to pay the electric, water, and phone bills. Lost time at work and increasing copays for Tess's medications have taken their toll on the family budget.

Barbara (Grandmother, Kathy's Mother)

Grandmother (Barbara), age 86, widowed eight months ago. Can drive but does not like to. Kathy takes Barbara to her appointments and social events. Strong Catholic faith and weekly church attendance is important. Has fallen eight times at home since her husband's passing. No severe injuries. Does not want to leave home, is still experiencing many symptoms of grief and loss. Barbara is on a fixed income, receiving social security every month. Barbara has lost the benefit of her husband's pension since his passing. She is currently able to cover all expenses without dipping into savings.

Presented in a series of four modules emphasizing the primary IPEC competencies (IPEC Expert Panel, 2011), the case study engages students with one another to respond to basic prompts such as these from the Roles and Responsibilities Module: "List and describe three areas where you see your professional role in relation to the family unit" and "Discuss other healthcare professionals who would be appropriate to engage in this family's care." Other questions prompt students to consider interacting with the clients around interprofessional topics, as in the following example:

> You meet with the family to discuss a new collaborative care model at clinic. Present are Kathy and Mike. Mike is here for his annual evaluation. Initial response from Kathy is uncertainty and hesitation. Kathy states, "I'm not sure what's going on or why things are different. Every year we come in, the nurse puts us in a room and then leaves. Sooner or later the doctor or nurse practitioner comes in, writes out the scripts for Mike, and we are on our way for another year. We saw a social worker once years ago, but we pretty much just figure things out on our own." Respond to Kathy by explaining the value and benefit of interprofessional team work.

Although the focus of IPE has been on the MSW program, inroads are being made to include interprofessional content at the BSW level as well. For example, students in a required practice course during their senior year, Generalist Practice with Individuals, Families, and Groups, participate in an online referral activity with undergraduate students in the nutrition department. As an application of their learning about clinical documentation, students practice receiving and making referrals to one another via e-mail. The activity is based on an unfolding case study that features a client with both nutritional and psychosocial needs. As nutrition students "meet" with the client, they learn about some of her psychosocial needs, which they then pass on to a social work partner via an online referral. Social work students then "meet" with the client to further assess those psychosocial needs and learn more about the client's nutritional needs, which they refer back to the nutrition student with a brief description of their social work intervention plan. There is no actual "client" in this activity; rather, students receive unfolding information that reveals what they have learned as if they had met with the client in practice. The online nature of the assignment helps to foster student collaboration when course schedules do not allow face-to-face interaction and prepares students for electronic collaboration, which is common in Arizona health care settings.

Mode of Delivery

ASU has found that interprofessional content reaches more students when delivered via a range of modalities. Students have expressed a preference for frequent brief online learning activities when training occurs external to the field setting. As such, the electronic learning bursts described above were developed to address students' voiced needs. Online learning also eliminates barriers associated with scheduling mismatches across professional programs. At the same time, students also recognize that in-person learning activities are most conducive to building relationships with students from other disciplines. The face-to-face student gatherings described above meet this need and are offered one to two times each semester during the early evening, a time that students have identified as most convenient for their busy schedules. Macy "ripple" interprofessional events, developed by Macy Project faculty apart from the formal Macy curriculum, are also face to face and occur regularly throughout the year (as reviewed in Table 9.2). Typically, these events are integrated in at least one discipline's curriculum such that student attendance is required. Social work has not mandated participation in any specific event, but graduate students in the health/behavioral health specialization must attend at least one interprofessional event from a menu of approved options during fall semester (Table 9.3); students in the health specialization also attend a second event during the spring semester. The final learning modality occurs face to face in interprofessional field sites through interprofessional coaching discussed above. As noted previously, a capstone project designed by a DNP student has further strengthened the interprofessional learning for students in nursing, medicine, and social work at one primary care site through monthly student-led discussions of care needs for a shared panel of patients.

Clinical and Field Practicum Experiences

Students placed in Macy Project field sites gain skills in foundation or advanced practice skills through the ongoing supervision of the traditional MSW-prepared field instructor. They also develop skills in interprofessional collaboration through regular meetings with an interprofessional social work coach, whose role is not to help the student build direct practice competencies but rather to enable the student to consider his or her role on the interprofessional team, how social work can assist the team to more effectively meet patients' needs, and strategies to troubleshoot communication or relationship challenges within the team. Onsite and external interprofessional learning opportunities are incorporated in students' learning contracts to acknowledge the importance of developing collaborative skills as well as direct practice skills. For example, MSW students at Woodmark Health Center are required to attend monthly case discussions with students in nursing and medicine to collaborate with panel patients' care and are also required to participate in student gatherings.

Apart from students placed in Macy clinical partner sites, the Macy Project and ASU School of Social Work recognize that interprofessional content reaches more students by extending learning opportunities to all social work students placed in health settings. Therefore, graduate students interning in hospitals, hospice organizations, skilled nursing facilities, rehabilitation centers, and similar settings receive the interprofessional learning bursts and are invited to attend the student gatherings. Regular Macy coach communication with field instructors reinforces the value of incorporating these activities into students' learning contracts. Advancements in standardizing health/behavioral health learning contracts for the 2015–2016 academic year will formalize students' involvement in interprofessional events as official components of the learning experience.

Evaluation

Interprofessional education at ASU is evaluated in two ways. The Macy Project curriculum and associated activities are evaluated using a pre- and posttest design that captures students' self-assessed competencies for interprofessional practice at the beginning and end of semester-long experiences, such as a field internship or course that integrates interprofessional content. Macy "ripples" and other brief extended reach projects are evaluated independently to assess the impact of each event on students' learning.

Macy Project Evaluation

Students complete either an online or pen-and-paper questionnaire that assesses competencies in the following areas: communication and teamwork, dimensions of relationship, interprofessional learning, interprofessional interaction, and communication processes. The measurement instrument contains 53 Likert-scale questions; 35 are from the University of West England Interprofessional Questionnaire (UWE-IQ; Pollard, Miers, & Gilchrist, 2004, 2005), and the remaining 18 are from a newly developed measure specifically designed to capture the impact of Macy interventions: the Interprofessional Collaboration Readiness Questionnaire (IP-CQR) (Lamb & Saewert, 2013). Example questions from the UWE-IQ include "I am comfortable expressing my own opinions in a group, even when I know that other people don't agree with them" and "It's easy to communicate openly with people from other health care disciplines." Responses are measured on a 5-point scale where 1 = strongly agree, 2 = agree, 3 = neutral, 4 = disagree, and 5 = strongly disagree. Example questions from the IP-CQR include "I am confident in my readiness to communicate my professional role and responsibilities to patients and other health care team members" and "I am confident in my readiness to respectfully listen to recommendations from other health care team members that reflect a different point of view other than my own." Responses are measured on a 4-point scale where 1 = strongly agree, 2 = agree, 3 = disagree, and 4 = strongly disagree.

At the end of the primary care internship experience, interprofessional students also participate in a qualitative interview to share highlights of their experience and recommendations for improvement. Evaluation of the Macy Project has been approved for inclusion in the National Center Data Repository (NCDR), housed within the National Center for Interprofessional Education and Practice. Data generated by the project will join that from other interprofessional education initiatives to create "big data" that can support future research to form an evidence base linking IPE to desired triple-aim health outcomes (better health, better care, lower costs). SHOW, the student-run free health clinic, also has an approved evaluation project for the NCDR. This evaluation will include measures of student perceptions of interprofessional competence, their evaluation of preceptor IPE, and diabetes and hypertension outcomes for patients. A third evaluation project is currently under review and, if approved, will examine the impact of providing on-site interprofessional supportive services to tenants of a low-income senior housing community; measures of interest include student perceptions of interprofessional competence and tenant outcomes related to health, quality of life, emotional well-being, and community integration.

As an example of the evaluation process and associated outcomes, the questionnaires were administered during the first and last class session to all consenting students enrolled in Advanced Social Work Practice in Health Settings, the course described above that includes seven online interprofessional learning bursts, an interprofessional OSCE, and required participation in at least interprofessional activity. Although the sample size was small ($n = 11$) with a response rate of 69 percent, results suggest positive movement in student self-ratings of their comfort in various collaborative skills, such as justifying their recommendations to senior-level colleagues, working with peers, leading groups, and expressing opinions in groups. There also was positive movement in perceptions of confidence in readiness to coordinate care for patients with multiple health and social problems.

Macy "Ripples" and Extended-Reach Project Evaluation

Shorter interprofessional events and experiences use less rigorous evaluation approaches that aim to capture the impact student participation in the activity has on attitudes and values toward interprofessional learning and practice, as well as students' input for improving the experience. Each event uses a different evaluation approach depending on the needs to the faculty members designing the experience. For example, the Team Arizona Interprofessional Healthcare Summit, briefly described in Table 9.3, is a required activity for first-year medical students at the U of A, is one of the first interprofessional events that other allied health students experience, and features a complex geriatric case for clarification of team roles and responsibilities. Faculty responsible for the project are thus interested in identifying how involvement in the activity affects students' values of interprofessional teams and their understanding of roles and responsibilities in care delivery, especially those related to working with older adults. The evaluation instruments include select questions from the Geriatric Interdisciplinary Team Training Program (John A. Hartford Foundation, n.d.) and a faculty-designed instrument that assesses students' knowledge of the roles and training requirements of the eight disciplines featured in the event (medicine, nursing, pharmacy, social work, nutrition, physical therapy, occupational therapy, and physician assistant).

The Bertha Strong Stoke Simulation, in comparison, focuses on teamwork and team decision making for intervention planning. The Interdisciplinary Education Perception Scale (Luecht, Madsen, Taugher, & Petterson, 1990) is used to assess changes in students' attitudes toward team practice, and a faculty-designed series of Likert-scale questions examine students' self-assessed confidence in applying the four overarching IPEC competencies in collaborative practice (IPEC Expert Panel, 2011). As another example, the interprofessional referral assignment between undergraduate social work and nutrition students also reaches students early in their preparation for practice and is one of their first exposures to IPE. Faculty use the Readiness for Interprofessional Learning Scale (Parsell & Bligh, 1999) to capture students' reactions to the experience of interprofessional learning.

IMPLEMENTATION CHALLENGES

Challenges were experienced to a greater extent by the Macy Project team in implementing the overall IPE intervention in contrast to the smaller "ripple" or extended-reach events. A primary area of difficulty was recruiting clinical partner sites willing to accept student teams for field internships or clinical rotations. There are several health professions training programs in the Phoenix area, which creates competition among schools for student placements. Many primary care sites deemed appropriate to provide students with high-quality interprofessional learning experiences were unable to accommodate additional students. The initial year of the 2013–2016 implementation grant began with two clinical partner sites, Woodmark Health Center, a federally qualified health center serving underinsured and uninsured patients in the greater Phoenix area, and Southwest Health Outreach, a primary care clinic offering federally qualified health center services. Later that year, Southwest Health Outreach experienced transitions that hindered its ability to host students, including the loss of an MSW field instructor and a change in the volume of patients served.

Difficulties recruiting clinical partners resulted in Macy faculty focusing efforts on bringing IPE to field sites already in place rather than developing new sites. Faculty mapped out where students across the four disciplines were placed and identified places of overlap, recognizing that IPE is defined as "two or more professions learning from, with, and about each other" and that Macy goals could be accomplished even if only two disciplines were concurrently placed at a site. The Macy team also put greater emphasis on SHOW, the student-run free health clinic under development, as a promising resource for interprofessional learning.

Within the primary clinical partner site, Woodmark Health Center, leadership was strongly invested in collaborative practice and students' learning of interprofessional skills. However, this on-site support could not help with scheduling challenges at the university level. Students' clinical rotations and internship schedules often did not overlap, making face-to-face interprofessional collaboration difficult. Again, the Macy team strove to make use of what was available, and Macy coaches took advantage of students' interest in case-based consultation to bring interprofessional topics into weekly team meetings, often involving discussion of a panel of patients with whom students were working. Although students might not see patients at the same time or the same day, they were knowledgeable about patient conditions and needs and could collaborate with other disciplines around shared patients during these meetings.

Another challenge experienced exclusively by the social work component of Macy involved occasional disconnection between project goals and field instructor goals. Although administration at Woodmark Health Center was highly supportive of IPE and actively strove to ensure a good learning experience for student interns, service delivery staff struggled to balance the need to prepare social work interns for direct practice with the need to prepare them to work effectively with interprofessional colleagues. Student participation in team meetings and panel patient discussions was at times viewed as interfering with the students' primary work, that is, delivering direct social work services. Incorporating team meeting attendance as a requirement listed in students' field learning contracts proved an effective way to convey the importance of both types of student learning.

PROGRAM SUSTAINABILITY

Program sustainability is fostered through adherence to Kennedy's (2009) model, which highlights the importance of four key elements for project longevity:

1. Maintenance of mission and activities
2. Institutionalization of organizational infrastructure
3. Community visibility
4. Strategic response to change.

The following is an example of an annual sustainability plan:

Maintenance of Mission and Activities—Priorities
- Core curriculum refinements, such as coach meetings with students, workshops, bursts, integration of modules
- Completion of distance learning modules
- Evaluation, emphasis on data collection and analysis
- Recruitment of additional coaches

Institutionalization of Organizational Infrastructure—Priorities
- Completion and integration of course curriculum maps
- Plan for common evaluation across program
- Evaluation—scale-up development and implementation of projects that include patient outcomes, development, and implementation of core IPE database

Community Visibility—Priorities
- Publications on coaching model
- Publication on curriculum model and evaluation
- Interprofessional communication blogs featuring social work and IPE
- Presentations for Collaborating across Borders V conference

Strategic Response to Change—Priorities
- Maintenance and expansion of clinical partner sites in the community
- Identification and development of projects to work on with primary partners

As part of the sustainability plan, the Macy team and team-identified content experts are currently developing a series of online learning modules that can be used in a variety of courses currently and as faculty development. The modules take advantage of innovative Web-based technology to create an engaging learning platform that addresses foundational concepts for interprofessional practice and advanced concepts for collaborative practice in primary care. Example topics include "What is IPE? Why is it important to your practice?"; "High performing teams: What to look for"; and "Developing an integrated plan of care." A student advisory board reviews all modules before finalization to provide highly detailed feedback to maximize both the utility and the content of the modules. It is important to note that students' recommendations identify any points of professional bias present in the learning content so that materials can be revised to present information in an unbiased manner. The development team has discovered that it is easy to subtly insert one's professional point of view inadvertently; students' identification of such unintentional and unrecognized bias is critically important to creating a learning resource that effectively models interprofessionalism. The modules will be made available to other universities upon dissemination.

In addition, a newly approved Center for Advancing Interprofessional Practice, Education, and Research will sustain and accelerate interprofessional initiatives across the participating universities and clinical partners. This endeavor will help connect the diverse interprofessional activities occurring independently and jointly with ASU, U of A, NAU, and other universities in Arizona. In particular, it will help streamline efforts in event scheduling, quality improvement, student recruitment, and data collection.

LESSONS LEARNED

Macy Project faculty and others involved in "ripples" and extended-reach projects have learned it pays to listen to students' feedback. Students across the four original Macy disciplines (medicine, nursing, social work, and pharmacy) repeatedly indicated a preference for brief online training materials scheduled frequently rather than lengthy readings, seminars, or workshops scheduled less frequently. The online learning bursts were an effective way to meet students' learning needs in the format and timeline they requested. Yet it was evident that students did not always take advantage of these brief learning materials even when they requested them. For example, in a final exam in Advanced Social Work Practice in Health Settings, students were not able to articulate basic learning from the seven assigned bursts. An additional level of accountability to engage with the online learning material, such as through brief in-class writing assignments or student-led discussion groups, appears a promising approach to ensure students actually read or view the materials.

Similarly, student feedback regarding the first Team Arizona Interprofessional Healthcare Summit indicated that a cultural sensitivity activity that comprised a significant portion of the students' time together was not helpful. Rather, they preferred to spend more time together working in small groups on the geriatric case study. Results from the faculty-developed questionnaire assessing students' recognition of colleagues' roles, responsibilities, and training requirements revealed that participation in the event did not contribute to greater understanding for the majority of students. Faculty used students' insights to strengthen the program for the second Team Arizona event, eliminating the cultural sensitivity activity, incorporating a lively introduction to roles, responsibilities, and training requirements of the eight professions listed above, and enriching a small-group component to include professional role discussions and team treatment planning. Students' evaluations significantly improved following the second Team Arizona event, as did their recognition of colleagues' roles, responsibilities, and training requirements.

Macy team members also developed an appreciation for keeping evaluation simple. During initial planning, a highly complex and rigorous data collection plan was devised. It involved weekly student and faculty electronic logs detailing various types of collaborative experiences in the field and in the community. Although this evaluation plan would have yielded rich data regarding student and faculty learning and the impact of various Macy-sponsored events and activities, it proved too cumbersome and response rates were low. Team members recognized that a simpler data collection was needed and instead instituted the online questionnaires and exit interviews described, which led to improvement in response rates.

In addition, it is important to recognize that developing interprofessional curricula takes time, as does building relationships with community partners. It is important to be patient and avoid becoming overly discouraged. Consistent with social work values, ASU IPE faculty recommend identifying and building on the strengths already present in one's program, rather than starting completely from scratch or trying to duplicate another university's program that may not fit one's particular academic structure or community setting. In other words, avoid reinventing the wheel, but improve the wheel you already have. For example, look for places in the curriculum where two disciplines are already working together and strengthen the existing learning experience by bringing in a new collaborative tool, focusing on an additional IPEC learning competency, or adding a third discipline. Identify interprofessional faculty who are already working together in a research or service capacity and build on those relationships for interprofessional curricular development. Many of the allied health disciplines must master the same material, especially early on in their professional education, including medical terminology, medical ethics, and basic physiology and pathology. Rather than offering separate courses across numerous disciplines, consider devising core courses that enable interprofessional students to learn with, about, and from each other.

A final word of advice is that students do not naturally recognize the importance of interprofessional collaborative skills and may not link these skills with positive patient outcomes. To ensure student buy-in and engagement in IPE, it is vital to place such skills in context. Include curricular content that links effective interprofessional collaboration to quality patient care, using examples from the Institute of Medicine, the National Center for Interprofessional Practice, and the Interprofessional Education Collaborative. For example, undergraduate students participating in the interprofessional referral assignment commented that the assignment was a "waste of time" and that "working well with other disciplines is not necessary for good care." After a brief PowerPoint presentation reviewing the value of interprofessional collaboration was included as part of the learning experience, students' negative comments diminished.

REFERENCES

Bronstein, L. R. (2003). A model for interdisciplinary collaboration. *Social Work, 48,* 297–306.

Graham, J. R., & Barter, K. (1999). Collaboration: A social work practice method. *Families in Society, 80,* 6–13.

Hyer, K., Heinemann, G. D., & Fulmer, T. (2002). Team Skills Scale. In G. D. Heinemann & A. M. Zeiss (Eds.), *Team performance in health care: Assessment and development* (pp. 159–163). New York: Plenum.

Interprofessional Education Collaborative. (2016). *Core competencies for interprofessional collaborative practice: 2016 update.* Washington, DC: Interprofessional Education Collaborative.

Interprofessional Education Collaborative Expert Panel. (2011). *Core competencies for interprofessional practice: Report of an expert panel.* Washington, DC: Interprofessional Education Collaborative.

John A. Hartford Foundation. (n.d.). *Geriatric interdisciplinary team training program: Resource Center NYU.* Retrieved from http://www.johnahartford.org/grants-strategy/geriatric-interdisciplinary-team-training-program-resource-center-nyu

Kennedy, T. (2009). *Geriatric education centers and the academic capitalist knowledge/learning regime.* Saarbrücken, Germany: VDM Verlag.

Lamb, J., & Saewert, K. (2013). *Interprofessional Collaboration Readiness Questionnaire (IP-CRQ).* Unpublished questionnaire. Arizona State University College of Nursing and Health Innovation.

Luecht, R. M., Madsen, M. K., Taugher M. P., & Petterson, B. J. (1990). Assessing professional perceptions: Design and validation of an Interdisciplinary Education Perception Scale. *Journal of Allied Health, 19,* 181–191.

Myers, I. B., & McCaulley, M. H. (1998). *A guide to the development and use of the Myers-Briggs Type Indicator* (2nd ed.). Palo Alto, CA: Consulting Psychologists Press.

Oliver, C. (2013). Social workers as boundary spanners: Reframing our professional identity for interprofessional practice. *Social Work Education, 32,* 773–784.

Parker-Oliver, D., & Peck, M. (2006). Inside the interdisciplinary team experiences of hospice social workers. *Journal of Social Work in End-of-Life and Palliative Care, 2*(3), 7–21.

Parsell, G., & Bligh, J. (1999). The development of a questionnaire to assess the readiness of health care students for interprofessional learning (RIPLS). *Medical Education, 33,* 95–100.

Pollard, K. C., Miers, M. E., & Gilchrist, M. (2004). Collaborative learning for collaborative working? Initial findings from a longitudinal study of health and social care students. *Health and Social Care in the Community, 12,* 346–358.

Pollard, K. C., Miers, M. E., & Gilchrist, M. (2005). Second year skepticism: Pre-qualifying health and social care students' midpoint self-assessment, attitudes and perceptions concerning interprofessional learning and working. *Journal of Interprofessional Care, 19*(3), 251–268.

10

UNIVERSITY AT BUFFALO

Diane E. Elze, Paul T. Wietig, and Patricia J. Ohtake

The University at Buffalo (UB) Interprofessional Education and Collaborative Practice (IPE/IPCP) Initiative, systematically launched by the health sciences schools in 2011, but with important groundwork laid by the School of Public Health and Health Professions in 2007, has focused on involving other key academic units, training faculty and community stakeholders, building university–community partnerships to promote IPE/IPCP, and developing IPE/IPCP curriculum. This chapter will provide an overview of UB's institutional environment; the evolution of the IPE/IPCP initiative; the curriculum development process and curriculum content; implementation challenges encountered and lessons learned by the IPE leadership team; and efforts under way toward achieving program sustainability.

OVERVIEW OF UB'S INSTITUTIONAL ENVIRONMENT

UB is the largest among the 64 campuses that make up the State University of New York (SUNY) system. Figure 10.1 shows the organizational chart of UB's academic units involved in the UB IPE/IPCP initiative. Five health sciences schools, housing six health professions education programs, comprise UB's Academic Health Center (AHC); all are located on the South Campus in the city of Buffalo: the School of Medicine and Biomedical Sciences, School of Dental Medicine, School of Pharmacy and Pharmaceutical Sciences, School of Nursing, and School of Public Health and Health Professions. The vice president for health sciences and dean of School of Medicine and Biomedical Sciences oversees the AHC, including the health professions schools' programs in IPE/IPCP.

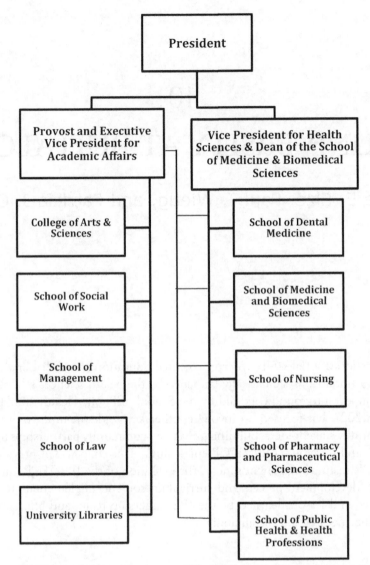

Figure 10.1: Organizational Chart of University at Buffalo's Academic Units Involved in the Interprofessional Education and Collaborative Practice Initiative

Most AHC schools house multiple departments, and all offer a diversity of undergraduate and graduate programs. The Department of Rehabilitation Science, with accredited professional programs in occupational therapy (OT) and physical therapy (PT), and the Department of Exercise and Nutrition Sciences are located within the School of Public Health and Health Professions. UB is the only AHC within the SUNY system without its own hospital, relying on multiple affiliations with area hospitals, health systems, and research institutes.

The UB Behling Simulation Center, a state-of-the-art simulation facility within the AHC, was the first center in the United States that was specifically designed to provide students in all six AHC health professions (that is, medicine, nursing, pharmacy, dentistry, occupational therapy, and physical therapy) with experiential, team-based IPE/IPCP learning opportunities that emphasize patient-centered care (Goldbaum, 2011a). The center's advisory committee is composed of at least one member from each AHC school and the School of Social Work (SSW). A new UB School of Medicine and Biomedical Sciences building, which will house an expanded Behling Simulation Center, is under construction on the Buffalo Niagara Medical Campus in downtown Buffalo in closer proximity to affiliated hospitals and health care systems (Unger, 2015).

Joining the AHC in the IPE/IPCP initiative are the Department of Communicative Disorders and Sciences within the College of Arts and Sciences, located on South Campus, and the SSW, the School of Management, and SUNY Buffalo Law School, all located on North Campus in Amherst. The University Libraries, particularly the Health Sciences Library, and the Center for Educational Innovation (the latter within the Division of Academic Services, also under the provost and executive vice president for academic affairs) have provided the IPE/IPCP initiative with important support services.

EVOLUTION OF THE IPE/IPCP INITIATIVE

Interprofessional Activities at UB Prior to the IPE/IPCP Initiative

Although health professions education has largely been delivered in silos with students minimally exposed to the roles and responsibilities of other health professions, faculty across the AHC, the SSW, and other academic units have long collaborated at the University at Buffalo on interprofessional research and clinical training of students. IPE/IPCP activities that had occurred prior to the start of the initiative relied largely on the interests and efforts of individual faculty, often in collaboration with the Behling Simulation Center. However, lacking an infrastructure to support, coordinate, and evaluate IPE/IPCP, the health professions schools had not been systematically exposing all students to IPE/IPCP experiences.

AHC schools, to varying degrees, did incorporate IPE/IPCP into their curricula. The School of Nursing had woven IPE activities into course requirements throughout the undergraduate nursing curriculum. The School of Dental Medicine, the School of Pharmacy and Pharmaceutical Sciences, and the Department of Rehabilitation Science had included some IPE content in their curricula and periodically used interprofessional simulations. Although all AHC schools had been using the Behling Simulation Center, not all simulations incorporated interprofessional teams; the School of Pharmacy and Pharmaceutical Sciences, the School of Nursing, and the School of Medicine and Biomedical Sciences had been increasing their use of interprofessional simulations. Third-year medical students typically participated in interprofessional teams in the Behling Simulation Center. A faculty member in the School of Nursing had conducted IPE/IPCP-related research with nursing and medical students to determine whether simulations enhanced learning and collaboration. For many years, faculty from multiple professions have taught PT and OT students, with students across these professions also collaborating in classroom and laboratory sessions. Some courses for OT and Department of Exercise and Nutrition Sciences students have been cotaught by Department of Rehabilitation Science and Department of Exercise and Nutrition Sciences faculty. The importance of advancing and achieving competency in IPE/IPCP is embedded in the School of Pharmacy and Pharmaceutical Sciences' vision statement and program outcomes for the doctor of pharmacy students.

The SSW had been and continues to be involved in several interprofessional initiatives. The School of Dental Medicine and the SSW, since 2001, have collaborated on the UB CARES (Counseling, Advocacy, Referral, Education, and Service) Program, a social work program within the School of Dental Medicine. Social work staff and interns receive referrals from dental faculty and students and link dental patients, many of whom present with complex health and psychosocial concerns, to needed community resources. The UB CARES Program addresses barriers preventing new and existing dental patients from receiving oral health care, such as lack of transportation, mental health problems, housing instability, legal problems, and chronic pain. UB CARES staff and MSW interns participate in consultations with the dental students and faculty, and MSW interns present case studies to dental students in a clinical rotation course (Schuman, 2005).

Inspired by the national Joining Forces initiative launched in 2010, the SSW and the School of Nursing formed the UB Partnership for Excellence in Veteran Care, now called Joining Forces-UB. Funded by the UB provost's E Fund, Joining Forces-UB provides graduate-level nursing and MSW students with specialized clinical training and IPE on the mental and physical health needs of veterans and their family members. As part of the project, a Veteran and Military Family (VMF) specialization and a VMF focus area were developed within the MSW and doctor of nursing practice (DNP) programs, respectively.

For several years, MSW students, under the supervision of a clinical associate professor in the SSW, have worked once a week alongside medical students at the Lighthouse Clinic, a free drop-in medical clinic operated and staffed by UB medical students for uninsured and underinsured residents of Buffalo's East Side. Interested MSW students register for a credit-bearing course, Community Social Work in Action, which is part of a faculty member's course load.

Development of UB's IPE/IPCP Initiative

UB was well positioned to embark on an IPE/IPCP initiative, given its AHC with its full array of health professions schools; a simulation center deeply committed to IPE/IPCP from its inception; and enthusiastic IPE/IPCP champions among the AHC and SSW faculty and administrative leadership. Important groundwork toward IPE/IPCP had been laid by the School of Public Health and Health Professions when the faculty, supported by a grant from the Josiah Macy Jr. Foundation in 2007, developed a new core curriculum that reflected common professional and interprofessional competencies across the school's diverse health disciplines (Fish et al., 2011). Through its core curriculum development process, the School of Public Health and Health

Professions strengthened its interprofessional culture, leading several faculty to participate in national and international IPE/IPCP meetings (Fish et al., 2011). The School of Public Health and Health Professions faculty wrestled with how best to implement the core curriculum and deliberated on multiple strategies, such as asynchronous learning experiences, video-captured seminars and special presentations, online modules, new courses, and enhancing existing courses. The IPE/IPCP initiative benefited from the expertise of the School of Public Health and Health Professions faculty in curricular mapping and IPE integration. Milestones described in the following sections are summarized in Table 10.1.

IPE Leadership Team Forms

Prior to 2010, the deans of the five health professions schools regularly convened to advance the mission of the AHC. Beginning in June 2010, the AHC associate deans for academic affairs began to meet regularly to address curricular and other academic issues of mutual interest. With a growing emphasis on interprofessional teams in health care delivery, emerging accreditation standards that incorporated IPE/IPCP, and the School of Public Health and Health Professions' experience in developing core competencies across its disciplines, the associate deans soon shifted their focus to the development of an IPE/IPCP curriculum for students across the health professions (Ohtake, Fish, et al., 2013).

During 2011, the associate deans submitted a grant proposal to UB's 3 E Fund, which supported university initiatives judged to be high impact with high return on UB 2020 initiatives (Hill, 2012). The IPE leadership team proposed a three-year project to develop, implement, and evaluate a sustainable IPE model for the health sciences and other disciplines. The plan included the development of an IPE infrastructure to coordinate and support curriculum development, implementation, and evaluation; faculty development in IPE/IPCP; and the expansion of IPE beyond the health professions to include law and management.

IPE Leadership Team Receives a Directive

In early February 2012, the associate deans received word that the E Fund proposal was not funded. Later that month, the vice president for health sciences directed the associate deans to proceed with an IPE plan without funding and identify the resources needed to accomplish the goals. Over the next two months, the IPE leadership team expanded beyond the associate deans to include the SSW's MSW program director; the Behling Simulation Center director; the School of Public Health and Health Professions' core curriculum coordinator, who, at the time, was also the interim director of UB's Teaching and Learning Center (now the Center for Educational Innovation); and an associate professor in the Department of Rehabilitation Science with considerable expertise in IPE and simulation. Participating faculty assumed these responsibilities without additional compensation or reduction in their teaching loads because of their strong belief in the importance of IPE/IPCP to health professions education.

The IPE leadership team began to inventory their health professions programs' curricula for alignment with the IPE core competencies (Interprofessional Education

Table 10.1: Timeline of Milestones

Year	Milestone
2010	• Associate deans in the Academic Health Center (AHC) form IPE leadership team to develop strategies for implementing IPE/IPCP. • Behling Simulation Center is piloted. • Associate deans examine schedules across AHC schools and inventory course content.
2011	• Associate deans explore how best to integrate IPE into programs. • Behling Simulation Center becomes fully operational. • SON takes lead on E Fund proposal focused on IPE.
2012	**Spring** • Vice president for health sciences and AHC and SSW deans direct AHC associate deans to develop IPE core curriculum, integrating the Behling Simulation Center, and to explore options for delivery. • Associate deans receive notice that IPE-focused E Fund proposal was not funded. **Summer** • UB sends faculty team to Interprofessional Education Collaborative 2012 Institute, "Building Your Foundation for Interprofessional Education," in Virginia. • Two IPE leadership team members attend five-day certificate ehpic (Educating Health Professionals in Interprofessional Care) course, led by University of Toronto's Centre for Interprofessional Education. • IPE leadership team presents proposal, to the vice president for health sciences and the AHC deans, for a Center of Interprofessional Education Excellence. Team revises proposal during the rest of the summer. **Fall** • IPE Faculty Curriculum Team forms and develops IPE pilot curriculum for Spring 2013 delivery. • IPE leadership team presents revised proposal to establish an administrative structure for the UB IPE/IPCP Initiative to the vice president for health sciences and AHC and SW deans.
2013	**Spring** • UB IPE Pilot Curriculum Project launched in February. • In February, the Office of Interprofessional Education is established within the AHC; assistant vice president of interprofessional education is appointed. • Dr. Ivy Oandasan, University of Toronto, a world-renowned IPE/IPCP expert, delivers the Third Annual Glen E. Gresham Visiting Professorship Lecture for the Department of Rehabilitation Science. • The AHC and M&T Bank host the Interprofessional Education and Western New York Health Care Leadership Forum, drawing 50 university and community leaders in health care.

(continued)

Table 10.1: Timeline of Milestones (Continued)

Year	Milestone

Summer

- The vice president for the health sciences and AHC and SW deans sponsor a three-day ehpic faculty development course, led by the University of Toronto's Centre for Interprofessional Education.
- UB sends interprofessional faculty team to the 2013 Western New York Service Learning Coalition's Service Learning Faculty Fellowship Program.
- Office of IPE launches electronic newsletter for faculty and community partners.
- Office of IPE begins contributing to the National Center for Interprofessional Practice and Education blog.
- IPE leadership team expands to include the School of Management, the Department of Communicative Disorders and Sciences (College of Arts and Sciences), and the Department of Exercise and Nutrition Services (SPHHP).
- An ad hoc committee of designated associate deans works on developing a research and scholarship protocol for the Office of IPE.
- The vice president for health sciences and the AHC and SW deans identify priorities for Office of IPE (i.e., meeting schools' IPE accreditation requirements, developing a strategic plan, and developing four competency-based foundational IPE modules for integration across schools).

Fall

- The Office of IPE produces an IPE/IPCP strategic plan.
- The UB Curriculum and Assessment Task Force, chartered by the provost, convenes.
- UB participates in nationwide screening event, *Escape Fire: The Fight to Rescue American Healthcare*, which includes a panel discussion with AHC faculty and Western New York leaders in healthcare delivery.
- The UB Curriculum and Assessment Task Force issues a summary report supporting IPE/IPCP.

2014   **Spring**

- SPHHP, the Office of Global Health Initiatives, and the Office of IPE launch an IPE course, Health for Refugee Populations in Buffalo.
- AHC leadership approves Office of IPE strategic plan.
- The Office of IPE convenes IPE Faculty Curriculum Committee to develop online IPE modules to integrate across AHC schools. Work begins on modules.
- Planning begins for IPE Days, an interprofessional team experience for students across the AHC and SW.
- SUNY IITG grant awarded in May to UB Health Sciences Library and SUNY Buffalo State's E. H. Butler Library to design and evaluate technology-enhanced methods of evidence-based IPE instruction.
- Refugee Health Summit 2014 held, sponsored by the Office of Global Health Initiatives (SPHHP), with Office of IPE among the planners.
- SMBMS curriculum committee, joined by IPE leadership team members, convenes to discuss curricular initiatives for accreditation, including integration of IPE.

(continued)

Table 10.1: Timeline of Milestones (Continued)

Year	Milestone
	Summer
	• Two key IPE leadership team members depart UB.
	• Office of IPE develops communications plan for Web site development.
	Fall
	• Internal funding proposal for IPE Days submitted but rejected.
	• Funding search for Office of IPE Web site.
	• IPE leadership team suffers a profound loss with the sudden death of the senior associate dean for medical curriculum, an IPE champion.
2015	**Spring**
	• The IPE leadership team loses a key member to retirement.
	• The IPE Faculty Curriculum Committee presents overview of online IPE modules to the vice president for the health sciences and the AHC and SW deans.
	• Funding for IPE Web site approved by the vice president for the health sciences and the deans.
	• Plans initiated for a January 2016 IPE/IPCP development course, facilitated by UB faculty, for faculty and community partners.
	Summer
	• SUNY IITG IPE curriculum and conference planning completed.
	Fall
	• SUNY IITG project pilots individual and team-based IPE instructional strategies with 56 students from eight health professions.
	• SUNY IITG conference brings to Buffalo Dr. Amy Blue and Dr. Joseph Zorek, two national IPE experts.
	• IPE Web site is launched.

Notes: IPE = interprofessional education; IPE/IPCP = interprofessional education and collaborative practice; SON = School of Nursing; SSW = School of Social Work; UB = University at Buffalo; SW = social work; SPHHP = School of Public Health and Health Professions; IITG = Innovative Instruction Technology Grant; SMBMS = School of Medicine and Biomedical Sciences.

Collaborative [IPEC] Expert Panel, 2011) and attempted to identify blocks of time across the health professions programs when interprofessional learning activities could be conducted with teams of students. The IPE leadership team planned to integrate IPE content into existing courses and clinical experiences, as well as bring students together from diverse professions for interprofessional teamwork experiences.

IPE/IPCP Faculty Development

Faculty capacity building for IPE/IPCP emerged as a priority for the IPE leadership team in 2012. UB sent four IPE leadership team members (two associate deans, one Department of Rehabilitation Science associate professor, and the Behling Simulation

Center director) to the 2012 Interprofessional Education Collaborative Institute, "Building Your Foundation for Interprofessional Education," held in May in Virginia. While at the institute, the UB participants drafted an IPE/IPCP vision for the IPE leadership team to present to the deans. Additionally, two IPE leadership team members attended the June 2012 ehpic (a trademarked abbreviation of Educating Health Professionals in Interprofessional Care) five-day certificate course, "Advancing the Future of Healthcare through Interprofessional Learning," aimed at developing IPE leaders, conducted by the University of Toronto's Centre for Interprofessional Education.

Infrastructure Proposed

The IPE leadership team presented its IPE/IPCP vision to the vice president for health sciences and the AHC and SSW deans in July 2012, proposing the establishment of the Center of Interprofessional Education Excellence, but without specific recommendations as to the administrative infrastructure. The center would promote team-based learning and patient-centered collaborative practices for UB students, provide faculty development opportunities in IPE/IPCP, and secure funding for research and scholarship on educational and practice models, assessment, and outcomes. The plan outlined a framework for a two-year curriculum and an implementation timeline, with the first year focused on exposing students to IPE core competencies through online didactics, small group discussions, experiential activities, and simulation experiences, and the second year focused on immersion in interprofessional team-based learning and collaborative care. With the approval of each AHC school's curriculum committee, the IPE leadership team proposed to pilot an IPE curriculum as a one-credit elective during the spring of 2013 and expanded curricular offerings during the 2013–2014 academic year.

Informed by information gathered at the Interprofessional Education Collaborative Institute and ehpic, the IPE leadership team revised their vision during the remainder of the summer and presented it to the vice president for health sciences and the AHC and SSW deans in September. The plan detailed an administrative structure for an office of interprofessional education within the AHC that included a coordinator (one full-time faculty member) and a full-time staff member. The coordinator would function under the direction of an Academic Associate Deans' Council for IPE/IPCP, composed of the associate deans for academic affairs from the AHC schools and the SSW. An IPE/IPCP faculty committee and an IPE/IPCP community advisory committee would collaborate with the coordinator in the development and implementation of IPE curriculum and IPCP opportunities.

The plan identified important domains for continued work, including faculty development, curriculum development, instructional methodologies, online education, policy and regulation, assessment of student performance, evaluation of IPE/IPCP outcomes, research and dissemination, and proposals for external funding. Priority tasks for the Office of IPE and a timeline were also proposed (for example, seeking external funding, completion of curriculum inventories of IPE/IPCP competencies). The team also requested financial support to host a three-day ehpic course, led by the University of Toronto's Centre for Interprofessional Education IPE/IPCP, for 42 UB faculty and community partners.

Pilot Curriculum Development Begins

At the IPE leadership team meeting in October 2012, four faculty volunteered to develop a one-credit, semester-long elective, Interprofessional Education and Collaborative Practice, grounded in the IPEC core competencies (IPEC Expert Panel, 2011), that would be piloted in the spring of 2013 with approximately 56 students from the AHC schools and the SSW. The course would involve online activities, biweekly small-group activities with interprofessional teams of students, and a simulation experience in the Behling Simulation Center. Curriculum development continued from October 2012 through January 2013, and the pilot project was held from February 2013 to April 2013. The curriculum development process and the pilot project are explained in detail later in this chapter.

Office of IPE Instituted

A status report from the IPE leadership team to the vice president for health sciences and the AHC and SSW deans in November 2012 again advocated for an Office of Interprofessional Education, with at least an interim director appointed and a part-time support staff. The IPE leadership team shared the proposed pilot curriculum with the deans and requested financial support for use of the Behling Simulation Center in the pilot project. Funding for the spring three-day faculty and community development workshop conducted by the University of Toronto was also requested. The IPE leadership team emphasized the importance of forming a community IPE/IPCP advisory group, identifying IPCP outcome measures, and developing key IPCP practice sites. The team also reported that curriculum inventories across the schools were still in process.

The UB Office of Interprofessional Education (Office of IPE) was established within the AHC in February 2013. The interim director of the Teaching and Learning Center and the School of Public Health and Health Professions' core curriculum coordinator was appointed as the assistant vice president for interprofessional education and reported to the associate deans and the vice president for the health sciences. The structure included an IPE/IPCP faculty committee and an IPE/IPCP community advisory committee. The assistant vice president for interprofessional education, now full time in that position, remained as the interim director of UB's Teaching and Learning Center well into 2014, until the Teaching and Learning Center and the Office of Assessment were merged to form the Center for Educational Innovation.

Faculty Development and Community Engagement Events

Along with the 2013 pilot project, faculty development and community engagement were major foci for the Office of IPE, which sponsored or collaborated on four significant IPE/IPCP events that year.

The Department of Rehabilitation Science hosted Dr. Ivy Oandasan, a world-renowned expert in IPE/IPCP from the University of Toronto, for its Third Annual Glen E. Gresham Visiting Professorship Lecture.

The AHC and M&T Bank sponsored the "Interprofessional Education and Western New York Health Care Leadership Forum," which brought together faculty, administrators, and community leaders in health care to engage with internationally recognized IPE experts: Dr. Barbara Brandt and Dr. Frank Cera, both associated with the National Center for Interprofessional Practice and Education housed at the University of Minnesota, and Dr. Madeline Schmitt, professor emerita at the University of Rochester.

An interprofessional UB faculty team (representing physical therapy, social work, nursing, public health, pharmacy, and medicine) was accepted to the 2013 Service-Learning Faculty Fellowship Program, a three-day intensive training program in service learning pedagogy, sponsored by the Western New York Service Learning Coalition and the University at Buffalo. The team focused on both expanding existing and developing new interprofessional service learning activities for students in health care settings.

The vice president for the health sciences and the AHC and SSW deans financially supported the IPE leadership team's request to host a three-day ehpic leadership development course, led by the University of Toronto's Centre for Interprofessional Education. Approximately 40 faculty, researchers, and health care administrators and clinicians convened for the purpose of advancing IPE/IPCP in Western New York, which built momentum for IPE/IPCP among faculty and community partners. The course included a simulation experience at the Behling Simulation Center. The University of Toronto leadership team also provided mentorship in leading IPE/IPCP faculty development to the UB Department of Rehabilitation Science IPE leadership team member during this course.

Acting on ehpic participants' recommendations, the Office of IPE generated an electronic newsletter to keep faculty and community partners updated about university and community IPE/IPCP activities and arranged with the Health Sciences Library to develop an IPE/IPCP resource collection for faculty and community use. Also emerging from the workshop were new collaborations with community partners to promote IPE/IPCP in their settings. The Office of IPE continued to cultivate partnerships with other UB units (for example, Center for Health Informatics, Institute of Person Centered Care, SUNY Buffalo Law, the Research Institute on Addictions), area hospitals, the county health department, and the New York State Area Health Education Center System, a health care workforce development initiative with its statewide and western regional office based in Buffalo.

During the fall semester of 2012, as part of a nationwide screening event, the Office of IPE, the School of Public Health and Health Professions' Office of Public Health Practice, the School of Medicine and Biomedical Sciences, the School of Management, the SMBM, and the American Medical Association Medical Student Section and Physicians for Human Rights sponsored a showing of the documentary *Escape Fire: The Fight to Rescue American Healthcare*. The screening was followed by a panel discussion that was attended by approximately 200 students, faculty, and community partners. Panelists included AHC faculty and western New York leaders in health care delivery.

Priorities Clarified

In June 2013, the vice president for health sciences and the AHC and SSW deans clarified priorities for the Office of IPE (that is, meeting each school's IPE accreditation requirements, developing an IPE/IPCP strategic plan, and developing four competency-based foundational online IPE modules for integration across schools). The IPE leadership team also identified the need to further analyze the pilot data, pursue external funding to support IPE/IPCP initiatives, and convene a committee to develop policies governing Office of IPE-related scholarship and research.

During the summer of 2013, the team endeavored to complete an environmental scan of the scope and variety of IPE/IPCP activities within and across academic health professions education units and with community partners. A template for the scan was developed. Data to be gathered were descriptions of current IPE/IPC activities, names of participating faculty and community partners, the health professions programs, and the number and academic level of students involved. Using this information, the team anticipated further development and expansion of interprofessional activities and collaborative partnerships by building on existing opportunities. However, the environmental scan was not completed because of several faculty departures from the university and time constraints on remaining leadership team members. The Office of IPE assumed the coordination of this task.

Strategic Plan

By October 2013, the Office of IPE had produced a document, *IPE/IPCC Strategic Plan–Essential Concepts*, which was accepted in February 2014 by the AHC leadership. The plan delineated the vision, mission, and governance structure of IPE/IPCP and identified strategic parameters, key result areas, and domains requiring attention for implementing the vision. At the time, it was deemed necessary to have the assistant vice president for interprofessional education formulate a strategic plan. Financial support for a formal strategic planning process was requested but not granted at the time. Thus, the IPE leadership team members and other key university and community stakeholders were not involved. The Office of IPE plans to conduct a more formal and inclusive process within the next two years.

Focus on Integrating IPE into Curricula

Although the IPE leadership team rarely met during 2014, much work occurred outside of meetings. The Department of Rehabilitation Science IPE leadership coordinated the online IPE modules in January. Online module development continued into 2015 and is discussed in detail later in this chapter. The AHC schools developed plans for integrating the modules into their curricula, and members from the School of Management and Department of Rehabilitation Science joined faculty within the School of Medicine and Biomedical Sciences to discuss curricular initiatives related to accreditation, including IPE.

Within the School of Medicine and Biomedical Sciences, an IPE leadership team member in family medicine surveyed course and clerkship directors to identify situations where medical students were already learning from health care professionals in other disciplines or learning with students in other health care professions. He also asked colleagues to suggest how courses and clerkships might increase such opportunities for medical students. The faculty member from each school then provided the IPE leadership team with specific examples of how medical education could develop or expand interprofessional learning activities in classroom and clinical settings. This built on existing learning opportunities, which helped other team members conceptualize possibilities within their own schools.

Among the suggestions were to (a) add interprofessional participation to grand and working rounds; (b) expand existing initiatives where medical students engage with nurses on care coordination and postdischarge follow-up and with pharmacy students on medication reviews with high-risk patients; (c) develop interprofessional online modules addressing common learning needs, such as ethics and team communication; (d) create an interprofessional simulation for fourth-year medical students in the simulation center; (e) invite students from other health professions to an existing personal narrative presentation on patient safety, currently delivered to medical students by the daughter of a woman who died from polypharmacy and multiple hospital-acquired infections (Goldbaum, 2011b), and follow the presentation with small-group interprofessional discussions; (f) expand and formalize the involvement of nursing faculty and senior nursing students with first-year medical students who are learning to administer injections, a practice that has been occurring periodically and informally; and (g) develop a service learning clearinghouse to connect students from diverse health professions with interprofessional service learning opportunities.

Collaboration between UB and SUNY Buffalo State

To advance IPE, UB's Health Sciences Library and SUNY Buffalo State's E. H. Butler Library successfully partnered to secure a SUNY Innovative Instruction Technology Grant (IITG) in May 2014. The project, completed in Fall 2015, aimed to design, pilot, and evaluate technology-enhanced methods for instruction of evidence-based practice knowledge and skills to interprofessional student teams to facilitate collaborative decision making. Collaborators on the grant included the Office of IPE; faculty from the AHC, the School of Social Work, and the School of Management; library faculty in UB's University Libraries; and faculty and librarians from SUNY Buffalo State's health professions programs.

Online curriculum modules on evidence-based practice, study designs, and strategies for finding evidence to support patient care were developed during the summer of 2015. Participants also accessed the Office of IPE's online modules describing interprofessional collaborative practice and the roles and responsibilities of nine different health professionals. After completing the online modules in September 2015, approximately 56 students from UB's AHC and social work schools and SUNY Buffalo State's dietetics and speech language pathology programs were assigned to interprofessional teams. Using SUNY Buffalo State's technology-enhanced active learning classrooms, the interprofessional student teams, facilitated by faculty and librarians, used case studies and classroom technologies to work collaboratively to locate, evaluate, and discuss the available evidence and develop patient care plans.

Project collaborators convened for a morning session in October to review the program and its outcomes as well as the feedback from the participating students, faculty, and librarians. This session was followed by an afternoon IPE conference, with presentations by IPE experts: Dr. Amy Blue, associate vice president for Interprofessional

Education at the University of Florida, Gainesville, and Dr. Joseph Zorek from the University of Wisconsin–Madison School of Pharmacy.

Office of IPE Web Site

By July 2014, the Office of IPE had developed a communication plan for a Web site that would meet UB's new communication standards and branding guidelines. The plan delineated the goals and objectives of an IPE Web site integrated with the AHC. Several years ago, UB embarked on the Digital Communications Transformation, a university-wide initiative to use state-of-the-art technology for the development and maintenance of more effective, well-branded, and user-friendly Web sites (Hill, 2012). The Digital Communications Transformation requires each unit to commit a substantial amount of time to strategic planning around Web site development, training in the UB Content Management System, and content development, implementation, and maintenance. The Office of IPE lacked sufficient personnel to embark on such a venture, and it was necessary to secure external site developers. Funding for Web site development was approved by the vice president for the health sciences and the AHC and SSW deans in January 2015; by April, the developers were identified and contractual arrangements were in process. Web site development was targeted for completion in Fall 2015. Each academic unit involved in the IPE/IPCP initiative identified an IPE content specialist to both supply and approve unit-related content for the Office of IPE Web site.

Student-Led IPE Initiatives

Student organizations from physical therapy, occupational therapy, social work, and nursing, with the support of the Office of IPE, the UB Graduate Student Association, and the UB Institute for Person-Centered Care, organized a showing of the award-winning documentary film *Alive Inside: A Story of Music and Memory* followed by an interprofessional panel discussion. During 2015, plans were also laid to organize an IPE Student Association at UB, which would be associated with the Institute for Healthcare Improvement Open Schools Project and composed of leaders from health professions student organizations.

Professional Development Course

A three-day UB-developed IPE/IPCP professional development course for faculty and community stakeholders is being planned for January 2016, with the organizing effort led by the Department of Rehabilitation Science IPE leadership team member. To apply for the course, interprofessional teams will be required to submit abstracts describing an interprofessional project they will undertake upon completion of the course.

Other IPE Activities

During 2015, work continued on the online IPE modules, and the IPE leadership team presented an overview to the vice president for health sciences and the AHC and SSW deans. With collaborative relationships built among IPE leadership team members, faculty also partnered with each other to provide their students with interprofessional experiences. For example, two faculty, one in the School of Medicine and Biomedical Sciences and one in the Department of Rehabilitation Science, brought medical (third-year) and physical therapy (second-year doctoral) students together in a two-hour IPE seminar to share information about their professions, discuss the management of a patient with acute low back pain, and determine a plan of care. The seminar concluded with a faculty-facilitated discussion of the patient's interprofessional collaborative care plan and a debriefing.

The Office of IPE focused on expanding university–community partnerships, pursuing external funding and Web site development, and investigating the feasibility of bringing faculty and students from across the health professions schools together for IPCP experiences.

IPE Movement at the University Level

During the summer of 2013, the provost, following multiple campus-wide conversations, launched seven task forces to develop implementation strategies for achieving goals and initiatives set forth in the university's strategic plan (Office of the Provost, 2014). IPE for all AHC health professions programs, social work, management, and ultimately all professional programs was identified as a strategic necessity for curricular innovation and student success (Office of the Provost, 2013). The Curriculum and Assessment Task Force, charged with developing and overseeing "the implementation of curricular innovations that achieve the outcomes we promise every UB student" and proposing "new and more extended processes of assessment to measure the success of our curriculum in meeting desired educational outcomes" (Curriculum and Assessment Task Force, 2013, p. 1), was explicitly directed to create a plan, with the IPE leadership team, to extend IPE to all professional programs. The Inter-Professional Education Subcommittee, one of five task force subcommittees, was composed of the deans of the School of Nursing, the School of Public Health and Health Professions, the School of Management, and the Graduate School; the chair of the Department of Rehabilitation Science; and the assistant vice president of IPE and interim director of the Teaching and Learning Center.

Among the Curriculum and Assessment Task Force's final recommendations were (a) fiscal support for training faculty and staff in IPE; (b) identification of time periods within the academic calendar for all students in the health professions to engage in interprofessional activities; (c) fiscal support for students' participation in simulation experiences; (d) involvement of all health professions at UB in AHC IPE activities; (e) pursuit of external funding to support IPE initiatives; (f) faculty and student engagement in research and scholarship as an integral component of the IPE initiative; and (g) expansion of IPE beyond the health professions (Curriculum and Assessment Task Force, 2013). At this point in time, despite IPE's standing as a strategically necessary curricular innovation, the resources required from UB's central administration have not been allocated.

IPE CURRICULUM DEVELOPMENT PROCESS AND CONTENT

IPE Pilot Program

The development and implementation of the IPE pilot curriculum was a 10-month process that involved ongoing input and feedback from the IPE leadership team on content, format, and structure and multiple revisions of implementation logistics. Faculty flexibility, commitment, and good humor were critical to moving forward.

IPE Pilot Curriculum Development

In April 2012, the associate dean in the School of Medicine and Biomedical Sciences drafted a three-year IPE curriculum for the leadership team's consideration. He suggested that the team pilot a curriculum with a small group of students and faculty volunteers during the 2012–2013 academic year in order to strengthen funding applications to support the initiative. Curriculum development began in earnest in September 2012, with the formation of a four-member IPE Faculty Curriculum Team (including representatives of physical therapy, social work, nursing, and pharmacy), and continued through January 2013. The curriculum involved team-based learning both online and in the classroom. Content was linked to the *Core Competencies for Interprofessional Collaborative Practice* (IPEC Expert Panel, 2011). Participating students would be divided into teams composed of at least one student from each of the seven participating units (that is, dentistry, medicine, nursing, pharmacy, social work, occupational therapy, and physical therapy). Although the team deliberated on holding simulations in less expensive facilities (for example, patient assessment rooms in the School of Pharmacy and Pharmaceutical Sciences or the simulation labs in the School of Nursing), the team decided that a simulation experience in the Behling Simulation Center was critical for the pilot project, given the center's capability to provide high-quality simulation and debriefing experiences.

Originally, the IPE leadership team planned a four-semester curriculum for students in the health professions but had to scale back this plan several times between October 2012 and January 2013. By November 2012, members of the IPE Faculty Curriculum Team had developed a template for a semester-long, one-credit IPE elective for 56 students (that is, eight students from each of the seven academic units). It shared this template with the vice president for the health sciences and the AHC and SSW deans while it was awaiting administrative decisions about the course from the AHC leadership. This course would involve online activities, biweekly small-group activities with interprofessional teams of students, and a simulation experience in the simulation center. The team also requested from the vice president for the health sciences and the AHC and SSW deans workload accommodations for key faculty in each professional program to acknowledge effort devoted to continued curriculum development during summer 2013, with a planned Fall 2013 rollout of IPE/IPCP across the schools.

By mid-December, with some administrative questions still unanswered, the spring semester rapidly approaching, insufficient time to secure course approval from the schools' curriculum committees, and the lack of certainty over the number of students that could be funded for participation in the simulation center, the IPE leadership team decided to pilot the curriculum with a student task force on interprofessional education and collaborative practice. The task force would be composed of 28 student volunteers, four from each academic unit. The students would act as consultants to the faculty, testing out the curriculum modules and providing critical feedback; the modules would then be refined for a Fall 2013 delivery. A major challenge was finding a time for task force meetings that worked for each of the seven academic units. The meeting schedule was determined by late January 2013, and every unit successfully recruited at least four students. Institutional review board (IRB) approval was secured several days before the first scheduled session. Faculty from all seven professions participated.

Student Recruitment for Pilot Project

All schools were successful in recruiting a sufficient number of students for the pilot project. The pilot was conducted with 31 students: five undergraduate nursing students, four MSW students, four medical students, four dental students, six pharmacy students, four occupational therapy students, and four physical therapy students. Student experience in their health professions program ranged from first to final year. Students were assigned to one of four teams, with each profession represented on every team. Twenty-two students completed the program.

Students were recruited within the academic units via strategies congruent with each unit's culture. Strategies included lottery selection of interested students, random selection of interested students, and first-come, first served via in-face or e-mail announcements.

Pilot Curriculum Content

The pilot curriculum, outlined in Table 10.2, consisted of four 90-minute classroom-based sessions, pre-session online learning activities, and a culminating simulation experience at the simulation center for students whose schedules could accommodate that activity. Students were asked to complete learning activities prior to three of the four classroom sessions. Each session consisted of a welcome, the articulation of the learning objectives, and team-based interactive class activities (for example, small- or large-group discussions, case studies, team-building exercises). Brief videos were often used as pre-session or in-class learning activities. Every session ended with students completing a written KWLA assessment (that is, what is known, what is wanted, what was learned, what will be applied, and overall reflections; Almerico, 2011) and participating in a semi-structured group debriefing facilitated by a faculty member. In the debriefing, students shared detailed reflections on what worked and did not work for them in the session, ideas for improving both the pre-session and the classroom-based learning activities, the extent to which the session met the learning objectives, and any additional information about the session that they would have liked to have been different. For future IPE/IPCP promotional purposes, the cultural competency session was filmed, and a high-quality video was produced by UB's Center for Educational Innovation.

Table 10.2: Outline of University at Buffalo Interprofessional Education Pilot Curriculum

Date and Topic	Core Competencies from IPEC Report	Pre-Session Learning Activities	Classroom Activities
Session #1, 2/5/2013: Welcome, Introduction to IPE/ IPCP, Purpose of the Pilot Seminar, Roles and Responsibilities	VE1, VE3, VE4 RR1, RR2, RR3, RR4, RR6 CC3, CC4, CC6	• None	• Distribute name tags and team assignments. • Faculty introductions. • Brief introduction to IPE and purpose of pilot program. • Team-based activity: students introduce selves and professions; discuss case study, identifying the patient's problems across medical, clinical, functional, and psychosocial domains; and discuss how each profession contributes to patient's care and well-being. • Large-group discussion of case study.
Session #2, 2/26/2013: Teams and Communication, Roles and Responsibilities	TT1, TT3, TT5, TT6, TT8 RR1, RR2, RR4 CC1, CC4, CC5, CC6	• Complete brief questionnaire describing one's profession. • Complete Teamwork Attitudes Questionnaire. • Complete Strategies for Handling Conflict Self-Assessment. • View online TeamSTEPPS modules.	• Individual sharing of professional roles and responsibilities with team members. • Paper Chain Team Exercise. • View patient's health care team meeting video; team discussion of teamwork and communication issues. • Large-group debriefing of video.
Session #3, 3/19/2013: Cultural Competency	VE3, VE6, VE4 RR2, RR3 CC7, TT6	• Complete two readings. • Complete cultural self-reflection exercise. • Online discussion board applying readings to case study.	• Small-group discussion of cultural self-reflection exercise facilitated by faculty. • Viewing of 10-minute Worlds Apart vignette, small-group discussion, followed by large-group discussion.
Session #4, 4/2/2013: Values and Ethics	VE1, VE2, VE3, VE4, VE5, VE6, VE7, VE8, VE9, VE10	• Online discussion board: sharing of personal values; values underpinning professional codes of ethics; compare three codes of ethics. • Team develops a shared ethical code.	• Large-group discussion of shared ethical codes and core values. • Team case study analysis using team's ethical code. • Large-group discussion of teams' case study analyses.

Notes: IPEC = Interprofessional Education Collaborative; IPE/IPCP = interprofessional education and collaborative practice; VE = Values and Ethics; CC = Interprofessional Communication; TT = Teams and Teamwork; RR = Roles and Responsibilities.

Three one-hour simulation experiences were scheduled at the Behling Simulation Center; students and faculty were assigned to one session on the basis of their availability and the need to have at least two different professions represented on each team. A Department of Rehabilitation Science IPE leadership team member with expertise in facilitating and debriefing simulations (Ohtake, Lazarus, Schillo, & Rosen, 2013) spent considerable time organizing, scheduling, and developing the simulation experiences for the participating students and faculty, with assistance from other team members. Three to six students representing three to five different professions participated in each simulation (total of 15 students). Standardized patients (roles: patient and his daughter) were trained prior to the simulation sessions and were provided with questions developed by faculty across the health professions involved. Two faculty members were assigned to lead the debriefings. A case study that was used in an earlier classroom-based session was revised for the simulations (that is, a patient with multiple chronic health problems who had made an office visit to his physician was now being discharged from the hospital after a 10-day stay). All students and faculty received the case study ahead of time. After the simulation experience (that is, a discharge planning conference with the patient and daughter) was completed, a debriefing was held to permit the volunteer student participants to provide feedback on the simulation experience.

Student Evaluation

The Interprofessional Education Perception Scale (IEPS) (McFadyen, Maclaren, & Webster, 2007), administered at the first and last classroom sessions, was used to assess students' interprofessional attitudes and perceptions. Students completed the Team-STEPPS Teamwork Attitudes Questionnaire (T-TAQ) (Baker, Amodeo, Krokos, Slonim, & Herrera, 2010; Baker, Krokos, & Amodeo, 2008) at the beginning and end of the second classroom session and at the end of the last classroom session. The simulation participants completed the KidSIM ATTITUDES (Attitudes in Teamwork in Training Undergoing Designed Educational Simulation) Questionnaire (Sigalet, Donnon, & Grant, 2012) before and after their simulation experience. Fifty-eight percent of the students completed two administrations of the IEPS and the T-TAQ, and fewer completed the third T-TAQ administration. Students' mean scores on the IEPS significantly increased from pre- to posttest, with the significant increase explained by the rise in scores on the Perceived Actual Cooperation subscale (pretest: $M = 4.73$, $SD = 0.63$; posttest: $M = 5.07$, $SD = 0.62$, $p = .014$) (Lucke et al., 2013).

Student Feedback

Faculty found the participating students to be highly engaged in the classroom-based activities. Lessons learned from the debriefings with students included the following: (a) face-to-face teamwork was essential; (b) students recognized and respected faculty modeling IPE/IPCP; (c) the physical environment should support group work, such as having tables to convene around rather than fixed desks in a lecture hall; (d) students highly valued learning each other's roles and responsibilities; (e) cultural competency and health disparities content was new to many students; (f) students had difficulty completing some of the preparatory online activities because of time constraints; (g) online content should be tailored for mobile devices; and (h) case studies were critical for team-based learning.

UB Foundations of Interprofessional Collaborative Practice Module Series

Building on the success of the pilot project and the positive student response to the curriculum, in January 2014 the Office of IPE recruited faculty to develop an online module series, "The Foundations of Interprofessional Collaborative Practice." This series was composed of six 50-minute modules based on the *Core Competencies for Interprofessional Collaborative Practice* (IPEC Expert Panel, 2011), with a Department of Rehabilitation Science faculty member coordinating the project. When completed, the series will provide students in the AHC professions and social work with foundational knowledge essential for face-to-face engagement in interprofessional collaborative care. The six modules are

- Module 1: Introduction to Interprofessional Collaborative Practice, which provides an overview of IPCP and is composed of short video cameos from multiple health professions faculty (lead faculty: Rehabilitation Science).
- Module 2: Roles and Responsibilities (lead faculty: Rehabilitation Science).
- Module 3: Teams and Teamwork (lead faculty: School of Management).
- Module 4: Communication (lead faculty: School of Management).
- Module 5: Values and Ethics (lead faculty: School of Nursing).
- Module 6: Cultural Engagement, Cultural Competence, and Cultural Humility: Essential for Interprofessional Collaborative Practice (lead faculty: School of Social Work).

Each module will include interactive activities to promote student engagement, an individual student assessment, links to relevant materials to enrich the students' learning experience, and an instructor's guide to assist faculty in integrating the modules within their courses.

An introductory video and an additional promotional overview of IPE/IPCP, "The Foundations of Interprofessional Collaborative Practice: Transforming Health Education at UB," were completed in February 2014. Although the original goal was to have all modules completed by the end of the Fall 2014 semester, module development took longer than anticipated because of personnel changes. The modules were completed in summer 2016 and embedded in relevant courses across the academic units in the fall. The modules were delivered using UB's course management system, UBlearns (Blackboard). During 2014, the AHC associate deans began identifying where the online modules would be placed in their curricula.

Faculty received assistance in module development from instructional design and video production staff within the School of Public Health and Health Professions and the School of Medicine and Biomedical Sciences. Faculty largely worked independently through the summer and fall of 2014. A Department of Rehabilitation Science faculty member held focus groups with physical therapy graduate students to gather data on what students liked and did not like about online modules and specific suggestions for the Roles and Responsibilities module.

Although some discussion had occurred around the need for a common template for the online modules, nothing definite was decided until January 2015. At this time, the Office of IPE had secured funds from the vice president for health sciences for additional instructional design and video production assistance from UB's Center for Educational Innovation. Fortunately, no completed work had to be redone. Center staff gave the modules a common format and design to provide students with consistency and also improved the quality of the audio in all the modules.

UB IPE Days

Since spring 2014, the IPE leadership team has been organizing and securing funding for "IPE Days," originally conceived as a half-day event in which students from the seven health professions programs would be assigned to interprofessional teams and engage in IPCP activities. The IPE leadership team believes that face-to-face, team-based, interprofessional collaboration is an essential component of a foundational IPE curriculum. Thus, "IPE Days" was envisioned as a means to provide students with introductory exposure to interprofessional team-based learning. The plan was to have students observe a case study scenario (role-played by live actors) of a patient who is experiencing multiple chronic health conditions and social, economic, and cultural barriers to care and a family member of the patient. Following the scenario, students would work in small, interprofessional teams to develop and discuss a collaborative patient care plan.

The Office of IPE pursued both internal and external funding and investigated how best to align the programs' diverse schedules to support the event. In the summer of 2015, the plan was reconfigured to circumvent the scheduling challenges posed by trying to convene students from seven health professions. The Office of IPE secured internal funding to hire a videographer to produce a video of the case study scenario, which was role-played by professional actors. This enabled faculty from two or more health professions to bring their classes together to view and discuss the video within small interprofessional student teams. This plan is not only more cost-effective but also provides faculty with greater flexibility and more opportunities to schedule face-to-face, interprofessional activities with their students.

The vision of an IPE Day, however, finally came to fruition in November 2016, with plans commencing the previous spring. The newly named Jacobs School of Medicine and Biomedical Sciences set aside a day in November for all second-year medical students to participate in IPE Day, and they were joined by students in dentistry, nursing, occupational therapy, physical therapy, pharmacy, social work, law, and management. Approximately 850 students participated, along with faculty from each of the schools.

IMPLEMENTATION CHALLENGES

Challenges encountered by UB's Office of IPE and the IPE leadership team include (a) insufficient financial resources for the Office of IPE; (b) lack of centralized financial support for the IPE/IPCP initiative, including for the simulation center; (c) scheduling difficulties in coordinating classroom and clinical IPE/IPCP activities across the AHC and social work schools; and (d) lack of course release or workload compensation for faculty involved in the IPE/IPCP initiative.

The Office of IPE lacks a budget and support staff. Well into 2014, the vice president for interprofessional education was also acting as the interim director for UB's Teaching and Learning Center and the core curriculum coordinator for the School of Public Health and Health Professions. With no support staff, administrative tasks such as the environmental scan and a complete curriculum mapping have yet to be completed.

The Behling Simulation Center relies on a "pay-to-play" model; students in the AHC are charged additional fees for their simulation experiences, with some schools adding additional funds to relieve the burden on students. The faculty of all seven health professions programs must determine if, when, and how they can provide students with the simulation center's high-quality, interprofessional simulation experiences, the dilemma being the utilization costs and an aversion to imposing additional fees on students.

Scheduling difficulties are a major hurdle in planning classroom and clinical IPE/IPCP activities across the health professions programs. The hope is to scale up IPE/IPCP for over 800 health professions students. The Office of IPE and the IPE leadership team continue to strategize around resolving the scheduling challenges.

As the Office of IPE and the IPE leadership team work toward creating an IPE/IPCP-supportive culture at UB, the deans, associate deans, and chairs of the academic units will need to address workload compensation issues if more faculty are to embrace and actively participate in the IPE/IPCP initiative. Over the last five years, IPE leadership team members volunteered their time (over and above their standard teaching and research workloads) to develop curricula, teach in the pilot project, and collaborate on the IITG grant, which required more curriculum development and teaching. If the initiative is to scale up, many more faculty will need to be involved.

LESSONS LEARNED

Lessons learned include the importance of (a) faculty commitment, enthusiasm, flexibility, and good humor in moving an IPE/IPECP initiative forward within a university composed of academic siloes; (b) a strategic planning process to build community among the IPE leadership team and other stakeholders and to generate a shared vision, goals, and priorities; (c) faculty and community stakeholder professional development in creating organizational and community cultures that support IPE/IPCP; and (d) interprofessional teamwork within the IPE leadership team, as tasks and projects are planned, implemented, and completed.

The Office of IPE and the IPE leadership team needed to respond to administrative directives, changing timelines, resource constraints, and diverse requirements across the health professions programs. Their dedication, flexibility, and good humor were essential to the success of the pilot curriculum project and to the rollout of the online modules. The IPE leadership team was, and continues to be, composed of faculty that strongly believe in the importance of IPE/IPCP to health professions education and to more effective, high-quality, and patient-centered health care delivery. Although the team members volunteered their time for the IPE/IPCP initiative, with no additional compensation or workload release from their units, the Office of IPE and the deans of participating schools will need to consider incentives to increase faculty involvement in the IPE/IPCP if the initiative is to expand within the university.

Because of time constraints in 2013, the assistant vice president of IPE, without funding to support a formal strategic planning process, developed a general framework of strategic directions to guide the IPE leadership team. The Office of IPE and the IPE leadership team anticipate organizing a strategic planning process inclusive of IPE leadership team members and university and community partners that value and wish to expand IPE/IPCP in academic and clinical settings. Such a strategic planning process can solidify commitment among the participants; secure buy-in around a shared vision, goals, objectives, and priorities; and help with future planning and division of roles and responsibilities.

The provision of faculty and community stakeholder professional development has strengthened UB's IPE/IPCP initiative by building more skilled and knowledgeable advocates among the faculty, generating enthusiasm for incorporating IPE/IPCP activities into existing courses, and establishing productive partnerships among faculty across the AHC, social work, and management schools. The School of Nursing received a three-year Health Resources and Services Administration Advanced Nursing Education training grant for nursing and dental students to work together on interprofessional teams to improve patients' oral health care (Saldi, 2013). A team of four UB students, representing School of Medicine and Biomedical Sciences, School of Pharmacy and Pharmaceutical Sciences, School of Social Work, and School of Nursing, submitted a proposal (which was one of 10 selected) for the 2015 Interprofessional Student Hot Spotting Mini-Grant Project learning collaborative, sponsored by the Camden Coalition of Healthcare Providers, Primary Care Progress, and the Association of American Medical Colleges (Association of American Medical Colleges, 2015; Gawande, 2011). With a medical student taking the lead, faculty on the IPE leadership team helped identify the students from the other professions for the hot spotting project.

The continuous engagement of new faculty in IPE/IPCP activities, through outreach and professional development opportunities, has also been essential in preserving a strong IPE leadership team. Faculty departures from the university and the unexpected death of another team member necessitated the recruitment of new IPE/IPCP champions for the leadership team.

Overall, the IPE leadership team functioned well as a collaborative, interprofessional team, respecting members' professional roles and responsibilities and different areas of expertise. However, on two key decisions, team members failed to communicate and achieve consensus as a team, which caused some avoidable distress later on: the pilot curriculum's evaluation plan and the protocol for generating scholarship from the pilot project, particularly the data analytic plans to answer the research questions.

As team members developed the pilot curriculum for the pilot project, IRB approval needed to be secured before the first classroom session convened. With some haste, because the decision to form a student task force was not made until well into December, two team members took the initiative and prepared the IRB proposal, using their best judgment on measures to be used. As would be expected, some differences of opinion later emerged on how best to use the data from some of the measures. The IPE leadership team recognized the importance of developing an evaluation plan as an interprofessional team.

The IPE leadership team was also reminded of the importance of an agreed-upon protocol for generating scholarship from any collaborative research project. As faculty prepared abstracts for conference presentations and publications following the pilot project, team members had differences of opinion on the data analytic plans for answering particular research questions. IPE leadership team members realized that, for Office of IPE-supported research, the Office of IPE needed to convene a committee to develop a protocol for deciding on (a) the products that would be generated from a project, (b) the lead and collaborating authors of each product, and (c) the data analytic plan for the research question.

Although no major difficulty arose, the faculty developing the online modules realized the need for sufficient pre-planning on the format, design, and content of each online IPE module. IPE leadership team members began online IPE module development in the spring of 2014, functioning fairly independently in how they were conceptualizing and developing their modules but consulting with an instructional designer within the School of Public Health and Health Professions. Not until January 2015, when assistance was secured from UB's Center for Educational Innovation, did the team decide on a common template and consistent format and design for the modules. Fortunately, no content had to be redone; center staff were able to reformat existing content and improve sound quality for audio in the modules. Ideally, all participating faculty, instructional designers, and videographers would have convened before module development began to decide on format, design, and content. The Center for Educational Innovation had produced two videos for the IPE/IPCP initiative in early 2014 but was not brought back into the project until 2015.

PROGRAM SUSTAINABILITY

Program sustainability continues to be high on the agenda for the Office of IPE and the IPE Leadership Team. The team suffered a profound loss with the death of the assistant vice president for IPE in spring 2016. Although UB's IPE/IPCP initiative is not yet sustainable, sustainability is inevitable given accreditation requirements, particularly for the AHC schools. The Office of IPE is tasked with marshaling the necessary resources to develop and implement a business plan, including a strong marketing plan, for program sustainability. Internal and external funding were being sought by the assistant vice president for IPE, in collaboration with faculty and community partners. Following the assistant vice president's death, the IPE leadership team pursued internal funding and continued developing the online modules and plans for IPE Day. By the beginning of the fall semester, the position at the Office of IPE had yet to be filled.

The Office of IPE and the IPE Leadership Team view several elements as essential in building toward sustainability: (a) institutionalizing the Office of IPE's involvement in key university initiatives, (b) broadening the scope of outreach to more diverse community partners, and (c) supporting students in becoming IPE/IPCP advocates and powerful change agents as they move from the classroom to clinical settings and then into the workforce.

To achieve program sustainability, it is imperative that key initiatives at UB institutionalize the Office of IPE's inclusion. For example, the Office of IPE is a key partner in the Community of Excellence in Global Health Equity, aimed at reducing global health disparities and funded by the UB Provost's E Fund during the 2014–2015 academic year (Stern, 2015). The National Institutes of Health–funded UB Clinical and Translational Research Center also incorporated the Office of IPE into its plan. The Clinical and Translational Science Award establishes UB as the lead institution of the Buffalo Translational Consortium, also composed of Roswell Park Cancer Institute; the Great Lakes Health System; UBMD, the largest physicians' group in western New York; and community health organizations (Goldbaum, 2015).

The Office of IPE is committed to conducting outreach to a broad scope of potential community partners to support future sustainability. In August 2014, UB partnered with the Federal Bureau of Investigation and the Centers for Disease Control and Prevention to host a two-day workshop for faculty, students, and law enforcement and community health on emergency preparedness and epidemiological investigations related to bioterrorism, in which IPE was an integral theme (Saldi, 2014). The symposium was grounded in interprofessional principles, especially the importance of teamwork and communication in collaborating around emergency preparedness and responses. This university–FBI partnership led to a seminar for faculty and students, sponsored by the School of Public Health and Health Professions and the UB Police Department, on gang behavior as a public health emergency and the essential role of interprofessional collaboration in solving complex community problems.

In spring 2016, the Office of IPE partnered with the Erie County Department of Health to address the opioid abuse epidemic in Western New York. The partnership will focus on educating health practitioners in safe acute-pain management and educating providers, consumers, and the larger community about the risks of opioid pain medications (Goldbaum, 2016). Also on the agenda for the Office of IPE is the strategic selection of a Community Advisory Council for IPE that will add significant strength to the IPE/IPCP initiative in areas of public relations, marketing, financing, and systems change.

Finally, the IPE Leadership Team views students as fulfilling a critical role in creating an IPE/IPCP culture at UB and in the community, particularly in the settings in which they practice their profession. A priority for the Office of IPE is to facilitate the convening of student leaders in the health professions schools for an IPE Student Association, which would be connected to the Institute for Healthcare Improvement Open Schools Project. Students can be powerful change agents within their clinical placements as advocates for IPE/IPCP and can continue to promote a culture of IPE/IPCP as they enter the workforce.

REFERENCES

Almerico, G. M. (2011). Secondary content area reading: Challenging sell for professors in teacher education programs. *Research in Higher Education Journal, 14,* 1–16.

Association of American Medical Colleges. (2015). *Hot spotters.* Retrieved from https://www.aamc.org/initiatives/hotspotter/

Baker, D. P., Amodeo, A. M., Krokos, K. J., Slonim, A., & Herrera, H. (2010). Assessing teamwork attitudes in healthcare: Development of the TeamSTEPPS teamwork attitudes questionnaire. *Quality and Safety in Health Care, 19*(6), e49. doi:10.1136.qshc.2009.036129

Baker, D. P., Krokos, K. J., & Amodeo, A. M. (2008). *TeamSTEPPS Teamwork Attitudes Questionnaire manual.* Retrieved from http://www.ahrq.gov/professionals/education/curriculum-tools/teamstepps/instructor/reference/teamattitude.pdf

Curriculum and Assessment Task Force. (2013). *Summary report: Realizing UB 2020–Curriculum and Assessment Task Force.* Retrieved from http://www.buffalo.edu/content/www/ub2020/archives/archives/realizing-ub-2020/task-forces/_jcr_content/par/download/file.res/CurriculumandAssessmentTaskForceFinalReport.pdf

Fish, D. R., Tona, J., Burton, H., Wietig, P. T., Trevisan, M., & Ohtake, P. J. (2011). Integrating public health and allied health education through a core curriculum: An action research approach. *Journal of Allied Health, 40*(1), e7–e14.

Gawande, A. (2011, January 24). The hot spotters. *New Yorker.* Retrieved from http://www.newyorker.com/magazine/2011/01/24/the-hot-spotters

Goldbaum, E. (2011a, September 20). Behling Patient Simulation Center transforms health sciences education at UB. *UB News Center.* Retrieved from http://www.buffalo.edu/news/releases/2011/09/12884.html

Goldbaum, E. (2011b, August 22). Future doctors at UB hear personal story on medical errors' tragic toll. Web initiative fires up. *UB News Center.* Retrieved from http://www.buffalo.edu/news/releases/2011/08/12802.html

Goldbaum, E. (2015, August 13). NIH awards UB $16 million clinical and translational science grant. *UB News Center.* Retrieved from http://www.buffalo.edu/news/releases/2015/08/016.html

Goldbaum, E. (2016, January 21). UB and Erie County join forces to fight opioid abuse. *UB News Center.* Retrieved from http://www.buffalo.edu/news/releases/2016/01/028.html

Hill, D. J. (2012, February 2). Web initiative fires up. *UB Reporter.* Retrieved from http://www.buffalo.edu/ubreporter/archive/2012_02_02/dct_rollout

Interprofessional Education Collaborative Expert Panel. (2011). *Core competencies for interprofessional collaborative practice: Report of an expert panel.* Washington, DC: Interprofessional Education Collaborative.

Lucke, K. T., Ellis, A., Havard, P. F., Elze, D. E., Ohtake, P., Antsonson, D., et al. (2013, June). *From classroom to community: Building social accountability in health professions' education and collaborative practice.* Presentation session at Collaborating across Borders IV, Vancouver, British Columbia.

McFadyen, A. K., Maclaren, W. M., & Webster, V. S. (2007). The Interdisciplinary Education Perception Scale (IEPS): An alternative remodeled sub-scale structure and its reliability. *Journal of Interprofessional Care, 21,* 433–443.

Office of the Provost. (2013). *Realizing UB 2020: Achieving academic excellence.* Retrieved from http://www.buffalo.edu/content/www/ub2020/realizing-ub-2020/realizing-ub-2020-planning-documents/_jcr_content/par/download_5/file.res/Realizing-UB2020-Final-2013-10-7.pdf

Office of the Provost. (2014). *Realizing UB 2020 task force recommendations.* Retrieved from http://www.buffalo.edu/ub2020/archives/archives/realizing-ub-2020/task-forces.html

Ohtake, P. J., Fish, D. R., Wietig, P. T., Lucke, K. T., Havard, P. F., Elze, D., et al. (2013, June). *What's good for the goose is good for the gander: Using an interprofessional leadership approach to develop a university IPE curriculum.* Poster session presented at Collaborating across Borders IV, Vancouver, British Columbia.

Ohtake, P. J., Lazarus, M., Schillo, R., & Rosen, M. (2013). Simulation experience enhances physical therapist student confidence in managing a patient in the critical care environment. *Physical Therapist, 93,* 216–228. doi:10.2522/ptj.20110463

Saldi, S. (2013, August 14). *UB gets $1 million HRSA grant to educate nurses on oral health.* Retrieved from http://www.buffalo.edu/news/releases/2013/08/009.html

Saldi, S. (2014, August 14). FBI-CDC workshop focuses on bioterrorism. *UB Reporter.* Retrieved from http://www.buffalo.edu/ubreporter/campus/campus-host-page.host.html/content/shared/university/news/ub-reporter-articles/stories/2014/August/fbi_bioterrorism.detail.html

Schuman, N. (2005, January 6). CARES delivers "more than a set of teeth." *UB Reporter.* Retrieved from http://www.buffalo.edu/ubreporter/archive/vol36/vol36n16/articles/CARES.html

Sigalet, E., Donnon, T., & Grant, V. (2012). Undergraduate students' perceptions of and attitudes toward a simulation-based interprofessional curriculum. *Simulation in Healthcare, 7,* 353–358. doi:10.1097/SIH.0b013e318264499e

Stern, R. (2015, May 28). UB invests $25 million to address pressing societal problems. *UB News Center.* Retrieved from http://www.buffalo.edu/ubreporter/research/news.host.html/content/shared/university/news/ub-reporter-articles/stories/2015/05/communities_of_excellence.detail.html

Unger, S. A. (2015, Summer). The right team with the right tools. *UB Medicine, 3*(2), 18–20. Retrieved from http://issuu.com/ubaa/docs/ub_medicine_summer_2015

11

HUNTER COLLEGE AND WEILL CORNELL: PUBLIC–PRIVATE ACADEMIC PARTNERSHIP

Kathleen M. Nokes

Hunter College, located on the East Side of Manhattan, is the largest college in the publicly supported City University of New York (CUNY) higher educational system. More than 23,000 students attend Hunter, pursuing undergraduate and graduate degrees in more than 170 areas of study. The college is composed of the Schools of Arts and Sciences, Education, Nursing, Social Work, and Health Professions and was the lead member of the CUNY School of Public Health. More than half of Hunter students are employed, and more than a third are the first in their families to attend college. Despite the challenges they face, their level of academic achievement is extremely high (Hunter College, n.d.).

Weill Cornell Medical College is the biomedical research unit and medical school of Cornell University, a private Ivy League university located in upstate New York. The medical college is located within walking distance of the main campus of Hunter College. One of the most selective medical schools in the United States, approximately 100 students enroll annually (Weill Cornell, n.d.).

All of the educational programs participating in this project are located on the East Side of Manhattan. The Hunter College Schools of Social Work and Public Health are in East Harlem (119th Street); Weill Cornell and the main Hunter College campus are at 68th Street; and the Nursing School is in Gramercy at 25th Street. Public transportation systems, including subways and buses, are accessible.

INTERDISCIPLINARY ACTIVITIES HELD PRIOR TO THE DEVELOPMENT OF THE PROGRAM

Nursing faculty at Hunter College had a long history of collaborating with social work faculty, especially related to aging issues; nursing faculty involved in the geriatric nurse practitioner program had actively collaborated with social work faculty since the 1980s. During the 1990s budget crises, the School of Nursing merged with public health and other health professions faculty into a School of Health Professions located on 25th Street. With the creation of the CUNY School of Public Health and the move of that program to the School of Social Work, geographical proximity decreased. Additionally, the organizational changes prompted by the new building at 119th Street occurred around the same time that the School of Nursing was again independent. The graduate program in the School of Nursing offers combined master's degrees in community and public health nursing and public health and has maintained a steady enrollment of approximately 40 nursing students since the program was created in the early 1990s. Nursing students take courses at both 119th and 25th Streets.

The National Institutes of Health Clinical and Translational Science Awards (CTSA) create an academic home for clinical and translational research. Nursing faculty were involved in the development of the award to Weill Cornell Medical School. The School of Nursing is one of the units within Hunter College that has been an institutional partner from the beginning of that CTSA award. That opportunity opened the door for future collaborations, including the interprofessional work described in this chapter.

HOW INTERPROFESSIONAL EDUCATION (IPE) FACULTY EMERGED

In light of the incorporation of interprofessional competencies into accreditation standards for the undergraduate and graduate nursing programs, nursing faculty were interested in strengthening the curriculum. The dean of the School of Nursing had expertise in public health and interdisciplinary work and was supportive of reaching out for external funding. A working group within Cornell and Hunter (Table 11.1) met to develop a proposal for a one-year planning grant from the Josiah Macy Jr. Foundation, which was funded in 2010. The purpose of the planning grant was to design, demonstrate, and institutionalize a program of integrated, interprofessional educational experiences that would provide nursing, public health, social work, and medical students with new competencies in collaborative teamwork. One of the highlights of the planning year was visiting with the interprofessional faculty at Vanderbilt in September 2010 (Schorn, Wu, Davidson, Black, & Rockhold, 2014) and learning about their two-year immersion program. During the planning year, the core nursing and medical faculty identified additional faculty in the Hunter Schools of Social Work, Public Health, and Nursing who were interested in implementing the program. A three-year grant was developed and funded (2011–2014) by the Macy Foundation. The first-year grant faculty are identified on Table 11.1. The project came to be called ITEACH (Interprofessional Training and Education at Cornell-Hunter).

Table 11.1: Hunter and Cornell Faculty Involved in the IPE Projects (2010 to 2014)

Planning Grant (2010) Project Directors and Faculty	Organizational Title
Joyce Griffin-Sobel, PhD, RN, CNE, ANEF	Assistant dean, curriculum and technology professor and director, undergraduate nursing programs (Hunter)
Carol Storey-Johnson, MD	Senior associate dean (Education), associate attending physician (Cornell)
Neal L. Cohen, MD	Distinguished lecturer in public health and social work (Hunter)
Byron P. Demopoulos, MD	Associate professor of clinical medicine (Cornell)
Mattia Gilmartin, RN, PhD	Clinical nurse leader, Graduate Program (Hunter)
Kathleen Nokes, PhD, RN, FAAN	Director of Graduate Program (Hunter)
Joseph F. Murray III, MD	Associate professor of clinical psychiatry (Cornell)
Darrell P. Wheeler, PhD, MPH	Associate professor, School of Social Work (Hunter)

Years 1–2 Faculty/Staff (2011–2013)	Organizational Affiliation
Joyce Griffin-Sobel, PhD, RN, CNE, ANEF	Nursing, Hunter College, principal investigator
Carol Storey-Johnson, MD	Weill Cornell Medical College, principal investigator
Joseph Murray, MD	Medicine, Weill Cornell Medical College
Byron Demopoulos, MD	Medicine, Weill Cornell Medical College
Kathleen Nokes, PhD, RN	Nursing, Hunter College
Pamela Mahon, PhD, RN	Nursing, Hunter College
Alexandra Plavskin, MSN, RN	Nursing, Hunter College
Lorna Thorpe, PhD	Public Health, Hunter College
Stacey Plichta, PhD	Public Health, Hunter College
Carmen Morano, PhD	Social Work, Hunter College
William Trochim, PhD	Cornell University, evaluation consultant
Michelle Sembetrand, RN, MS	Weill Cornell Medical College, home health nurse
Shawn McGinniss	Project coordinator

Year 3 (2013–2014)	Organizational Affiliation
Carol Storey-Johnson, MD	Weill Cornell Medical College, principal investigator
Joseph Murray, MD	Medicine, Weill Cornell Medical College
Byron Demopoulos, MD	Medicine, Weill Cornell Medical College
Kathleen Nokes, PhD, RN	Nursing, Hunter College
Kenya Beard, EdD, GNP-BC, NP-C, ACNP-BC	Nursing, Hunter College

(continued)

Table 11.1: Hunter and Cornell Faculty Involved in the IPE Projects (2010 to 2014) (Continued)

Stacey Plichta, PhD	Public Health, Hunter College
Carmen Morano, PhD	Social Work, Hunter College
William Trochim, PhD	Cornell University, evaluation consultant
Michelle Sembetrand, RN, MS	Weill Cornell Medical College, home health nurse
Shawn McGinniss	Project coordinator
Martin Dornbaum, MS	Health Professions Education Center, Hunter College
Barbara Glickstein, RN, MPH, MS	Senior project director, Hunter College
Gail C. McCain, PhD, RN, FAAN	Co-principal investigator, Hunter College

Notes: IPE = interprofessional education; PhD = doctor of philosophy; RN = registered nurse; CNE = certified nurse educator; ANEF = Academy of Nursing Education Fellow; MD = doctor of medicine; FAAN = Fellow of the American Academy of Nursing; MPH = master of public health; MSN = master of science in nursing; EdD = doctor of education; GNP = gerontology nurse practitioner—board certified; NP-C = certified nurse practitioner; ACNP-BC = acute care nurse practitioner—board certified; MS = master of science.

FACULTY SUPPORT

The nine-month, 21-credit Hunter College faculty workload is negotiated by a union contract. Many of the grant faculty were already assigned to the required number of credits. Traditionally, faculty receive summer salary equal to the amount of credits assigned to the grant. This practice was used to support the participation of grant faculty. To illustrate, if a faculty member was expected to contribute 1.5 credits to the project, she or he would receive that amount of money over the summer months based on the usual salary scale. Release time was given to Cornell faculty to support their involvement by reassigning their usual workload.

DEVELOPMENT PROCESS OF THE PROGRAM

From the outset, four key professions were included in the project: nursing, medicine, social work, and public health. By the end of the planning year, key faculty were identified, and some of them continued to the end of the three years of funding. As Table 11.1 illustrates, there were significant changes in personnel over the four years of funding. The project coordinator joined the team during the first year and remained with the project for entire grant period.

MILESTONES

Key milestones were offering the three-credit course from September 2011 through May 2012 and again from September 2012 through May 2013. It was decided not to offer the course during the third year of funding because it became clear that external funding was needed to support the course and so the project faculty decided to develop the videos based on the IPE competency domains during the final year of funding (2013–2014).

OVERVIEW OF PROGRAM FEATURES

During the planning year the faculty made a number of key decisions:

- The course would be offered as an elective (the course would be given a distinct nursing, social work, or public health course number and code at Hunter College). This was done so that students could use the course to fulfill requirements in their specific discipline. The course would be offered over one year rather than one semester.
- The course would be offered over two semesters between early September and mid-May, with each session lasting three hours. Although the course was divided between two semesters, the total class hours and the credit allocation amounted to what would normally be allocated to a single course.
- To comply with the Hunter College registration and grading protocols, an incomplete grade would be entered at the end of the first semester and a final grade at the end of the second semester.
- All the classes would include both didactic and group activities, with the students graded only on work that emerged from their team activities.
- A free learning platform, specifically Canvas (https://canvas.instructure.com/), which is not associated with either Hunter or Cornell, would be used as it did not require school-specific e-mails.
- The faculty would participate in each of the classes and be responsible for creating the student team consisting of students from all of the disciplines. Each faculty member would be responsible for two student teams.
- Faculty planning meetings would be scheduled one hour before the start of the class.
- The class locations would be rotated between the Hunter and Cornell settings.
- The course would be organized according to the four domains identified in the core competencies for interprofessional collaborative practice (values and ethics, roles and responsibilities, interprofessional communication, and teams and teamwork) (Interprofessional Education Collaborative Expert Panel, 2011) and with population health and financing issues.
- The course would be grounded in the relational coordination (Gittell, Seidner, & Wimbush, 2010) theoretical framework.

OVERVIEW OF CURRICULUM

The three-credit course, Transdisciplinary Teamwork in Healthcare, was designed to explore teamwork in health care settings with nursing and medical clinicians, social workers, and public health practitioners through a transdisciplinary lens. Seminars, reflective exercises, and extensive small-group work along with practicum experiences focus on the consumer's perspective on interacting with the health care team.

There were six course objectives:

1. Use the knowledge of one's own role and the roles of other professions to appropriately assess and address the health care and wellness needs of patients and populations served (Roles/Responsibilities domain).
2. Work with individuals of other professions to maintain a climate of mutual respect and shared values (Values/Ethics domain).
3. Communicate with patients, families, communities, and other health professionals in a responsive and responsible manner that supports a team approach to maintaining health and treatment of disease (Interprofessional Communication domain).
4. Apply relationship-building values and the principles of team dynamics to perform effectively in different team roles to plan and deliver patient- or population-centered care that is safe, timely, efficient, effective, and equitable (Teams and Teamwork domain).
5. Describe the major ways in which the provision of health care is financed and delivered in community-based settings.
6. Analyze and describe how the various approaches for paying for health care affect the care provided to patients.

CONTENT

The Vanderbilt team emphasized the importance of building rapport among the students early in the semester, scheduling a one-week immersion held on their campus. We decided to offer a weekend immersion, which included a trip to Lincoln Center for the Performing Arts for a classical music concert. Each class was organized according to the core competencies with an emphasis on how interprofessional collaboration promotes patient safety and higher quality health and social care. We used a variety of teaching strategies, including simulated cases, standardized actors, videos, team-building exercises (such as a toy drive for a foster care agency during holiday time), a guided visit to a museum, and lecture discussion by faculty teams. Articles that drew from the different disciplines were assigned as required readings.

Students were assigned to small groups on the basis of their discipline. Faculty were assigned to each group for the duration of the course. We hoped to have one student from nursing (graduate and undergraduate programs), medicine, social work, and public health on each team.

MODE OF DELIVERY

Clinical and Field Practicum Experience

The course description included an expectation of 50 hours of field practicum. We wanted the student team to meet a hospitalized patient and follow that patient's progress upon discharge. The physician and Cornell nursing members of the faculty team identified hospitalized patients who agreed to be followed by the team. There were a number of challenges that emerged from this experience, including death of two of the identified patients before hospital discharge. During the second time that the course was offered, teams were assigned to a onetime community experience in either a homeless shelter or community-based health fair. Both of the community settings were part of the established curriculum in the Cornell medical and Hunter nursing programs, and the IPE student teams joined those efforts. These experiences were supervised by at least one of the course faculty because the learning outcome was focused more on team work and not necessarily on specific clinical skills.

EVALUATION

Student teams completed two scholarly papers on assigned topics, reflecting the core themes of Healthy People 2020 (see https://www.healthypeople.gov), teamwork, and cultural competency; gave an oral presentation focusing on issues related to how the team functioned with the identified clients; and attended and participated in seminars, blogs, and other team activities, including the practicum experience described above.

A logic model was developed by the faculty team to ensure that the learning activities were consistent with overall course objectives. The project evaluator led this part of the project; Table 11.2 describes part of the logic model and how student outcomes were aligned with the course objectives.

IMPLEMENTATION CHALLENGES

Recruitment of social work, medical, and undergraduate nursing students was not difficult. Although the director of the graduate nursing program was a team faculty member and recruited vigorously, it was difficult to enroll registered nurses completing their graduate program. There were also challenges recruiting public health students into a course with more of a clinical focus. Although we originally planned an immersion weekend, a major hurricane closed New York City transportation down and the college canceled all courses over the scheduled weekend. We found that a onetime introductory session followed by a light dinner and a trip across town to Lincoln Center for a Mostly Mozart concert was effective. We used the orchestra model as an illustration of a highly functioning team (Lancaster, Kolakowsky-Hayner, Kovacich, & Greer-Williams, 2015). Although the one-year time frame was preferred by the Cornell students, most of the Hunter students did not like that schedule. The grant-funded program coordinator greatly assisted in addressing the scheduling and logistic challenges, and he also made himself available to the students.

There were multiple implementation challenges that ultimately resulted in the decision not to offer the course during the third year of funding. Changes in key leadership positions made sustainability difficult, and it became apparent that, without external funding, the course could not be sustained. The remaining team decided to produce

Table 11.2: Logic Model (March 2013)

Inputs	Activities	Outputs	Short-Term Goals	Mid-Term Goals	Long-Term Goals
External funding	Student recruitment and selection	A scholarly paper (5–10p)	Students can describe the health care system in the United States	Students can advocate effectively for their patients	Graduates value different professional identities
Classroom space with multiple sites with breakout room	Faculty role modeling	Discussion forum posts	Students can identify key legislation in U.S. health care policy	Students can discuss what makes an effective team	Graduates deliver transdisciplinary patient-centered care with chronically ill patients
Curriculum materials	Student relationship building	Graduates of ITEACH		Students can identify health care financing and impact on patient populations	
Faculty from nursing, medicine, social work, public health	Student team building	Readiness for Interprofessional Learning Scale	Students can understand the role of transdisciplinary team in chronic illness and death		Graduates effectively care for patients as a team
Food as an incentive	Introduce students to multiple professional roles		Students can describe business aspects of health care and how financing can affect patient care	Students can integrate perspectives of other disciplines into their own practice	Graduates can advocate for health care system improvement
Hospital partnership	Challenge biases and perceptions				
Online learning management system	Lectures			Students can process as a team the occurrence of deaths and near misses	
	Readings		Students have insight into how health care education is delivered in both private and public settings		
Students	Patient voice			Students understand transdisciplinary patient-centered care	
	Discussion of videos				
	Group work		Students are aware of how they express themselves and what effects this has on colleagues		
	Discussion of board and blog posts				
	Conflict resolution activities				
	Simulations		Students describe process of team development and the roles and practices of effective teams		
	Debriefing journaling, patient identification				

Note: Prepared by the project evaluation consultant from Cornell University Cornell Office for Research Evaluation with the IPE project faculty team during Year 1 of funding.

a product that could be used by health and social care faculty who wanted to integrate interprofessional content into the content of any course. Third-year project faculty are listed in Table 11.1.

During the final funding year, four modules, organized according to the four IPE domains, were produced as open-source stand-alone teaching tools (http://ipelab .commons.gc.cuny.edu/ipe-elearning-resources/). Each module uses exercises and the unfolding patient case of Mrs. Garcia (described throughout this text). The modules are presented in a series of video vignettes to illustrate the effects of teamwork and communication on care providers, patients, and their support networks. Every module contains approximately six to 10 minutes of video, interactive quiz questions and learning activities, content presentation, and feedback centered on a core competency domain. These resources are accompanied by an instructor's guide, providing additional debriefing, class discussion, and extension topics.

LESSONS LEARNED

A total of 39 students during the first year and 55 students during the second year completed the course. Five-person interdisciplinary student teams that remained stable over the duration of the course were effective and achieved positive evaluations overall. Although most health and social care professions value the benefits of interprofessional collaboration, faculty are hard pressed to identify sustainable, cost-effective strategies. Logistic issues related to scheduling, course progression, and creation of teams that reflect students' level of clinical expertise cannot be underestimated. The teaching strategies that we used, such as hiring standardized actors and field trips for cultural experiences, were valued but expensive. It was helpful to schedule faculty team meetings immediately before the class and use an open-source teaching platform such as Canvas. Canvas served as a two-way repository for course-related and logistic information that was not impeded by having an e-mail address from either Hunter or Cornell. Inclusion of public health faculty on the IPE team broadened everyone's perspective and identified how financial and other social determinants issues affect interprofessional collaboration. We created short modules that can be integrated into a variety of different health and social care courses. This sustainable product can enhance the education of providers who are effective members of high-functioning teams. These modules could also be used as part of continuing education or in-service programs for professional staff. Although the guide questions are directed toward pre-professional students, the high-quality videos can stand alone.

Our faculty team enjoyed working together, which facilitated our modeling of interprofessional team work for the students. While students from different disciplines would approach faculty from that discipline when they had concerns, the team faculty were able to redirect the issue back to the entire team. Students were disappointed when they learned that the course would not be offered again. Although the way forward is not clear at this point for the IPE collaboration between Hunter and Cornell, a sound platform was established.

REFERENCES

Gittell, J., Seidner, R., & Wimbush, J. (2010). A relational model of how high-performance work systems work. *Organization Science, 21*, 490–506.

Hunter College. (n.d.). *Welcome to Hunter College.* Retrieved from http://www.hunter .cuny.edu/abouthunter

Interprofessional Education Collaborative Expert Panel. (2011). *Core competencies for interprofessional collaborative practice: Report of an expert panel.* Washington, DC: Interprofessional Education Collaborative.

Lancaster, G., Kolakowsky-Hayner, S., Kovacich, J., & Greer-Williams, N. (2015). Interdisciplinary communication and collaboration among physicians, nurses, and unlicensed assistive personnel. *Journal of Nursing Scholarship, 47*, 275–284.

Schorn, M., Wu. A., Davidson, H., Black, E., & Rockhold, R. (2014). Interprofessional education (IPE): Synchronous, asynchronous, clinical practice, simulation across disciplines, across universities. *Medical Science Educator, 24*(Supp. 1), S9–S11.

Weill Cornell. (n.d.). *About us.* Retrieved from http://weill.cornell.edu/education/ index.html

12

INTERPROFESSIONAL EDUCATION: ISSUES IN EVALUATION

James C. Norton and James A. Ballard

The purpose of this chapter is, first, to comment from the point of view of one interprofessional education (IPE) program and identify the challenges we face in trying to evaluate the effect of our efforts. We will also discuss some of the evaluation strategies we have used and what we have learned both about the instruments themselves and about the effectiveness of our curricular efforts. Finally, we share some ideas regarding a way forward in this arena. In doing this, we do not mean to suggest that our program is exemplary in terms of evaluation. Rather, we are very much learning as we go and expect that many other programs find themselves similarly situated.

One final point to make by way of introduction concerns the meaning of the word *evaluation*. In this context, the term has two related meanings. On the one hand, evaluation refers to the assessment of student performance or student characteristics. Tests given at the end of a course are examples of this meaning of evaluation. On the other hand, evaluation also refers to the curriculum itself, attempting to determine whether the curriculum leads to the outcomes for which it is intended. The answer to that question is, in part, dependent on what is found using evaluation in the first sense. That is, if assessment of students does not show movement toward improved performance in the areas the curriculum is designed to teach, the curriculum clearly has failed. In this chapter, we will be discussing IPE evaluation in terms of assessing both student progress and curriculum quality.

THE CHALLENGES

If we agree that the ultimate purpose of IPE is to create health professionals who are effective and collaborative in their approach to health care delivery and health promotion, a challenge to evaluation of that outcome is immediately evident. At the most fundamental level, the greatest challenge to evaluating IPE that is provided as part of health professions education is the fact that, even assuming we have valid tools to evaluate such practice parameters (a challenge in itself), these parameters cannot be assessed at a time even remotely close to the end of the curricular experience. At the University of Kentucky (UK), we have worked diligently to develop an IPE experience for students entering the health-related professions. Assessing the effect of that experience on the clinical practice of those students cannot be done for at least several years and, in some cases (for example, a medical student pursuing a career in neurosurgery), for a decade or more. Furthermore, even if we live very long lives, are very patient, and have remarkable tracking capabilities allowing us to evaluate students when they are in practice, relating what we find to a curricular experience provided years before is not going to be straightforward.

Given this reality, a second challenge facing IPE evaluation is the identification of attributes that are relevant to attainment of the ultimate objective but that can be assessed in students at the time of an IPE experience. These would be attributes that, if present at the time of training, should predict effective and collaborative clinical practice once practice has begun. Identification of such attributes can be pursued on both theoretical and empirical grounds.

Empirically, one could look for traits that differentiate highly effective and collaborative practitioners from their less effective peers, then measure those traits in students, the assumption being that increases in such traits after IPE will predict attainment of the ultimate objective when the students becomes practitioners. (Incidentally, such attributes, if well validated, might also figure in the admissions process to health professions programs.) An article by Joan Sargeant, Elaine Loney, and Gerard Murphy (2008) illustrates this approach. They performed structured interviews with functioning primary care teams and identified through content analysis five attributes that characterized the members of highly effective teams. Examples included respect for team members, ability to work together, and excellent communication skills. Based on these findings, it would follow that an IPE intervention might focus, for example, on the specifics of how to work together to address a problem. Participants would then be evaluated on their acquisition of those skills, perhaps using a pre- and posttest methodology.

A more purely theoretical approach might entail application of, for example, social identity theory (Tajfel, 1981) to the task of identifying key attributes that an IPE intervention should address and, similarly, that evaluation of that intervention should track. Borst (2011) discussed identity theory in the context of interprofessional collaboration, noting that identity formation in the process of professional education can create barriers to collaboration after graduation. That is, to the extent that students strongly identify themselves as members of a particular profession, in-group/out-group dynamics that work to protect identity might conflict with the attitudes necessary for collaborative care. If this is true, an argument could be made that IPE should address the issue of subjective feelings of professional identity and, in terms of evaluation, measure their intensity before and after IPE intervention, with reduction in such attitudes being the goal. The appropriate tools for evaluating students might be an adaption of the Implicit Association Test (Greenwald, McGhee, & Schwartz, 1998). This tool typically used to assess preferences for one social group over another could be adapted to detect preferences by profession. In terms of evaluating the curricular intervention, movement in the direction of more equitable valuation would be a positive sign.

In an article on IPE in the context of continuing education (CE), Sargeant (2009) discusses, among other theories, complexity theory (Pisek & Greenhalgh, 2001) and how it might inform CE offerings. Briefly, and with much oversimplification, complexity theory posits that the performance of individuals in complex systems must be studied and understood in the context of the system as a whole. Such systems are affected by their environments, and interactions within such systems are nonlinear and unpredictable. To be effective, then, a practitioner must acquire the skills and attitudes necessary to operate in such complex systems. This is certainly not the sort of content traditionally associated with CE, but, Sargeant argues, it is essential that CE train practitioners differently going forward, in terms of both methods and content. Specifically, it would seem to follow from this theory that clinically oriented CE is more likely to be effective if training is provided to caregiving teams, rather than to individuals in professionally segregated venues.

From an evaluation perspective, addressed training variables would include communication patterns and other elements essential to collaboration in addition to or, in some cases, instead of acquisition of discipline-specific clinical knowledge. Relating this to the training of health professions students, it would suggest that we should be teaching the skills necessary for effective team work in complex systems. This content is not traditionally included in, for example, the core curriculum of colleges of medicine. Moreover, looking back at the dual focus of evaluation, there is a tension between evaluating the movement of the individual student along a trajectory toward interprofessionalism and evaluating the combined efforts of the entire team toward this same end. Either approach provides the benefits and risk of making one salient over the other. That is, if individuals are evaluated, they will have a better understanding of their performance, but the function of the team as a whole is implicitly deemphasized. Conversely, if the team is the object of evaluation, individual members may not understand their specific contribution.

The point here is not to advocate either of these theories but rather to illustrate that IPE evaluation and IPE content can be derived from theoretical constructs. Many have argued that theory is essential if we are to advance in our understanding of interprofessional practice and the training necessary to promote it.

In a 2013 editorial, Scott Reeves and Sarah Hean wrote that

> the use of theory in the interprofessional field has evolved and matured over the past few years . . . from a position of implicit and sometimes tentative use of theory, with broad skepticism of its ability to enrich our education, practice and patient care processes and outcomes, to a position of acceptance (and even celebration) of how theory can generate some insightful, helpful and, importantly, practical accounts for educators,

practitioners, researchers and also policy-makers. Although we have advanced some distance, with an increasingly sophisticated use of theoretical approaches, to support the design and evaluation of interprofessional activities, there is still some way to go. Encouragingly, the steady growth of theories from the disciplines of education, social psychology, organizations and systems and psychodynamics has enhanced and deepened our knowledge about the interprofessional field. (Reeves & Hean, 2013, p. 2)

Angus McMurtry makes the same point, giving examples from four theoretical perspectives: communities of practice, cultural historical activity theory, complexity science, and actor-network theory (McMurtry, 2013). Although these theories differ in many ways, they share the fundamental idea that social groups and the material artifacts they generate are fundamental to all human knowing. An example of a material artifact could be a medical record system, the expectation being that the format of such a system generated by a high-functioning interprofessional team would differ in fundamental ways from one created by homogeneous groups of professionals working in isolation. Also common across these approaches is the acknowledgment that optimal practice and optimal learning require four elements: diverse perspectives, common ground, negotiated resolution of conflicts, and ultimate synthesis. Thus, an effective health care delivery team would include various professionals (diverse perspectives) who share an understanding of what is good patient care (common ground). However, for an effective treatment plan to be generated (ultimate synthesis), rules for working through differences of opinion (negotiated resolution of conflicts) must be ingrained in their process. In terms of IPE, one could argue that curricula should allow students to experience these four elements in meaningful and progressive ways that take into account the level of professional knowledge students possess at the time of each intervention. Student evaluation from this perspective might logically focus on uncovering the changes, if any, in the definition of common ground or the creation within the group of more effective mechanisms for resolving conflict resulting from students' participation in IPE curricula.

A final challenge in IPE evaluation is balancing the relative ease of application and scoring of objective, quantitative instruments with the potentially richer data that are generated using more subjective, qualitative methods, such as structured interviews and reflection papers. Validated, objective instruments have the great advantage of generalizability. The Attitudes toward Health Care Teams Scale (ATHCTS; Heinemann, Schmitt, Farrel, & Brallier, 1999) is a good example as it has been widely used and validated. It is relatively short and easy for students to complete and for staff to score. Conversely, end-of-course debriefings and student reflections on course experiences can provide insights into what was important to the students and how they see themselves as changed by the experience. Such methods do this in a way that quantitative scales do not and, importantly, may lead to identification of variables for which no scale exists. However, such methods are time-consuming for the students, faculty, and staff involved, both in data collection and in data analysis. Making sense of 50 student reflection papers in terms of identifying variables, represented by themes that have been affected by the IPE experience, requires skills in content analysis techniques and the time to apply them. Scoring quantitative inventories such as the ATHCTS takes minutes and can be done by a staff assistant. All of that said, it seems that a mixed methodology makes the most sense given the point in development of IPE at which we currently find ourselves. Such an approach, in fact, was recommended by a recent report by the Institute of Medicine (2015) on measuring the impact of IPE and collaborative practice. The challenge, however, is in doing the qualitative work in a way that is not unduly burdensome to either the students or the faculty.

In this section, we have identified three challenges to evaluation of IPE. The first is the time frame separating IPE delivery and the opportunity to assess the ultimate goal. The second, which derives from the first, is identifying attributes that can be defended as reasonable surrogates for the ultimate goal and which can be evaluated in temporal conjunction with IPE interventions. We have seen that choices of which attributes to assess can derive from both empirical observations of effective practitioners and from theories concerned with the dynamics of people working in groups generally or specifically in health care delivery. Finally, we noted that deciding on the appropriate balance between quantitative and qualitative approaches presents challenges in evaluation design. We turn now to an account of the approach we have taken at UK to evaluate both our students and our curricula.

IPE EVALUATION AT UK

At the University of Kentucky, I think it is fair to say that our evaluation approach has been pragmatic in at least two senses. First, our initial curricular efforts were primarily focused on students early in their educational journeys toward professional practice, and the interventions we envisioned were relatively small in terms of total contact time. So, thinking pragmatically, the sorts of changes or outcomes we could reasonably expect to document following these experiences were limited to some increase in knowledge about professions other than the students' own and, possibly, shifts in attitudes relevant to IPE. A pragmatic approach also is reflected in the fact that we have tried to be sparing in the amount of time we expect students to devote to the evaluation process. Regarding quantitative measures, it has often been demonstrated that the more questions you ask on a survey, the less meaningful the answers become (Maloney, Grawitch, & Barber, 2011). We have taken this finding to heart, as will be evident when we describe the specific instruments below. Similarly, as regards qualitative methods, we have tried to be judicious in their application and respectful of students' time.

From a theoretical perspective, our initial efforts were informed by a logic model that said, basically, if students' attitudes can be shifted in the direction of greater acceptance of a collaborative approach, it seems likely that, as they progress through their training, such attitudes will lead to collaboration with other students in clinical training settings and with other practitioners when in practice. This perspective is guided by the theory of planned behavior that argues that one's ultimate behavior is, in part, dependent on one's motivations and an intention to perform those behaviors (Ajzen, 1991). Drinka and Clarke's (2000) description of professionals coming to understand the "cognitive maps" of their team members seems relevant here. Our tool, though not based on their work, seems consistent with their thesis. This essentially commonsense approach grew primarily within the leadership of the Center for Interprofessional Health Education at UK, with occasional input from faculty members involved in the development of the IPE curricular elements. It was also informed by the literature then in place and by interaction with colleagues pursuing IPE at other institutions.

In this section, we will discuss two curricular initiatives, one that is fully managed by the center and a second offered with center support. We choose these to illustrate concrete examples of our evaluation approach in practice. We will look first at the Deans' Interprofessional Honors Colloquium (DIHC) and then turn to Interprofessional Teamwork in Global Health (ITGH). Both these courses are described in more detail in chapter 7.

Deans' Interprofessional Honors Colloquium

DIHC, launched in 2009, was our first formal curricular offering. It is a semester-long course built annually around a cross-cutting health issue, such as obesity or pain management, and consisting of six sessions. The first four sessions begin with a short didactic presentation, followed by faculty-facilitated interprofessional small groups in which the presentations are discussed and the groups work on a project relevant to the health issue. The projects are then presented to the class and to medical center leadership at the last two sessions.

The evaluation model created for the DIHC was both quantitative and qualitative in character and addressed both student outcomes and course acceptability. Many of the tools were developed specifically for this course and thus have limited generalizability. We have used this model, with some modifications, in other IPE offerings.

Evaluation of Students

Looking first at student quantitative evaluation in the DIHC, we have used the ATHCTS before and after the course from the beginning and continue to do so. Also applied is a scale developed here that assesses students' self-assessment of their knowledge of other health professions in terms of their educational requirements and scope of practice. Use of these tools proceeds from the logic model described above. Movement in the direction of more positive attitudes on the ATHCTS and greater knowledge about other professions are the expectations. Historically, both of these have been met. In terms of coming to understand other disciplines, the most dramatic changes observed are those for social work and public health in that students from the health professions apparently have very limited understanding of these professions when they enter professional school. This suggests that although student understanding of the roles and scope of all professions generally increase, they know less about, and as a result of the course have greater increases in this understanding for, these two professions. Using a 5-point scale, students also rate themselves and the others in their groups on team competencies in the areas of contributing to achieving group tasks, communication skills, and team-relevant attitudes. The variables are derived from the Interprofessional Education Collaborative (IPEC) Expert Panel (2011) Core Competencies. This Self/Peer Assessment of Team instrument was developed in collaboration with faculty at the Medical University of South Carolina. In addition, faculty members rate students in their groups using a point system in terms of variables such as attendance, engaged participation, and preparation, with perfect scores on all variables yielding a score of 100. Finally, the project presentations for each group are rated by faculty members using a behaviorally anchored rubric with a 3-point scale on variables including teamwork, evidence of interprofessional growth, organization, scope, and completeness.

Qualitative measures include a structured course reflection focused on, for example, misperceptions students may have had concerning other professions, personal areas of strength and weakness in teamwork, and roles the student might play in a team addressing the health issue discussed in the course. As part of the course, students shadow a practitioner outside their profession and write a reflection on that experience. Finally, there are open-ended questions on the above-mentioned rating of self and others on team competencies. Examples are "What was the most significant thing that your group accomplished?" and "What could you have done to contribute more effectively to that work?"

Evaluation of the Course

In terms of evaluation of the course itself, we used a fairly standard quantitative format in which students rate aspects of the course on a 5-point scale. Variables are things like "The overall quality of this course was good" and "My facilitator(s) encouraged teamwork in my small group." In addition, there is a section in which students rate variables addressing specific core competencies (IPEC Expert Panel, 2011), for example, "By participating in this course I learned to . . . Respect the unique cultures, values, roles, responsibilities, and expertise of other health professions," one of the Values and Ethics Core Competencies, and "Engage other health professionals—appropriate to the specific care situation—in shared person-centered problem-solving," one of the Teams and Teamwork Core Competencies.

Qualitative methods include a large-group debriefing conducted by the course director in which students are asked to discuss things they liked or that they thought could be improved. There also are open-ended questions at the end of the quantitative evaluation described above. For example, "Please share one thing you learned that you plan to apply in your future practice/career" and "Please share any other comments about this course."

Finally, we evaluate the course based on some of the results of the student outcome evaluation data. Specifically, the movement of attitudes in the intended direction and the increase in knowledge about other health professions provide validation that the course is meeting its objectives and, from the point of view of the logic model, potentially contributing to achieving the ultimate goal of effective and collaborative practice.

The model described for the DIHC illustrates the approach to evaluation we have taken. The use of the standardized ATHCTS pre- and postcourse allows a degree of generalization, suggesting that the course is meeting national expectations for IPE. The evaluation process is not unduly burdensome in terms of student time, and for the qualitative elements, a pedagogical as well as an evaluation purpose is served. That is, the process of reflection represents an opportunity for students to consolidate learning and provides data that can be analyzed from the perspective of documenting student progress toward interprofessional competency acquisition. These data, to the extent they show movement in a positive direction, also serve to evaluate the course in terms of effectiveness.

Interprofessional Teamwork in Global Health

ITGH is a course for a select group of learners from all health professions colleges and residencies as well as some other undergraduates. It is a preparation for the Shoulder-to-Shoulder Ecuador Health Brigade, a one-week experience in which students work firsthand alongside faculty, medical professionals, and local Ecuadorian staff. The course meets six times in small groups during the spring semester, with the Ecuador experience scheduled for the summer break. Like DIHC, its design is based on a constructivist theoretical foundation, and therefore, the pedagogy uses a significant amount of interprofessional small-team discovery learning as students apply concepts from the course to work through an unfolding case. This case consists of multiple members of a family at various ages, from childhood to advanced age, and is based on real persons encountered during previous Health Brigades to Ecuador. This allows for incorporating the need for multiple professions in an authentic way without locating all of the medical issues within a single individual.

Evaluation of Students

The quantitative evaluation of students in this course follows the same pattern described above for DIHC. What is unique to ITGH, however, is that an intensive, qualitative evaluation was performed on the first offering that revealed important findings. Students submitted reflections done before and after the experience, addressing their understanding of principles of collaborative care and cultural competency. Based on a constructivist model, it was expected that the students would show a more articulated and complex pattern of responses to the questions asked after the experience as compared with results from reflections done before. Content thematic analysis of these data, guided by a narrative approach, confirmed this expectation.

Two major themes were identified. The first theme can be described by the construct of decentering (Piaget & Inhelder, 1969). This was demonstrated by movement from the worldview of an individual practitioner working effectively with patients to an integrated focus (culture, profession, and patient)—that is, a movement from what "I," or "my" profession, can do for the patient to what the team can do with the patient. This was observed at the cultural and professional levels. At the cultural level, it was expressed by an increased respect for the values of other cultures and an understanding of, and reflection on, one's own cultural biases. At the professional level, decentering was expressed by an increased respect for other professions, an understanding of others' roles, and an acknowledgment of the importance of interprofessional communication defined as the ability to take the perspective of other professionals and to recognize biases held toward other professions. This would seem to be another instance of understanding complementary cognitive maps characteristic of other professions as a result of an IPE experience (Drinka & Clarke, 2000).

The second theme discovered in this evaluation involved an anticipated transformation in how students expect to practice. Specifically, they intend to place greater focus on communication with patients and other professionals, seek out interprofessional practice opportunities, actively promote interprofessional collaborative practice, embrace the need to better understand cultural differences, and increase systematic thinking by embracing a broader perspective of health care.

In this initial evaluation, these qualitative outcomes were triangulated with the quantitative data. This yielded a rich picture of the changes in both attitudes and competencies, with a commitment to change consequent to this IPE offering.

Evaluation of the Course

We have described an evaluation methodology for ITGH that was very labor intensive. Many institutions (including our own) do not have the resources necessary to perform such an elaborate evaluation each time such an experience is offered as, in this case, it happens annually. However, it seems prudent to make this investment in a mixed approach to evaluation in initial offerings of significant IPE courses. In our experience, the rewards are substantial in terms of discovering what is happening to students as a result of the experience and assessing the value of the course. The outcomes revealed by the qualitative evaluation of students serve as strong evidence of the efficacy of the intervention, particularly when combined with conventional, quantitative measures of course acceptability, which, in this case, were strongly positive.

GOING FORWARD

We conclude this chapter with some thoughts on how we intend to go forward with our evaluation process at UK. In doing so, we will comment on what seems to be working and what we think may need to change. This discussion will also be informed by the work of others who are involved in IPE evaluation.

In a seminal article, Amy Blue and her colleagues drew the following conclusion (among others) regarding IPE evaluation, based on their review of the literature, focused interviews with IPE leaders, and expert panel discussion (Blue, Chesluk, Conforti, & Holmboe, 2015): "Multiple methods of learner assessment that measure knowledge, skills, and behavior over time in various contexts are needed" (p. 80). Among the tools suggested are portfolios in which students track their progress in acquiring interprofessional collaborative practice skills over the course of their training; behaviorally based assessment, such as objective structured clinical exams (OSCEs), that are team based; and evaluation instruments in clinical courses that define teamwork behaviorally and require faculty observation and evaluation. These authors further argued that longitudinal evaluation of students is essential and suggested the use of milestones as a vehicle. In medical education at the postgraduate level, such a methodology has been implemented (Swing et al., 2013), and translation to the undergraduate level is under way (Morgan et al., 2014). Although much of this work is focused on traditional clinical skill acquisition, the inclusion of interprofessional care is both possible and desirable, provided valid behavioral measures can be identified. The authors also noted that the use of milestones is consistent with the call for more use of contemporary developmental learning theory to guide both teaching and evaluation:

> As learners progress through a continuum of learning and attendant acquisition of knowledge and skills, markers to assess this development can be aligned to ensure progression and appropriate advancement and to identify points of remediation when necessary. Improvement of individual assessment practices will likely lead to enhanced program evaluation, particularly if the evaluation framework is explicit and includes agreed-upon metrics. (Blue et al., 2015, p. 80)

All of these recommendations seem beneficial to our program. The issue going forward is how, in fact, to implement them. For some of the suggested innovations, there are many challenges to implementation in our program and, we expect, in some others. OSCEs, for example, though validated as a methodology, are labor and time-intensive, even when pursued within a single discipline. Designing and implementing them across disciplines complicates that process considerably. In fact, developing such an OSCE might represent an interesting case study in teamwork for the faculty and programs involved. Using the essential elements of sociomaterial theories of learning as described by McMurtry (2013), we have multiple perspectives (the involved disciplines), common ground (shared commitment to IPE), a sufficiently collegial atmosphere for differing perspectives and needs to be reconciled (negotiated resolution of conflicts), and, in the end, if all goes well, a functioning interprofessional OSCE (synthesis). Viewed this way, the creative process is a learning opportunity for the faculty involved and one that, if effective, could potentially change the culture of the institution in subtle but meaningful ways. One of the greatest difficulties to be addressed at step three in this scenario, though, would be scheduling. At UK, we have had some success in that regard as we have implemented interprofessional simulations involving medicine, nursing, dentistry, physical therapy, physician assistant, and pharmacy students on a limited scale. However, the logistical problems were significant. Developing universal use of OSCEs across programs, although conceptually appealing, may exceed our capabilities at this point in time.

The idea of portfolios is an interesting one. Within some of our disciplines, a version of this methodology is already in place, and we have developed a database to track student involvement in IPE activities that could form one element in such a portfolio for each student. Related to this is the issue of a longitudinal approach to IPE and student evaluation. Our efforts to date have generated the framework for such an approach in that we have a universal curricular element (iCATS) for all beginning students, several opportunities for students to pursue IPE later in preclinical training (for example, DIHC and ITGH), and, finally, authentic clinical IPE during clinical training. What is not yet in place, however, is a complementary, longitudinal, systematic, and integrated evaluation strategy. Although we have a reasonably consistent evaluation suite for the preclinical IPE experiences, we have not yet articulated it with evaluation during the clinical years. We are beginning, however, to look at that.

REFERENCES

Ajzen, I. (1991). The theory of planned behavior. *Organizational Behavior and Human Decision Processes, 50,* 179-211.

Blue, A. V., Chesluk, B. J., Conforti, L. N., & Holmboe E. S. (2015). Assessment and evaluation in interprofessional education. *Journal of Allied Health, 44,* 73-82.

Borst, J. (2011). Interprofessional collaboration: An introduction. *Human Innovation Review, 2,* 32-37.

Drinka, J., & Clarke, P. (2000). *Health care teamwork: Interdisciplinary practice and teaching.* Westport, CT: Auburn House.

Greenwald, A. G., McGhee, D. E., & Schwartz, J. L. (1998). Measuring individual differences in implicit cognition: The Implicit Association Test. *Journal of Personality and Social Psychology, 74,* 1464-1480.

Heinemann, G. D., Schmitt, M. H., Farrel, M. H., & Brallier, S. A. (1999). Development of an Attitudes towards Health Care Team Scale. *Evaluation and the Health Professions, 22,* 123-142.

Institute of Medicine. (2015). *Measuring the impact of interprofessional education (IPE) on collaborative practice and patient outcomes.* Retrieved from http://iom.nationalacademies .org/Reports/2015/Impact-of-IPE.aspx

Interprofessional Education Collaborative Expert Panel. (2011). *Core competencies for interprofessional collaborative practice: Report of an expert panel.* Washington, DC: Interprofessional Education Collaborative.

Maloney, P., Grawitch, M. J., & Barber, L. K. (2011). Strategic item selection to reduce survey length: Reduction in validity? *Consulting Psychology Journal: Practice and Research, 63,* 162-175

McMurtry, A. (2013). Reframing interdisciplinary and interprofessional collaboration through the lens of collective and sociomaterial theories of learning. *Issues in Interdisciplinary Studies, 31,* 75-98.

Morgan, H., Marzano, D., Lanham, M., Stein, T., Curran, D., & Hammoud, M. (2014). Preparing medical students for obstetrics and gynecology milestone level one: A description of a pilot curriculum. *Medical Education Online, 19,* 25746. doi:10.3402/ meo.v19.25746

Piaget, J., & Inhelder, B. (1969). *The psychology of the child.* (H. Weaver, Trans.). New York: Basic Books.

Pisek, E. P., & Greenhalgh, T. (2001). The challenge of complexity in health care. *British Medical Journal, 323,* 625-628.

Reeves, S., & Hean, S. (2013). Why we need theory to help us better understand the nature of interprofessional education, practice and care. *Journal of Interprofessional Care, 27,* 1-3.

Sargeant, J. (2009). Theories to aid understanding and implementation of interprofessional education. *Journal of Continuing Education in the Health Professions, 29,* 178-184.

Sargeant, J., Loney, E., & Murphy, G. (2008). Effective interprofessional teams: "Contact is not enough" to build a team. *Journal of Continuing Education in the Health Professions, 28,* 228-234.

Swing, S. R., Beeson, M. S., Carracio, C., Coburn, M., Iobst, W., Selden, N. R., et al. (2013). Educational milestone development in the first 7 specialties to enter the next accreditation system. *Journal of Graduate Medical Education, 5*, 98–106.

Tajfel, H. (1981). *Human groups and social categories.* Cambridge, United Kingdom: Cambridge University Press.

Part 4

SETTINGS OF INTERPROFESSIONAL PRACTICE

13

INTERPROFESSIONAL PRACTICE IN THE VETERANS HEALTH ADMINISTRATION

Judith L. Howe and Louisa Daratsos

The Veterans Health Administration (VA) has a long-standing commitment to work-force development through interprofessional education and practice. Despite obstacles such as different disciplinary cultures, lack of dedicated time for clinical preceptors, and variability in academic schedules, interprofessional education (IPE) is viewed as a prerequisite to effective interprofessional practice (IPP) and better patient care (Gilman, Chokshi, Bowen, Rugen, & Cox, 2014). In this chapter, we focus on geriatric, pallia-tive, and rural health care in our discussion of IPE and IPP in the VA. The VA Office of Academic Affairs (now the Office of Academic Affiliations) was an early adopter of IPE with the creation of leading-edge training programs, such as the Interdisciplinary Team Training in Geriatrics program (ITTG) in the late 1990s. Through affiliation agreements with more than 1,800 health professions schools and colleges in the United States, numerous clinical training opportunities are provided to students in more than 40 professions, including nursing, medicine, pharmacy, dentistry, audiology, social work, physical therapy, and psychology. In 2013, 31,380 associated health trainees and 23,808 nurse trainees received training at a VA facility (Office of Academic Affiliations, n.d.-a). These placements provide the largest portfolio of IPE and IPP opportunities of any health care system in the United States.

The VA's commitment to IPE has included the exploration of new approaches for integrating IPE into clinical settings. In 2001, VA selected six medical sites, including the Geriatric Research Education and Clinical Center (GRECC) at the James J. Peters VA Medical Center, to host one-year interprofessional fellowships in palliative and end-of-life care. At the time, Dr. Stephanie Pincus, chief officer for academic affairs, said that the fellowships ensure that "the patient will be treated by a caring, training partnership of doctors, nurses, chaplains, and social workers" (U.S. Department of Veterans Affairs, Office of Public and Intergovernmental Affairs, 2001). This groundbreaking fellowship remains innovative even today as training programs and health care facilities continue to struggle with the many issues related to breaking down disciplinary silos to provide IPE.

More recently, the VA implemented the VA Centers of Excellence in Primary Care in an effort to prepare future health care practitioners to work in and lead patient-centered interprofessional teams. Launched in 2011, this initiative sought to develop strategies for integrating education into the VA's version of patient-centered medical homes, referred to as Patient Aligned Care Teams (Gilman et al., 2014). The five VA medical centers and university affiliates that were selected for this demonstration project developed a variety of clinical rotations that supported competency-based IPE approaches to prepare trainees to function effectively within interdisciplinary teams (Office of Academic Affiliations, n.d.-b).

GERIATRICS

Many VA IPE and IPP efforts have been sponsored by the GRECCs, which were established by the U.S. Congress in the 1970s to develop an infrastructure to prepare for the aging of the World War II veteran population. VA policy makers understood that the demographics of the VA population would require a variety of services as veterans aged (Daratsos & Howe, 2007).

The 20 GRECCs are centers of excellence composed of research, clinical, and education programs and are engaged in a myriad of educational, training, research, clinical, and dissemination activities (U.S. Department of Veterans Affairs, n.d.). The structure and composition of the GRECCs, with researchers, educators, and clinicians representing different disciplinary backgrounds, such as medicine, nursing, social work, and health services research, has promoted interdisciplinary collaboration in the development and implementation of research studies, clinical models of care, and educational programs and products.

The VA's Office of Academic Affiliations launched the ITTG program in 1979. It was conceptualized as a clinically oriented education program with multimodal learning opportunities for VA staff and students from three or more health professions (Tsukuda, 1998). This novel program focused on equipping health care providers with team-based knowledge and skills and promoting IPE leadership and mentorship in health care settings. ITTG was hosted at 12 VAs, providing financial support for coordinators, educational materials, and stipends for trainees in the allied health disciplines. Over the years, ITTG expanded its reach beyond geriatrics and was renamed the Interdisciplinary Team Training Program (ITTP). Within the VA, ITTP was an important catalyst in the institutionalization of IPE and increased recognition that IPE is foundational to successful IPP. The ITTG/ITTP program was also a building block for the John A. Hartford Foundation–supported Geriatrics Interdisciplinary Team Training program, which funded nine sites for three years in 1996, including the Icahn School of Medicine at Mount Sinai.

Since the GRECCs were founded, their mission has included the education and training of non-physician-associated health trainees with stipends provided by the Office of Academic Affiliations in a set-aside program. In 2014, 315 associated health trainees received GRECC-sponsored training. As an example, the James J. Peters GRECC in the Bronx, New York, sponsors 12 associated health trainees and four to five interprofessional palliative care fellows each academic year from disciplines including social work, pharmacy, nursing, and medicine. This GRECC's teaching and learning community is underpinned by IPE, IPP, and adult learning principles. The logistics and disciplinary cultural integration are time-consuming and often challenging but necessary for achievement of program goals. The clinical and didactic curriculum, though interdisciplinary in many respects, is also disciplinary focused to align with accreditation requirements and participants' professional identity.

There are interdisciplinary core competencies, discipline-specific competencies, and an array of interconnected classroom and clinical education. The curriculum includes a weekly one-hour interactive seminar for an interdisciplinary group of associated health trainees focusing on geriatrics, palliative care, and interdisciplinary teamwork by using a rotating faculty. This format facilitates an understanding and appreciation for all health care disciplines.

The seminar aims to integrate classroom content with the trainee's clinical rotations through activities such as case and article discussions, reflective journaling, and capstone presentations. The seminar's interdisciplinary team content lays the groundwork for IPP with trainees reflecting on their clinical teams (for example, communication, structure, role clarity) (James J. Peters VA Bronx Medical Center & Mount Sinai School of Medicine, n.d.).

PALLIATIVE CARE

Palliative and end-of-life care provides an excellent example of the VA's emphasis on IPE and IPP. In 2003, the VA issued a directive (Directive 2003-08) calling for each medical center to establish a palliative care consultation team (PCCT) with designated staff. The recommendation was for at least 25 percent of the team to be composed of a physician, social worker, nurse, and chaplain, with encouragement for greater contributions by these clinicians and the suggestion of participation by other disciplines. Updated five years later, VA Directive 2008-066 requires that each facility PCCT have one team member serve as coordinator, thus improving continuity of care and ensuring optimal communication among patients, families, and teams, among other tasks.

A significant wave of IPE initiatives in the VA occurred in palliative care beginning in 2003, with a national initiative requiring the establishment of PCCTs. Prior to this initiative, the VA had made efforts to create and sustain palliative care teams. In 1992, hospice consultation teams were developed with accompanying training both to support the teams and to promote consultation to these teams (Abrahm, Callahan, Rossetti, & Pierre, 1996).

Even in the late 1970s, according to Abrahm et al. (1996), there were interdisciplinary hospice teams at the Wadsworth VA Hospital (now West Los Angeles VA Medical Center) and the Philadelphia VA. The Philadelphia VA's pilot project is particularly interesting because it demonstrated cost savings associated with the team's efforts. This is notable given current discussions about using business models in palliative care, such as those developed by the Center to Advance Palliative Care and other organizations, to collect data showing financial and quality-of-life benefits. In the experience of one of the authors (Louise Daratsos), who worked in a VA medical center that had a hospice consultation team in the early 1990s, the team lacked multitiered administrative support. Thus, there was little incentive on the part of treatment teams to consult with the hospice team. The opportunity to collaborate on cases was often lost.

These early attempts at providing end-of-life care as an interdisciplinary effort came in part because leaders in the VA, such as the late Zelda Foster, recognized that quality services for patients in their last days of life could not be provided by any single profession. Foster's seminal article introduced the idea that social workers had a significant role to play in assisting patients during their terminal illness by having conversations that patients could not have with their physicians (Foster, 1965).

Very often, several disciplines contribute to meeting a patient's needs during a terminal illness, and no one profession can claim sole responsibility for assessing and treating a problem. Many social workers working in health care settings have had the experience of a patient being pleasant and conversational during encounters with physicians but more revealing to other team members.

Figure 13.1 illustrates the integrated nature of how health care professionals can work together to assess a symptom common to palliative care patients, such as pain. Suppose a patient with advanced cancer responded that he was fine during rounds with the interdisciplinary team. The nurse observes grimacing when the patient is moved during the physical examination. Assessment by the various disciplines confirms the patient's pain and speculates on some of the reasons why it was unreported.

Figure 13.2 shows how these disciplines can contribute to the resolution of this pain crisis. After discussing this patient in a team meeting with the physician present, nurses, social workers, and chaplains might each provide education and counseling regarding the benefits of good pain management, educate the patient about nonpharmacologic and integrative medicine techniques, and elaborate how these interventions might enhance that patient's quality of life. In sites fortunate enough to have pharmacists who are able to participate in team meetings and patient care, their expertise would be most welcome in situations such as this scenario. Pharmacists would suggest the most appropriate analgesic (for example, acetaminophen versus opioid) for the patient's particular pain site (bone pain versus muscle pain, etc.), pain quality (shooting, tingling, dull, etc.), and potential drug interactions, among other issues. The result of the combined expertise of all the professions should be a smooth resolution of a problem that, if untreated or inappropriately treated, may result in prolonged patient distress and dissatisfaction, an extended hospital stay, and other issues important in health care in today's climate. The case study of Mr. K. more fully illustrates how IPE

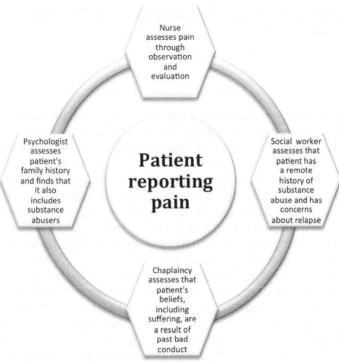

Figure 13.1: Assessing a Symptom

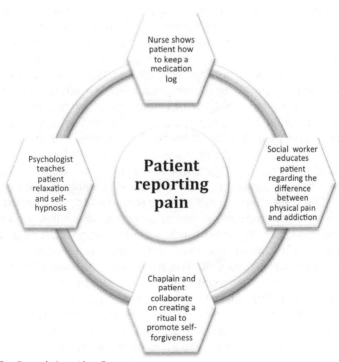

Figure 13.2: Resolving the Issue

and IPP contribute to assessment and intervention in palliative and end-of-life care for patients and their families:

Case Study: Mr. K

Mr. K is a 75-year-old man who lives in a home he built for himself in the Catskill Mountains. He is known by the owner and the staff of the coffee shop in town where he eats lunch most days of the week. He is described as pleasant but does not join in the banter with the other regular customers. He never discusses his military service, but he wears a frayed military jacket. The staff began to notice that he was not finishing his meals and his appearance began to change. His clothing was also noticeably looser and dirty. Sandra, his regular waitress, asks Mr. K if he is feeling alright, and he responds gruffly that there is nothing wrong with him. She offers to wrap up what remains of his meal, which he agrees to take home.

One day when Mr. K opens the door to the coffee shop, he is short of breath and dizzy. The hostess brings him a chair and asks when he last saw a doctor. He responds that it was when he checked out of the Army in 1969. He states he wants nothing to do with the government. When he tries to get up, he gets dizzy again. Sandra manages to convince him to let her drive him to the local VA Community Based Outpatient Clinic (CBOC) a few blocks away. There, he is registered, triaged, and sent via ambulance to the nearest VA medical center for further assessment.

Once Mr. K is admitted, it is soon clear that he is quite ill. He is coughing up blood, and his preliminary workup reveals he likely has metastatic lung cancer. He refuses more testing because he is sure he does not want treatment. He tells everyone who comes in his room that he needs to get home. The inpatient team feels he is unsafe to leave the hospital after receiving treatment, except to go to a long-term care facility. After consultation with the palliative care team for presenting issue about understanding of illness, he begins to comprehend that some treatments may relieve his symptoms and that without medical attention, he could feel worse and would never be able to achieve his goal of dying at home. Two members of the palliative care team, the social worker and the nurse practitioner, inform Mr. K that they have experience working with veterans who live in remote areas and are in the care of a home hospice program and the VA's Home Based Primary Care Program (HBPC). He then agrees to be transferred to the nearest VA medical center with a comprehensive cancer program, which is in an urban area.

Once he arrives at the larger medical center, Mr. K again begins to refuse to continue his workup. In the meantime, he develops pneumonia and is moved to the intensive care unit. The palliative care team of this hospital is consulted to help find a surrogate decision maker because Mr. K insists he has no one to fulfill this role. He is seen by the palliative care consultation team, including interprofessional palliative care fellows who are receiving their clinical training with the palliative care team. The social work fellow observes Mr. K's alienation and confusion. She has reviewed Mr. K's chart notes from his prior hospital stay and found the name and telephone number of the coffee shop employee who initially brought Mr. K to the VA. She discusses her findings with her clinical social work supervisor, and she is given guidance about how to make an assessment of a known Vietnam combat veteran with a life-limiting illness.

Mr. K has some lucid moments, and he consents to letting the social work fellow contact the coffee shop personnel. She learns that, in fact, Mr. K's family and the coffee shop owner's family have been acquainted for a few generations, and the coffee shop owner has contact information for Mr. K's adult daughter. Mr. K is delighted when the coffee shop owner visits him and takes him outside to sit on a bench in the courtyard.

A few days later, Mr. K's daughter arrives from California. The social work fellow facilitates a family meeting, which includes Mr. K and his daughter as well as the treatment and palliative care teams. They agree that Mr. K is too frail to get aggressive cancer treatment, and once he completes his course of antibiotics, he can go back to his cabin with a home hospice referral and a referral to HBPC. His coffee shop friends agree to deliver meals daily and run errands for him. The social work fellow's facilitation skills are evaluated by her supervisor, and she is given feedback after the meeting.

Mr. K returns to his cabin that weekend. His daughter is able to stay with him for the first two weeks of this plan. Two days before she is scheduled to leave, Mr. K dies peacefully while napping on his recliner in his living room with its picture window and its view of the yard and bird feeders. Mr. K's daughter later writes to the palliative care team to thank them for giving her and her father the gift of a peaceful death in the place they treasure the most, home.

The case of Mr. K. illustrates the sometimes complicated and nuanced nature of collaboration and separation among clinical team members as well as patients, families, and community members, such as the coffee shop waitress. The role of the interprofessional health care team in facilitating smooth transitions is something that students need to observe and participate in directly—a didactic approach will not sufficiently prepare students to practice in a complex and ever-changing health care arena.

RURAL HEALTH CARE

To better serve rural veterans, the Office of Rural Health was created in 2007 with the goal of increasing access to care and services. In 2014, 3.2 million rural veterans were enrolled in the VA health care system, representing 36 percent of the total enrolled population (U.S. Department of Veterans Affairs, Office of Rural Health, n.d.). Of the 924 VHA facilities nationwide, 404 have more than 60 percent of patients who are rural, with 298 of these facilities reporting that more than nine out of 10 of their patients come from rural areas (MacKenzie, Wallace, & Weeks, 2010; Weeks et al., 2004; Weeks,

Wallace, Wang, Lee, & Kazis, 2006). One strategy for building workforce capacity has been VHA's promotion of IPE and IPP to strengthen the workforce to provide health care to rural Veterans.

The Geriatric Scholars Program (GSP), funded by VHA Offices of Rural Health and Strategic Integration, delivers intensive core training in geriatrics to primary care providers and associated health professions that work in primary care (that is, social work, pharmacy, advanced nursing, physician assistants, and psychology). One component of GSP is the Rural Interdisciplinary Team Training (RITT) program, based at the James J. Peters GRECC, which provides a manualized team-based workshop to increase rural provider and staff capacity to address health issues facing older veterans. A major focus of the workshop is to enhance team-based solutions through more effective communication and role and goal clarity. Since 2011, the program has trained almost 850 individuals at 57 rural VA clinics throughout the United States.

The Team Development Measure (Salem-Schatz, Ordin, & Mittman, 2010) is used as an evaluation tool to assess the performance of the rural CBOC teams, measuring interdisciplinary team cohesion, communication, clarity of team roles, and clarity of team goals and means to achieve them over time. Pre- and postmeasurements have found a significant increase in these domains after the RITT workshop. Additionally, an action plan is put into place by the team members to continue the momentum of the training day. Teams develop a plan related to geriatrics or team dynamics and identify challenges, resources, and strategies available to overcome barriers, benefits of the goal, data collection processes for monitoring activities, and a time frame for completing specific activities by individual team members.

Another example of an Office of Rural Health–funded training and education program is the Rural Health Training Initiative. Based at the James J. Peters GRECC, the Hudson Valley Rural Geriatric Education Collaborative trains social work, psychology, physician assistant, pharmacy, nursing, and audiology students in rural geriatrics. This program prepares students to provide excellent health care to older rural veterans. The core of the program is a teaching and learning community that is interactive and interdisciplinary. With clinical and classroom education in several VA facilities, students learn about best practices for serving the health care needs of older veterans as well as the importance of considering all biopsychosocial issues that may arise for older adults living in rural areas. Learners participate in a variety of clinical experiences, including rotations at VA rural clinics and learning assessment and consultation techniques using various telehealth approaches. In addition, trainees participate either in person or remotely in the GRECC Associated Health weekly seminars and engage in self-paced learning by accessing various articles, resources, and videos on a learning community SharePoint site.

CONCLUSION

Although the VA system is a hospitable environment for IPE and IPP, implementation and sustainment of IPE and IPP are often challenged in the VA for a variety of reasons. Organizational factors enabling IPE and IPP, as well as hindering variables, are displayed in Table 13.1.

Table 13.1: VA System IPE and IPP Implementation Factors

Enabling Factors	Hindering Factors
Organizational commitment	Hiring delays and personnel changes
Funding streams	Dysfunctional teams
Dedicated time	Lack of or inconsistent buy-in from local administration despite national initiative
IPE-ready workforce	Lack of time, collateral responsibilities
Structured learning and curriculum	Confusion regarding goals and roles

Notes: IPE = interprofessional education; IPP = interprofessional practice.

Hindering variables include varying levels of commitment among the system's 160 medical centers and hundreds of community-based outpatient clinics. VA Central Office directives do ensure a relatively high level of consistency, however. The high level of agency commitment to IPE and IPP, as evidenced by funding streams, national program initiatives, and a culture of ongoing professional development in the context of IPE and IPP, have ensured an interdisciplinary workforce that is committed to team-based education and practice.

REFERENCES

Abrahm, J., Callahan, J., Rossetti, K., & Pierre, L. (1996). The impact of a hospice consultation program on the care of veterans with advanced cancer. *Journal of Pain and Symptom Management, 12,* 22–31.

Daratsos, L., & Howe, J. (2007). The development of palliative care programs in the Veterans Administration: Zelda Foster's legacy. *Journal of Social Work in End-of-Life & Palliative Care, 3,* 29–39.

Foster, Z. (1965). How social work can influence hospital management of fatal illness. *Social Work, 10,* 30–35. doi:10.1093/sw/10.4.30

Fulmer, T., Hyer, K., Flaherty, E., Mezey, M., Whitelaw, N., Jacobs, M. O., et al. (2005). Geriatric interdisciplinary team training program: Evaluation results. *Journal of Aging and Health, 17,* 443–470.

Gilman, S. C., Chokshi, D. A., Bowen, J. L., Rugen, K. W., & Cox, M. (2014). Connecting the dots: Interprofessional health education and delivery system redesign at the Veterans Health Administration. *Academic Medicine, 89,* 1113–1116.

James J. Peters VA Bronx Medical Center & Mount Sinai School of Medicine. (n.d.). *Geriatrics, palliative care and interprofessional teamwork curriculum.* Retrieved from http://www.bronx.va.gov/docs/GRECCTrainingModules.pdf

MacKenzie, T A., Wallace, A. E., & Weeks, W. B. (2010). Impact of rural residence on survival of male Veterans Affairs patients after age 65. *Journal of Rural Health, 26,* 318–324.

Office of Academic Affiliations. (n.d.-a). Associated health education program. Retrieved June 12, 2015, from http://www.va.gov/oaa/ahe_default.asp

Office of Academic Affiliations. (n.d.-b). VA Center of Excellence in Primary Care Education (CoEPCE). Retrieved June 24, 2015, from http://www.va.gov/oaa/coepce/index.asp

Salem-Schatz, S., Ordin, D., & Mittman, D. (2010). The Team Development Measure. Vancouver, WA: Peace Health.

Tsukuda, R. (1998). A perspective on healthcare teams and team training. In E. L. Siegler, K. Hyer, T. Fulmer, & M. Mezey (Eds.), *Geriatrics interdisciplinary team training* (pp. 21–37). New York: Springer.

U.S. Department of Veterans Affairs. (n.d.). Geriatric Research Education and Clinical Center. Retrieved June 2, 2015, from http://www.va.gov/grecc/

U.S. Department of Veterans Affairs, Office of Public and Intergovernmental Affairs. (2001, July 11). *VA selects six sites for end-of-life fellowships.* Retrieved from http://www.va.gov/opa/pressrel/pressrelease.cfm?id=295

U.S. Department of Veterans Affairs, Office of Rural Health. (n.d.). *Rural veterans' health care challenges.* Retrieved from http://www.ruralhealth.va.gov/aboutus/ruralvets.asp

Weeks, W. B., Kazis, L. E., Shen, Y., Cong, Z., Ren, X. S., Miller, D., et al. (2004). Differences in health-related quality of life in rural and urban veterans. *American Journal of Public Health, 94,* 1762–1767.

Weeks, W. B., Wallace, A. E., Wang, S., Lee, A. F., & Kazis, L. E. (2006). Rural–urban disparities in health-related quality of life within disease categories of veterans. *Journal of Rural Health, 22,* 204–211.

14

INTERPROFESSIONAL PRACTICE IN PEDIATRIC MEDICINE

Kanako Okuda

Caring for a sick child requires coordination of interactions between the child, the family, and the surrounding systems. In these situations, social workers use their skills to coordinate various services while responding to the child's and family's needs, the organizational mandates, and the expectations of the institution. The service settings in a hospital vary and may include inpatient, outpatient, primary care, and subspecialty services with a wide range of medical acuities and psychosocial concerns. Pediatric medicine serves children from the age of zero to 18 years old with a wide range of acuities and medical treatments, including scheduled medical procedures, medical emergencies, life-threatening illnesses, and catastrophic injuries that are both acute and chronic in nature. The length of the working process with a patient can vary depending on the service setting; some settings assign social workers on an inpatient or outpatient basis, and others allow the social worker to follow the patients throughout the course of their treatment. The role of pediatric medical social workers is unique because of the pediatric medicine and its service delivery structure. In general, pediatric medical social workers provide psychosocial services to children and their families that involve counseling, assessment, education, discharge planning, and advocacy, helping patients to access resources in the hospital and in the community (Stovall, 1993). This chapter will discuss the role of pediatric medical social work as part of interprofessional teams in inpatient settings.

When children need medical treatment, social workers work closely with their parents: the sick children are the patients, and their parents and family members are the clients. In most cases, parents are the primary caregivers for a child, and they are legally and financially responsible for the child's medical care; therefore, supportive parents are essential in this work because the child's treatment experience depends on both the internal and external resources of the parents. In a stressful situation, making medical decisions while managing other responsibilities can be very overwhelming. Social workers help the child, the parents, and the family to cope with medical diagnoses and adjust to treatment while continuing with their lives (Ross, 1993). Children's diagnoses bring the family and the interprofessional team together to achieve this common goal.

HISTORY AND EVOLUTION OF PEDIATRIC MEDICINE

The Children's Medical Department was established at Massachusetts General Hospital in 1910 (Cannon, 1952). Physicians within the department conceded that successful treatment outcomes for children and infants could not be achieved without addressing the support that surrounded them (Talbot, 1912). In 1911, Laura Beaton, a nurse, was assigned to the Children's Medical Department to assist with home care by visiting patients' homes, assessing the children's surrounding environments, and providing parents guidance and support so that they could carry out the care as physicians had directed (Cabot, 1912; Talbot, 1912). In addition, social workers assisted the hospital in minimizing duplications and unnecessary services (Cabot, 1912; Cannon, 1952). Over time, social work services for pediatric medicine have evolved in response to changes in society, in the surrounding systems, and in medical care delivery.

EVOLUTION OF INTERPROFESSIONAL PRACTICE IN PEDIATRIC MEDICINE

Policy changes and hospital administrative restructuring have influenced the role and utilization of social workers in hospitals (Abramson & Mizrahi, 1996). Consequently, hospital service delivery systems and health care policies have also influenced the nature of interprofessional practice. Some social workers are assigned to medical services, and others are members of social work departments and receive patient referrals through these departments at the request of patients or medical professionals. Physicians may identify their patients' psychosocial needs and refer them to social workers; social workers may identify patients during routine assessment, or on the basis of acuity and the known psychosocial risk factors designated by the hospital, social workers may explore possible needs for services. Members of nursing teams also seek social workers' assistance when they find their patients have psychosocial concerns. Social workers also work with other professionals in psychosocial services, such as psychiatrists; psychologists; child life specialists; speech, physical, and occupational therapists; and pastoral services. To coordinate care, social workers assess and identify the needs of children and their families and arrange care between multiple subspecialty medical services. Doing so involves arranging the child's access to care with an insurance company to ensure that the coverage interacts with another interprofessional team in an external organization. Additionally, social workers collaborate with other governmental organizations to advocate for the child and family, acting as a link to possible collaborations to ensure and enhance care for the child and family. Schools, local child protection services, and law enforcement frequently collaborate with hospital interprofessional teams to coordinate children's care.

The culture of the setting influences the way the members of an interprofessional team work together. Hospital settings promote a hierarchy with respect to medicine, and they shape a hierarchy within the team that fosters the structure of the priorities and decision making. The stage of treatment influences the priority of whom social workers collaborate with to utilize their skills in various professions; their skills are utilized to help the children and their families navigate the system at a time when these families are going through a time of great crisis as the child undergoes treatment. Although the organizational structure of health care appears to be hierarchical and rigid, the interprofessional team operates with creativity and flexibility for the benefit of the patients and their families.

Social workers also link the interprofessional team with outside organizations by collaborating with medical professionals in those organizations. When a patient's care transitions from a hospital to another location or facility, social workers become the link between the medical team in the hospital and the interprofessional team in the referred agencies, such as schools, home care companies, rehabilitation facilities, and other community-based organizations. In recent years, with implementation of the Patient Protection and Affordable Care Act, medical social workers ensure the safe transition of care from hospital to home, the coordination of care, and the integration of medical and mental health services (Allen, 2012; Andrews, Darnell, McBride, & Gehlert, 2013). The social worker's role has evolved in response to the way a modern patient experiences health care.

The relationships within an interprofessional team influence the ways in which the members of the team work together and how the children and families experience their treatment. Although the profession generally determines each member's role in caring for a child, the individuals are drawn to each other based on familiarity or natural affinity. Social workers assess this web of relationships and dynamics to establish the most effective paths for achieving the team's goal. When a parent is having a difficult time making decisions about a child's treatment, the social workers help to answer the most essential questions: Who will be the best person in the team to approach the parent? Who is the best person to talk to the parent? Who does this parent confide in about her vulnerability? How can the team create an environment in which the mother feels most supported? In many situations, it is also helpful when social workers use their skills to assess the relationships surrounding the child and family, making sure that the psychosocial needs are being met by those members of the interprofessional team who are most likely to be able to assist the family.

Fostering the support system that predates the child's illness is important because the members of the team have been part of the family's support system and will likely continue to provide the family with support regardless of the treatment outcome. When a child is in treatment for a prolonged period because of extended hospitalization, the hospital staff may not recognize the family's support system that existed before the child's diagnosis. Observing the fact that the family is receiving support from their friends and relatives (in addition to the help provided by members of an interprofessional team) and fostering this support are some of the most crucial roles for a social worker. Before meeting with a client for the first time, social workers can obtain as much information as possible by reviewing the chart and talking to the medical team. On the basis of this information, social workers approach the first meeting with the goal of engaging the clients while also assessing their needs.

The timing of entering into a working relationship with a child and family can vary depending on each situation. When the team receives a new patient, it is desirable for the social worker to meet the child and family as promptly as possible to provide support and to gather first impressions. The social worker can observe how the family is experiencing the introduction to the team and provide both the family and the team with support by filling the gaps in information, thereby ensuring communication between the family and the team. In most situations, families are anxious about the child's diagnosis or condition; at the same time, they are being given important information that is often difficult to absorb. The social worker can observe the communication and assess how the family both experienced the encounter and received the information from the team. Additionally, the social worker can "take the temperature" of the working relationship by observing the way the team interacts with the family. Social workers can also promote fluidity within the interprofessional team and foster mutual support among its members.

Balancing social work advocacy and the needs of the interprofessional team requires experience and is a continuous task for social workers. Hospital restructuring and changes in health care policy and management have forced social workers to be innovative in the ways in which they collaborate with other professionals (Abramson & Mizrahi, 1996). In health care, there has been a gap between social workers' professional identities and institutional expectations, and this gap influences the expectations other professionals have of social workers (Gregorian, 2005; Mizrahi & Berger, 2005; Silverman, 2008). With the patient's best interests in mind, social workers step in to fill service gaps within the boundaries of their responsibilities or to find other resources to fill those gaps. Doing so often involves obtaining information in a timely manner. With knowledge of the patient's treatment and schedule, as well as what is required of the patient and his or her family, social workers can utilize their skills to facilitate relationships within complex interpersonal and intrapersonal systems.

DIRECT PRACTICE EXPERIENCE AND TRAINING FOR INTERPROFESSIONAL PRACTICE IN PEDIATRIC MEDICINE

Pediatric medical inpatient services in a teaching hospital can be an exciting place for a social worker as they offer training opportunities from various professionals outside of the field of social work. Understanding how to work collaboratively in an interprofessional setting requires creativity, flexibility, and continuous exploration to discover ways to use one's skills in this new setting. Although the prior experience necessary to work in a health care setting may vary, in general, pediatric medical social work requires an MSW and a social work license for the state in which one practices.

Social workers receive both mandatory and voluntary training from hospitals and other sources. Training on important topics—such as patient confidentiality, the Health

Insurance Portability and Accountability Act, hand hygiene, fire safety, and patient safety—may be required to join the staff. Social workers and other professionals receive domestic violence assessment training and learn how to identify and report child maltreatment as a mandated reporter. In a hospital setting, these trainings are based on the premise of interprofessional collaboration: that one will know what is required of both oneself and of the other participants. In case of an emergency or crisis, the members are expected to assist one another. In a teaching hospital, students from various disciplines become part of these interprofessional teams, and training opportunities in medical and behavioral health are common. Additionally, some research opportunities are available for social workers to participate in, either as subjects or as part of the team conducting the research.

Working in health care is challenging as social workers try to meet the demands of their own profession and satisfy institutional needs as well (Gregorian, 2005). The hierarchical culture of health care may be confusing because many social workers are trained to think that social work's professional values are paramount to one's practice when working in a high-stress, fast-paced, and demanding environment. There are so many variables and contingencies that contribute to the demands placed on the social worker. A patient's condition may change rapidly and require a social worker's attention. At the same time, multiple patients are ready to be discharged, and the hospital needs their beds for patients waiting in the emergency room. Or the physician and team might be ready to discharge a child, but the parents are not present. This can cause a delay that can change aspects of the discharge plan and arrangements, such as transportation and home care visits for postdischarge care. Perhaps a social worker is ready to discharge a newborn baby and a mother, but there is no car seat for the baby. In still another scenario, a social worker might try to obtain authorization for a patient's discharge, but the insurance company needs additional information from a physician before authorization can be given. In a collaborative interprofessional setting, finding one's own working style requires creativity, flexibility, and adaptability.

Other "on-the-job" training comes only with experience. In a collaborative setting, asking for help creates room for the interprofessional team to work effectively. Some of the roles in an interprofessional setting can overlap, and it is important to prioritize one's own tasks to make sure that the patient's needs are met. Social workers may also need to assess the availability of resources to coordinate services. For example, if a family is scheduled to have a meeting with a physician about their child's treatment, and the team feels that the parents need additional emotional support, the social worker may work with other psychosocial professionals (such as a psychologist) if they are available. In this way, the social worker can get to know the family in an interprofessional setting, something that requires careful consideration of key participants in the process. When approaching a family, it is important to know which key individuals will be working closely with the patient. Social workers meet with clients at various times during the treatment process. Knowing the work style and personality of the treating physician will make clear the characteristics, culture, and expectations of the team as a whole. When social work service is provided in a host setting, many clients are not expecting to meet with a social worker or receive these services. In fact, they may be "mandatory clients," to whom social workers are assigned by the institution regardless of their individual needs or specific requests. Clients' ways of seeking help and the meaning behind them can vary. As in any engagement process, the social worker must first assess the client's response to meeting a social worker and the information about the services offered to them.

Last, supervision is another training method for social workers in an interprofessional setting. In general, for hospital social workers, the frequency and structure of supervision vary. Hospital social workers meet with their supervisor on an as-needed basis (which may change depending on circumstances). Peer consultations among line social workers are common, and the participants often become each other's sounding board.

INTERPROFESSIONAL SOCIAL WORK PRACTICE IN A PEDIATRIC MEDICAL SETTING

Common Members of the Team in Pediatric Medicine

An interprofessional team may consist of one or more members from each profession, and although some of them may be involved throughout a patient's treatment, others may change based on schedules and rotations. There are varying levels of involvement within the team, and participation changes based on patients' medical and psychosocial needs. Physicians, registered nurses, and pediatric nurse practitioners are the core members, but social workers are also involved in most of the patients' care. Additional members such as pharmacists, psychiatrists, psychologists, child life specialists, teachers, and pastors may also join the team.

Overview of the Roles of Team Members

The responsibilities of team members in an interprofessional setting may appear to be hierarchical, yet they can be flexible when meeting a patient's needs. The medical team consists of physicians and nurses. The team of physicians—including the attending physician—makes the overall decisions concerning the patient's care, including not only the medical but also the psychosocial services (based on recommendations from other members of the interprofessional team). Pediatric certified nurse practitioners (CPNPs) play an important role in facilitating medical care. CPNPs provide medical assessments, assist physicians, arrange for medical procedures, write prescriptions, and work together with floor nurses to coordinate their patients' care. Registered nurses (RNs) take care of patients at the bedside level in shifts. RNs administer medications and are some of the professionals who spend the most time with the patients and their families. To provide psychosocial care, social workers consult with patients and their families concerning matters such as discharge planning and coordination of care with the medical team and external organizations. Child life specialists prepare children for their medical procedures. Pastoral services are also available to patients. During this time, some patients and their families may form close bonds with their pastors. Some pediatric hospitals also have a public school on the premises for children who are hospitalized for an extended period. There, teachers play a very important role in the children's care by ensuring children continue their education, providing normalcy, and helping children attain a sense of achievement. During the course of treatment, various professionals involved in a patient's care participate in the interprofessional work to various degrees. Although the roles of the members are determined by their credentials and training, the nature of each relationship often determines their level of involvement in the patient's care.

Role of the Individual and Family

When a child is in the hospital, the whole family needs to adjust their lives to care for him or her. In these settings, the sick children are the patients, and the parents, care-takers, and other children in the family are the clients. Although the definition of the family unit varies by culture and life circumstances, in general, parents take the lead in making decisions—except in those cases where children are able to assent to their own medical decisions. The members of the interprofessional team work very closely with the parents, informing them about treatment options, providing education and support, and helping the child cope with treatment. Coordinating care and services for the siblings is also essential in supporting the family as a whole, and extended family members and friends often step in to help care for them.

Required Competencies in Knowledge, Attitudes, and Skills

Social workers practicing in this setting require the ability to execute unique and complex tasks, such as those articulated in Table 14.1. Both understanding the child and the family from a biopsychosocial perspective and perceiving how the medical condition and its treatment influence the child and the family's lives are necessary skills.

Logistics: Structure of Team Meetings, Their Frequency, and Methods of Communication

Coordinating patient care requires close communication among the interprofessional team members. Members of a team may meet during each shift for an update on the child's condition and schedule weekly patient rounds to provide updates on patient care and discuss treatment options. Pagers and cell phones are often used by team members to find each other throughout the day, and e-mail is used to disseminate written information among the various team members.

CHALLENGES AND STRATEGIES FOR INTERPROFESSIONAL PRACTICE IN A PEDIATRIC MEDICINE SETTING

Ethical Challenges

Ethical challenges often emerge concerning a very important question: What is best for the child? Medical treatment decisions for adolescent patients involve achieving

Table 14.1: Pediatric Interprofessional Competencies

Knowledge	Attitudes	Skills
Obtain medical information about the patient's diagnosis, the treatment and duration, and the possible side effects.	Follow the lead of the attending physician and the medical team.	• Review charts and attend rounds and team discussions. • Use empathy to anticipate how the patient and family will accept the information.
Evaluate the resources and systems that surround the patients and their families.	Help the family cope with the change and identify the resources to augment the gap.	• Anticipate the client's needs. Use supportive communication and respect the client's wants and needs. • Have basic knowledge of benefits and entitlements.
Understand the family history, relationships, and culture.	Observe the dynamics, paying attention to cultural cues and their meaning.	• Use one's clinical assessment and intervention skills to help the patient and family. • Assess communication patterns and communication outcomes and assist the team in communicating with the patient and family. • Fill in the gaps in communication with the involved parties.
Understand the dynamics within the institution and department.	Be aware of one's relationship with the institution and the department.	• Navigate roles and relationships within the institution. • Understand how the system works: the key players and the decision-making system and structure.

a balance between the wishes of the child and those of the parents. The difficulty of achieving such a balance can be seen in the following case study.

Case Study: Amal

Amal is a 16-year-old girl who was recently diagnosed with bone marrow disease and requires a bone marrow transplant. The medical team informed Amal's parent that her prognosis was uncertain: having a bone marrow transplant could either cure Amal or end her life. Amal's only parent, her mother, thought it was best for Amal to have the transplant; however, Amal pleaded with her mother to take her home. On the basis of Amal's medical condition and the risks of treatment, Amal's social worker understood that she was unlikely to ever go home. Amal pleaded with her social worker, crying, "I want to go home. Will you help me go home?" The social worker responded, "I understand and will do what I can to help you get better. You can go home as soon as you get better."

When an adolescent patient assents to treatment, it means involving the patient in the treatment decision. Therefore, the medical team must determine the age-appropriate level of medical information for that patient while protecting his or her emotional well-being; the physicians must also determine the adolescent patient's capacity to make these decisions (Kuther, 2003). Social workers participate in the assessment of adolescent patients' ability to make such decisions for themselves. Even if the medical team deems the adolescent capable of making medical treatment decisions, the team often discusses the matter with the parents. In some situations when the patient is unlikely to survive the treatment and wishes to go home, parents choose to stay in the hospital because they are overwhelmed and uncertain about their ability to care for the child at home. The interprofessional team supports the decisions of the parents who will be left behind, allowing them to believe that they did everything they could despite the eventual outcome.

INSTITUTIONAL CHALLENGES

Patient care needs to meet both the standards of the institution and the expectations of the child and the family. When the patient's wishes and the institution's policy are not congruent, the social worker and the interprofessional team face a challenge concerning how to mediate these differences. Social workers must work within the policies and resources that are available within that particular institution. The following case study is an example of a mismatch between institutional resources and client expectations.

Case Study: Jimmy

Jimmy, a seven-year-old boy with sickle cell disease, is admitted for a crisis. Jimmy has three siblings at home, and his parents cannot afford to miss work. Jimmy stays in a hospital room alone for most of the day. The social worker coordinates volunteers to tend to Jimmy while he is in the hospital. However, the hospital does not have a system in place for a staff person to stay with the patient throughout the day. When Jimmy is alone in his room, he activates various alarms in the room out of boredom. When he is well enough to go home, the team speaks to Jimmy's father, and the physician explains that Jimmy needs to stay home for a couple of days until he is well enough to return to school. The parents respond by saying that they can take Jimmy home only when he is well enough to go to school.

Institutions attempt to meet the needs of a diverse patient population. However, there continues to be an assumption of reasonable parental obligation. Some parents have multiple stressors and no resources to respond to some of the demands that relate to the child's medical care. Under the social worker's leadership, the interprofessional team addresses gaps in services, accesses available resources, and inquires about the institution's policies so that together the team can help the patient and the family to find a solution.

PROFESSIONAL CHALLENGES

Bearing witness to a child's battle with a disease and a family's ability to cope is a privilege. The process is intimate and can result in a close bond between the family and the members of the interprofessional team. Sometimes the team members become more involved with the child than do the patient's family and friends. In certain situations, a team member's relationship with patients or their families can create dynamics that can either pose a challenge to or enhance the relationship, as in the following case study.

Case Study: Samantha

Samantha is a 17-year-old young woman who has battled a blood disorder for many years. She is the oldest of four siblings, and she has been their caretaker since her father died suddenly four years ago. With limited skills and employment opportunities to support her own family, Samantha's mother had to adjust her life for single motherhood. Her extended family lives abroad, so the family's external support was limited. Samantha's mother is unable to be present for her daughter for treatment, and medical updates and consent are often given over the phone. As a medical student, Jennifer is assigned to Samantha's primary team, working tirelessly to help Samantha with her medical care and helping her cope with treatment. Jennifer visits Samantha at her bedside, sometimes even when she is not on shift. Jennifer vents to the social worker that Samantha's mother is neglecting her daughter. During patient rounds, Jennifer has difficulty accepting other team members' views of Samantha's psychosocial concerns and alienates Samantha's mother and other members of the interprofessional team.

Working in a fast-paced teaching hospital where tragedies and trauma are commonplace can provide the opportunity to reflect on intrapersonal dynamics. In the scenario above, the medical student experienced a strong reaction to what she saw during the course of treating the patient. Consequently, her reaction influenced the patient's care and the relationships within the team. In some situations, social workers need to view their colleagues as "clients" to facilitate professional and interpersonal dynamics, analyzing the relationships between the patient, family, and team member (Gregorian, 2005). The above scenario demonstrates triangulation, in which the patient's mother is excluded from the relationship. Dysfunctional relationships such as these are often temporary, and it is important for the social worker to understand the possible strengths of the relationship (Shapiro, 2001). Such situations can be resolved if the social worker acknowledges what is positive in the relationship and addresses any problems; doing so creates an environment in which the interprofessional team, the child, and the family can meet and help the team member to gain insight into his or her participation in the dynamic, thereby facilitating change in the way that member relates to the patient and family.

REFERENCES

Abramson, J. S., & Mizrahi, T. (1996). When social workers and physicians collaborate: Positive and negative interdisciplinary experiences. *Social Work, 41,* 270–281.

Allen, H. (2012). Is there a social worker in the house? Health care reform and the future of medical social work [Viewpoint]. *Health & Social Work, 37,* 183–186.

Andrews, C. M., Darnell, J. S., McBride, T. D., & Gehlert, S. (2013). Social work and implementation of the Affordable Care Act [Guest Editorial]. *Health & Social Work, 38,* 67–71.

Cabot, R. C. (1912). General statement. In *Sixth annual report of the Social Service Department of the Massachusetts General Hospital: January 1, 1911, to January 1, 1912* (pp. 7–12). Boston: Barta Press.

Cannon, I. M. (1952). *On the social frontier of medicine: Pioneering in medical social service.* Cambridge, MA: Harvard University Press.

Gregorian, C. (2005). A career in hospital social work: Do you have what it takes? *Social Work in Health Care, 40*(3), 1–14.

Kuther, T. J. (2003). Medical decision-making and minors: Issues of consent and assent. *Adolescence, 38,* 343–358.

Mizrahi, T., & Berger, C. S. (2005). A longitudinal look at social work leadership in hospitals: The impact of a changing healthcare system. *Health & Social Work, 30,* 155–165.

Ross, J. W. (1993). Understanding the family experience with childhood cancer. In N. M. Richardson & M. M. Lauria (Eds.), *Oncology social work: A clinician's guide* (pp. 199–236). Atlanta: American Cancer Society.

Shapiro, J. (2001). Using triangulation concepts to understand the doctor–patient–family relationship. *Families, Systems & Health, 19,* 203–210.

Silverman, E. (2008). From ideological to competency-based: The rebranding and maintaining of medical social work's identity [Commentary]. *Social Work, 53,* 89–91.

Stovall, A. (1993). Social work services for the child and family. In N. M. Richardson & M. M. Lauria (Eds.), *Oncology social work: A clinician's guide* (pp. 237–255). Atlanta: American Cancer Society.

Talbot, F. B. (1912). Report of the social work in children's clinic. In *Sixth annual report of the Social Service Department of the Massachusetts General Hospital: January 1, 1911, to January 1, 1912* (pp. 13–17). Boston: Barta Press.

15

INTERPROFESSIONAL PRACTICE IN GERIATRIC MEDICINE

Thomas V. Caprio

Case Study: Martha

Martha is a 92-year-old woman who lives alone and has multiple chronic health problems, including cardiac disease, lung disease, diabetes, and arthritis. After sustaining a fall at home, paramedics arrive and find her with right leg pain and unable to walk. She is taken by ambulance to the hospital and diagnosed with a hip fracture. She undergoes surgery and is discharged to a nursing home for rehabilitation. Martha's family is concerned about her living alone and reports a history of progressive memory problems and several falls at home prior to the hospitalization. Her daughter expresses concern that Martha wears dirty clothes, no longer cooks for herself, and depends on the daughter to buy groceries. A social worker interviews Martha and finds that she has been a widow for 14 years. Although she has been active in her faith community all her life, she has stopped leaving the house in recent months. The social worker notes that Martha's daughter is under increased stress as a caregiver. The geriatrics team at the rehabilitation center establish that Martha is afraid of falling again, feels depressed, has poor short-term memory, becomes short of breath just walking in the hallway, and has new onset of urinary incontinence. The pharmacist reviews her medications and finds that there are at least 12 prescription bottles from home. The pharmacist is unable to determine how Martha was managing these medications. The interdisciplinary team of the physician, nurse, social worker, physical therapist, and pharmacist share their findings and recommendations with each other and propose a plan to help Martha regain independence with a goal to return home. The planning goals include an increase in her mobility and endurance

---

so that she can get to the bathroom when needed. They also hope to reduce duplicative medications and use a pillbox to help manage the medications, as well as treat her depression. Finally, they identify caregiver resources in the community to support the family.

Older adults are often faced with complex medical and psychosocial problems that can be best assessed through the combined efforts of an interdisciplinary team of health care professionals. Each discipline brings unique training and perspective in evaluating the needs and formulating a plan of care that supports older patients and their family caregivers. With normal aging comes increased vulnerability for disease, functional losses (for example, physical, cognitive, and social–emotional), and progressing frailty. An overarching precept in geriatric medicine is that early identification of health and psychosocial challenges in older adults allows for interventions that can maintain the greatest level of independence and quality of life in older age.

COLLABORATIVE CARE MODELS

Collaborative care models focusing on the health and wellness of older adults have gained momentum in recent years given the rapid demographic trends of the aging population, rising health care costs, and concerns regarding the quality of health care. This is especially true with the growing gaps in meeting older patient needs caused by fragmentation of care. The new reality is that patients often see multiple health care providers with little continuity, are introduced to unfamiliar medications and techno-logical interventions, have medical histories stored and transmitted across different electronic or paper-based health records, and receive care across competing hospital systems. All of these factors can negatively affect the patient care experience and be disruptive to overall health and well-being. As a downstream consequence, the educa-tion of health professions across the continuum of clinical settings has emerged in the national dialogue (Institute of Medicine, 2003). Specifically within nursing, medicine, and pharmacy, national work groups have begun to establish recommendations for how to teach students to work together in collaborative teams. The World Health Organiza-tion's definition of interprofessional education as occurring "when students from two or more professions learn about, from and with each other to enable effective collabora-tion and improve health outcomes" (World Health Organization, 2010, p. 10) provides an ideal framework for the practice of geriatric medicine. Additionally, the national experts have proposed core educational competencies for health care interprofessional collaborative practice (Interprofessional Education Collaborative [IPEC] Expert Panel, 2011), which also intersect in the care of older adults.

Interprofessional education (IPE) and interprofessional practice (IPP) can effectively take place through the model of comprehensive geriatric assessment (CGA). CGA has been defined as a multidimensional diagnostic process designed to quantify an older adult's medical, psychosocial, and functional capabilities and problems, with the intention of arriving at a comprehensive plan for therapy and follow-up (Rubenstein, 1987, 1995). Health care providers with specialized training in geriatrics are uniquely positioned to provide this comprehensive clinical evaluative approach in addressing the complex needs of older adult patients. Unfortunately, as the Institute of Medicine has indicated, there are critical shortages in qualified health professionals to care for this aging, frail population (Institute of Medicine, 2008). This necessitates establishing robust team-based models to access expertise of geriatrics from multiple disciplines and to establish teaching programs to train future team members.

UNIQUE NEEDS OF OLDER ADULTS

Older adults are faced with a number of unique challenges with the intersection of the normal aging process and disease. Many older patients have multiple chronic medical conditions that often interact with and affect each other, creating complexity in both diagnosis and management. Furthermore, the compounding of multiple conditions can have a profound impact on functional ability. For example, an older patient may have difficulty breathing from chronic lung disease and chronic heart disease, but he or she also has arthritis affecting the joints. The convergence of these conditions profoundly affects the individual's mobility and endurance in daily activities. Another important factor to consider for older patients is the interactions, side effects, and indications for medications to treat disease. The concept of "polypharmacy" is common in geriatrics and refers to the growing list of multiple medications prescribed to patients and the complexity of managing these medications, some of which may be beneficial and others that could potentially do harm to patients in terms of side effects and adverse health outcomes. The nuances of medication management require a proactive team approach of physicians, nurses, and pharmacists working together to ensure a thoughtful approach to prescribing as well as providing adequate patient education, which encourages adherence to medication regimens and the recognition of potential emerging side effects.

There are also common geriatric syndromes associated with aging and disease, including vision impairment, hearing loss, incontinence, issues with falls and mobility, depression, and memory disorders. These conditions are an aggregate of health conditions that also affect daily functioning and quality of life. An interdisciplinary approach in assessing these geriatric syndromes is vital to addressing the multiple etiologies and developing effective treatment options individualized for a particular patient and family.

INTERPROFESSIONAL TEAMS

The ideal interprofessional team in geriatrics likely consists of physicians, nurses, psychologists, rehabilitation and allied health professionals, pharmacists, and social workers. This multidimensional perspective by the health professions makes for an ideal model for interprofessional practice in health care and can be applied across various clinical settings, such as clinics, hospitals, nursing homes, and home care. Currently, formal teaching curriculum or evaluative processes that extend across the disciplines in geriatric teams are limited. From a research perspective, there is also a knowledge gap regarding the clinical (patient-centered) outcomes that result from geriatric assessment teams.

HISTORICAL BACKGROUND

There have been mixed results in studies measuring clinical outcomes and cost-effectiveness for comprehensive geriatric assessment programs. Some of the reasons for these inconsistencies are due to the heterogeneity in the types of assessments conducted as well as in the patient populations evaluated. This heterogeneity also makes it difficult to make comparisons between individual assessment programs. However, controlled trials of comprehensive geriatric assessment have provided evidence that these programs can decrease the use of institutional services (for example, nursing homes), improve physical and mental functioning, and increase survival, particularly when the comprehensive assessment team continues to take primary responsibility for management and accomplishment of the goals determined through the evaluation (Rockwood et al., 2000; Stuck, Siu, Wieland, Adams, & Rubenstein, 1993; Stuck, Wieland, Rubenstein, Ziu, & Adams, 1995). Randomized clinical trials even suggest that a single comprehensive geriatric outpatient consultation, in combination with efforts to improve adherence to recommendations, could have effects on preventing functional decline and maintaining quality of life (Reuben, Burns, Nichols, Martindale-Adams, & Graney, 2000; Reuben, Frank, Hirsch, McGuigan, & Maly, 1999).

The Veterans Administration had been on the forefront of comprehensive assessment with the development of the Geriatric Evaluation and Management (GEM) model for inpatient and outpatient care. One controlled trial demonstrated reductions in functional decline for inpatient GEM units and improvement in mental health for outpatient GEM clinics, without significant effects on survival or costs (Cohen et al., 2002; Reuben et al., 2000). Boult, Boult, Morishita, Smith, and Kane (1998) were among the first to publish an outline regarding the program inputs and activities in adapting the GEM model to an outpatient setting. They also established survey methods to assess patient and primary care physician satisfaction with consultative geriatric assessment.

CGA has also been adapted within international settings, integrating itself in primary care practice (Mann, Koller, Mann, van der Cammen, & Steurer, 2004) or through mobile geriatric assessment teams (Rockwood et al., 2000). In both cases, studies have found a high prevalence of geriatric-associated health syndromes that could be targeted in management plans from the consultation. Reuben et al. (1999) advocated that pre-screening of participants in a clinic was necessary to identify those with these common geriatric syndromes that were most likely to benefit from CGA. Patients selected for evaluation had one or more areas of impairment, and these geriatric syndromes had evidence to support that the CGA intervention was linked to measurable improvement.

The current research literature appears to show that a team-centered approach in conducting a CGA is associated with at least short-term positive medical and social outcomes for patients and may be an ideal interprofessional setting for collaborative teaching and learning. A significant issue with the existing CGA literature that needs to be considered is that the majority of the groundwork research dates back over 20 years ago. This at least may suggest that characteristics of the current patient populations served by CGA (including overall health status and medical comorbidity) and the health care reimbursement structure (costs and payments) may be fundamentally different if examined today.

INTERPROFESSIONAL EDUCATION

The IPE model in geriatrics embraces the Institute of Medicine core competencies to cooperate, collaborate, communicate, and integrate care in interdisciplinary teams to ensure that care is continuous and reliable (Institute of Medicine, 2003). An education task force through the American Association of Colleges of Pharmacy took this a step further with specific recommendations for the implementation of IPE in health care settings (Buring et al., 2009). IPE appears to support positive research outcomes on patient satisfaction, teamwork, error rates, and mental health competencies (Zwarenstein et al., 2000), all of which are consistent with existing IOM goals.

Clark (2006) argued for a consistent theoretical framework to inform IPE in gerontology and made a direct challenge to the perceived "status quo," which is described largely as "descriptive, anecdotal, and atheoretical" in the current educational and clinical settings. This proposed framework of IPE includes emphasis on both social learning (collaboration) and experiential (clinical) learning. The social learning approach in IPE challenges the disciplinary biases by members of the interprofessional team. These biases are tied into the theory of social construction of knowledge in the professions in which communities of learners gradually evolve to share a common worldview (Bruffee, 1986). IPE, therefore, challenges this socialization as different disciplines learn to work together and appreciate each other's different perspective. For example, the training for doctors has traditionally occurred in relative isolation and provides limited exposure to interdisciplinary perspectives. Medical students learn from senior physicians and have little purposeful interaction with nurses, pharmacists, or social workers during their training. An interprofessional environment in which medical students learn to work with and learn from other disciplines challenges the status quo and allows for enrichment in health care perspectives when evaluating complex patients. Clark (2006) furthered his discussion with a focus on the "reflective practitioner" as a critical component in the interprofessional education, building on Schön's (1987) work describing the resolution of conflicting viewpoints by the learner as part of the professional development process. This underscores the need for reflection within interprofessional practice as part of the learning process.

Oandasan and Reeves (2005a) described the fundamental vocabulary shift internationally from "interdisciplinary" to "interprofessional" within the context of describing IPE in an effort to acknowledge the contributions of many health professionals. The factors for the implementation of IPE (Oandsan & Reeves, 2005b) have been described as creating a nonthreatening learning environment, emphasizing the creation of reflective practitioners, generating experiential learning opportunities, using a variety of teaching methods and settings, and developing core competencies in the IPE process. However, it is also argued that there should be a consideration of the social, political, and administrative structures for IPE implementation (Oandasan & Reeves, 2005b). These important contextual factors necessitate that outcome measurement be a part of any IPE model to demonstrate feasibility, cost, and impact. With ongoing changes in Medicare reimbursement and a growing emphasis in providing health care services in community-based and home care settings, this is particularly important in geriatric medicine.

Remington, Foulk, and Williams (2006) noted that curricular interventions in IPE implementation have included didactic and clinical teaching methods in addition to outcome evaluations consisting of pre- and posttest surveys of learners. Outcomes showed at least short-term learner and clinical (patient-oriented) improvements in outcome measures. Remington et al. (2006) argued that further research is needed that includes behaviorally oriented outcomes of trainees, the employment of control groups in evaluative designs, and the necessary validation of prior research studies. These are all gaps that currently exist with interprofessional geriatric training.

These emerging themes of IPE and IPP appear to have "face validity" with the overarching goals set forth in health care education from a variety of disciplines in the care of older adults. For an effective IPE curriculum and evaluation strategy to be implemented for the geriatric assessment model, the literature suggests that the implementation would need to use standardized patient screening tools and learner evaluations. Particularly in areas of depression screening and cognitive assessment (that is, screening for the presence of dementia), there is a wealth of standard clinical instruments that student practitioners can be trained in and immediately implement as part of the interprofessional team. The IPE efforts also need to consider specific contextual factors, such as social, political, and administrative interactions at academic medical centers that can either support or impede the model development. Patient-oriented clinical outcome measures may require longer-term evaluations to demonstrate overall effectiveness. IPE evaluation methods continue to have a need to move beyond satisfaction surveys and pre- and post-knowledge assessments, which currently exist in the literature, and instead expand the assessment framework to include behaviorally oriented outcomes for learners engaged in the care of older adults. The use of knowledge, satisfaction, and behavioral outcomes may give us the most comprehensive learner evaluation of IPE to date.

The most challenging task with IPE in geriatric medicine is determining how to formalize the learning and clinical processes. It is insufficient, based on this existing literature, to take a perspective of simply immersing trainees from multiple disciplines into one clinical setting caring for older adults and hoping that interprofessional learning occurs without some type of curricular framework and evaluation strategy.

GERIATRIC CORE COMPETENCIES

Fundamental to IPE in geriatric medicine is defining core competencies for trainees in the care of older adults. The American College of Graduate Medical Education has defined core competency areas for geriatric medicine fellowships, internal medicine, and family residents (Williams et al., 2010) and provides "milestones" for developing the requisite skill set in assessing and treating older adult patients. There are four core domain areas relevant to the CGA model:

1. Systems-Based Care for Elder Patients (care settings, transitions, elder abuse, hazardous driving, advocacy, community resources)
2. Complex Illnesses and Frailty in Older Adults (multimorbidity, prioritization of care, deviations from standards, family/caregiver needs)
3. Cognitive, Affective, and Behavioral Health (cognition assessment, depression, dementia)
4. Medication Management

These domains are defined specifically for medical providers but have clear intersections with the activities of other professions, such as social work, pharmacy, nursing, and physical therapy. This again underscores that the learning process cannot occur in isolation and that the team-based interdisciplinary model of geriatrics enhances the ability to fully assess the complex care needs of older patients.

One theoretical approach to fully embracing the core competencies of geriatric medicine as part of the Interprofessional Core Competences for Collaborative Practice (IPEC Expert Panel, 2011) is represented in Figure 15.1. In this approach, the core areas

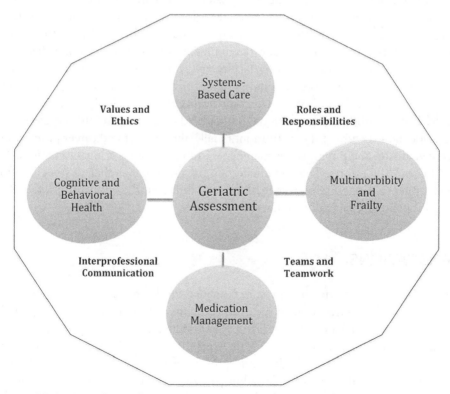

Figure 15.1: Interface of Geriatric Medicine and Interprofessional Core Competencies

are overlaid. This highlights the areas of importance for trainees in geriatric medicine when assessing the care needs of older adults within the context of the competency domains vital to interprofessional collaboration by learners. These core competencies can be used as the target endpoints of learning activities, particularly for physicians-in-training interacting with other health care disciplines. This can serve as the conceptual framework for curriculum development and can inform subsequent steps for teaching and evaluation activities within the geriatric assessment model.

TRANSFORMING THE FACULTY

The success of IPE hinges on committed, appropriate faculty in the respective disciplines who are knowledgeable about the best practices of teaching and learning within interprofessional settings of care for older adults. Most faculty at professional schools have likely been trained within the traditional models of education, which completely separated learners (such as nursing and medical students) during training. There may be faculty within professional schools who recognize the value of IPP. Many of them may have even successfully worked in collaborative clinical practice environments, such as the nursing home or rehabilitation center. However, these same faculty members may have never received specific training in IPE or its teaching methods, core competencies, or evaluation strategies. This argues for a system-level change within medical, nursing, and other health professional schools to create faculty development pathways in IPE. Core competency areas for IPE are important foundations that can be used at academic medical centers as part of their faculty development process. The challenges that remain are the institutional commitment for faculty time, effort, and financial resources to be devoted to building interprofessional programs. The development (and funding) of IPE "centers of excellence" at academic medical centers would allow for cross-linking faculty from the different professional schools and create a sense of legitimacy within the academic structure of the institution. Finally, the support and career promotion of recent graduates and junior faculty members within professions is paramount to sustaining IPE and IPP efforts. These graduates are the tangible beneficiaries of IPE efforts and represent a new generation of teachers and clinicians who "grew up" professionally within the transformed educational system.

IMPLICATIONS

Interprofessional education and practice remains a fundamental component of modern health care and is congruent with the goals and aims of geriatric medicine to provide a comprehensive team-based approach to patient evaluations to achieve the best clinical outcomes. There is a need to effectively integrate the tenants of comprehensive geriatric assessment with the core methods of interprofessional teaching to meet intended goals of affecting the health care of older adult patients. As a consequence of this process, it is also intended that trainees will develop positive attitudes toward the care of older adults and increase their knowledge related to geriatric medicine. This may actually increase their confidence as teachers of geriatric concepts themselves and ultimately improve the quality of care for all older adults in the future.

REFERENCES

Boult, C., Boult, L., Morishita, L., Smith, S. L., & Kane, R. L. (1998). Outpatient geriatric evaluation and management. *Journal of the American Geriatrics Society, 46,* 296–302.

Bruffee, K. A. (1986). Social construction, language, and the authority of knowledge: A bibliographical essay. *College English, 48,* 773–790.

Buring, S. M., Bhushan, A., Broeseker, A., Conway, S., Duncan-Hewitt, W., Hansen, L., & Westberg, S. (2009). Interprofessional education: Definitions, student competencies, and guidelines for implementation. *American Journal of Pharmaceutical Education, 73*(4), 59.

Clark, P. G. (2006). What would a theory of interprofessional education look like? Some suggestions for developing a theoretical framework for teamwork training. *Journal of Interprofessional Care, 20,* 577–589.

Cohen, H. J., Feussner, J. R., Weinberger, M., Carnes, M., Hamdy, R. C., Hsieh, F., et al. (2002). A controlled trial of inpatient and outpatient geriatric evaluation and management. *New England Journal of Medicine, 346,* 905–912.

Institute of Medicine. (2003). *Health professions education: A bridge to quality.* Washington, DC: National Academies Press.

Institute of Medicine. (2008). *Retooling for an aging America: Building the health care workforce.* Washington, DC: National Academies Press.

Interprofessional Education Collaborative Expert Panel. (2011). *Core competencies for interprofessional collaborative practice: Report of an expert panel.* Washington, DC: Interprofessional Education Collaborative.

Mann, E., Koller, M., Mann, C., van der Cammen, T., & Steurer, J. (2004). Comprehensive geriatric assessment in general practice: Results from a pilot study in Vorarlberg, Austria. *Biomed Central Geriatrics, 4*(4). Retrieved from http://www.biomedcentral.com/1471-2318/4/4

Oandasan, I., & Reeves, S. C. (2005a). Key elements for interprofessional education. Part 1: The learner, the educator and the learning context. *Journal of Interprofessional Care, 19*(Suppl. 1), 21–38.

Oandasan, I., & Reeves, S. (2005b). Key elements of interprofessional education. Part 2: Factors, processes and outcomes. *Journal of Interprofessional Care, 19*(Suppl. 1), 39–48.

Remington, T. L., Foulk, M. A., & Williams, B. C. (2006). Evaluation of evidence for interprofessional education. *American Journal of Pharmaceutical Education, 70*(3), 1–7.

Reuben, D. B., Burns, R., Nichols, L. O., Martindale-Adams, J., & Graney, M. J. (2000). Interdisciplinary geriatric primary care evaluation and management: Two-year outcomes. *Journal of the American Geriatrics Society, 48,* 8–13.

Reuben, D. B., Frank, J. C., Hirsch, S. H., McGuigan, K. A., & Maly, R. C. (1999). A randomized clinical trial of outpatient comprehensive geriatric assessment coupled with an intervention to increase adherence to recommendations. *Journal of the American Geriatrics Society, 47,* 269–276.

Rockwood, K., Stadnyk, K., Carver, D., MacPherson, K.M., Beanlands, H.E., Powell, C., et al. (2000). A clinimetric evaluation of specialized geriatric care for rural dwelling, frail older people. *Journal of the American Geriatrics Society, 48,* 1080–1085.

Rubenstein, L. Z. (1987). Geriatric assessment: An overview of its impacts. *Clinics in Geriatric Medicine, 3,* 1–15.

Rubenstein, L. Z. (1995). An overview of comprehensive geriatric assessment: Rationale, history, program models, basic components. In L. Z. Rubenstein, D. Wieland, & R. Bernabei (Eds.), *Geriatric assessment technology: The state of the art* (pp. 1–10). Milan: Editrice Kurtis.

Schön, D. A. (1987). *Educating the reflective practitioner.* San Francisco: Jossey-Bass.

Stuck, A. E., Siu, A. L., Wieland, G. D., Adams, J., & Rubenstein, L. Z. (1993). Comprehensive geriatric assessment: A meta-analysis of controlled trials. *Lancet, 342,* 1032–1036.

Stuck, A. E., Wieland, D., Rubenstein, L. Z., Siu, A. L., & Adams, J. (1995). Comprehensive geriatric assessment: Meta-analysis of main effects and elements enhancing effectiveness. In L. Z. Rubenstein, D. Wieland, & R. Bernabei (Eds.), *Geriatric assessment technology: The state of the art* (pp. 11–26). Milan: Editrice Kurtis.

Williams, B. C., Warshaw, G., Fabiny, A. R., Lundebjerg, N., Medina-Walpole, A., Sauvigne, K., et al. (2010). Medicine in the 21st century: Recommended essential geriatrics competencies for internal medicine and family medicine residents. *Journal of Graduate Medical Education, 2,* 373–383.

World Health Organization. (2010). *Framework for action on interprofessional education & collaborative practice.* Retrieved from http://apps.who.int/iris/bitstream/10665/70185/1/WHO_HRH_HPN_10.3_eng.pdf

Zwarenstein, M., Reeves, S., Barr, H., Hammick, M., Koppel, I., & Atkins, J. (2000). Interprofessional education: Effects on professional practice and health care outcomes. *Cochrane Database of Systematic Reviews, 3,* CD002213.

16

INTERPROFESSIONAL PRACTICE IN THE EMERGENCY DEPARTMENT

Martine Sanon and Gallane Dabela Abraham

Case Study: WB

WB is a 90-year-old man with multiple medical comorbidities, including mild cognitive impairment, coronary artery disease, chronic obstructive pulmonary disease, congestive heart failure (CHF), Parkinson's disease, and an unsteady gait. He presented to the emergency department (ED) with complaints of chest pain and shortness of breath. The patient is well known to the ED staff, is closely followed by a community primary care provider (PCP), and has had multiple previous short-stay admissions to the inpatient medical service. The patient has visited the ED many times before, usually during the evening and weekend hours. ED social workers have become familiar with WB's case through his prior visits and have learned that most of his ED visits are partly related to anxiety he feels when his aides leave. He lives at home alone with assistance from a home health aide 12 hours a day. His multiple chronic illnesses and chronic pain make it very difficult for him to leave his home. His pain is often worse at night when he has no one to assist him with his medications. He also has a fear of falling because of his worsening Parkinson's gait. Despite several attempts by his PCP and community social worker to increase his home care services, he remained ineligible for this increase.

In the ED, he is evaluated for chest pain and shortness of breath, with a full medical workup for acute coronary syndrome and other acute medical issues. His medical workup is negative for an acute medical illness; therefore, he is medically cleared by the emergency physician. The ED clinicians then decide to have WB evaluated by the interprofessional geriatric transitional care

---

team. A pharmacist was consulted to help simplify his medication regimen and ensure chronic pain relief, and a physical therapist was consulted for his gait instability and fear of falling. The ED pharmacist reviewed his medications and options for a simplified regimen. The physical therapist performed a full evaluation, and WB was deemed a good rehabilitation candidate. The case manager and social worker then evaluated WB for transfer to a subacute rehabilitation facility, and he has since moved into a skilled nursing facility, where he is less anxious, maintains his medication regimen, and is at less risk for falling. He adapted to his new environment and has not been to the ED in over a year.

EMERGENCY MEDICINE AND MODELS OF CARE

The ED is in a unique position to have an impact on a patient's trajectory once the patient enters the health care system. The ED is the transition point between outpatient community care and inpatient hospitalization. ED clinicians are responsible for making critical diagnoses and disposition decisions to admit or discharge a patient. These decisions have a major impact on a patient's health and the health system. The challenges of caring for patients in an ED setting remain a topic of particular interest because of the changing demographic trends of an aging patient population and growing numbers of vulnerable high-risk patients living longer with multiple comorbid conditions and complex care requirements. For these patients, an ED disposition decision is often difficult and requires input from a team of health care professionals that provide rapid assessments and interventions in the ED. In 2006, the Institute of Medicine highlighted the growing concern of the state of emergency care for an aging population with unique health and psychosocial needs that often cannot be met with the traditional emergency medicine model (Wilber et al., 2006). New models of emergency care are currently being implemented that utilize interdisciplinary teams and interprofessional education (IPE) to improve care for the geriatric patient. The principles of interprofessional practice (IPP) in geriatric emergency care may serve as a model of care for all vulnerable and high-risk patient populations. This chapter addresses the complex needs of the geriatric patient presenting to the ED and introduces key models of interprofessional clinical care that aim to improve quality of health care for geriatric patients.

THE GERIATRIC PATIENT IN THE EMERGENCY DEPARTMENT

Older adults age 65 years and older comprise 13 percent of the population and are projected to grow to approximately 20 percent by 2030. Although older adults represent 25 percent of all ED visits, they account for almost half of all ED admissions and 60 percent of those that are considered preventable. They are more likely to present with urgent and emergent medical conditions and are five times more likely to be admitted (Samaras, Chevalley, Samaras, & Gold, 2010). As the geriatric patient population continues to grow, this demographic shift and utilization pattern implies that the number of ED visits by older adults will only increase. Given the projected doubling of older adult ED visits, attempts should be made to make the ED more receptive to the needs of older adults (Hwang & Morrison, 2007).

Traditionally, emergency care for the older adult involved a focus on treating acute illnesses and injuries, as well as exacerbations of chronic disease. The older adult often presents with vague symptoms, atypical presentations of common diseases, multiple acute conditions, and confounding medical comorbidities. In addition, up to 40 percent of older adults will have cognitive impairment that is not readily apparent to emergency providers, further complicating their medical and psychosocial evaluation and disposition. ED physicians face a number of challenges while caring for the older patient: unrecognized dementia and delirium, the undertreatment of pain, the number of diagnostic tests, polypharmacy and adverse drug events, and time required in history and exam (Aminzadeh & Dalziel, 2002). Older adults are often discharged from the ED with unrecognized illness or unmet social needs, and 20 percent experience a change in the ability to care for themselves after an acute illness or injury. Complications commonly ensue, with an often rapid decrease in functioning and quality of life. Not surprisingly, 27 percent will experience ED revisit, hospitalization, or death within three months (Adams & Gerson, 2003). The combination of these clinical and psychosocial factors puts older adults at risk for delays in diagnosis, inappropriate and insufficient treatment plans, ED revisit, and hospitalization. Older adults are at high risk for accelerated cognitive and functional decline, delirium, adverse medication events, and falls during and subsequent to their ED visit or hospitalization and require intensive evaluation and management in the ED. Because of the medical and psychosocial complexity of many older adults, the ED is often an appropriate setting for care. The ED is often the only outlet for older adults with acute medical needs who cannot be seen urgently by their primary care provider and need expedited clinical workups. For many outpatient providers, the ED represents the only location that can conduct complicated medical workups for patients who cannot navigate the health care system, and it may be the sole safety net for older adults with complex geriatric syndromes who can no longer live safely on their own in the community (Pines, Mullins, Cooper, Feng, & Roth, 2013).

A visit to the ED marks a sentinel event for an older adult. This event is considered a critical transition point of the older adult's health-related quality of life. Older adults have complex care needs (such as cognitive impairments, functional limitations, multiple comorbidities, and psychosocial concerns), which make rapid triage, diagnosis, and clinical decision making difficult. The 2006 Institute of Medicine report recognized that the emergency care of older adults is accompanied by difficulties that cannot be solved by an individual emergency physician and emphasized the role of other professionals, such as physical therapists, pharmacists, social workers, and geriatric technicians, who can assist in care coordination, patient assistance, and safe discharge planning to optimize ED care of older adults (Wilber et al., 2006). The ED is uniquely positioned to assist and facilitate improvement in care for older adults and to have an impact on patient outcome trajectories. Successful inpatient and outpatient models of geriatric care highlight the benefits of interdisciplinary team effort in caring for older adults in acute care settings.

Geriatric Emergency Care Model

Recognizing the demographic changes of an aging population and need to improve patient care outcomes, the role of interprofessional teams in the ED setting is essential. To identify and address older persons' complex medical and psychosocial needs, emergency providers must account for baseline cognitive and functional limitations, obtain history from and collaborate with multiple sources, and develop a broad differential. An intensive case management approach will allow emergency providers to develop appropriate care plans that place older adults' needs in context. Optimal care for complex older adult patients requires emergency physicians to work as a team with the patient's primary physician, the ED nurses, geriatric nurses and nurse practitioners, physician assistants, pharmacists, social workers, case managers, and physical therapists. A highly functional team could theoretically optimize quality, efficiency, and satisfaction (Adams & Gerson, 2003). Most ED models of geriatric emergency care adapt elements from other care settings, and almost all utilize a case management approach, a collaborative assessment, planning, and care coordination process to improve outcomes for older adults.

In a 2011 systematic review of ED-based case management for older adults, Sinha, Bessman, Flomenbaum, and Leff (2011) identified eight operational components that can inform the development of a comprehensive geriatric emergency care model. Key operational components include

> implementation of an evidence based practice model; universal screening with validated risk assessment tools; nursing or midlevel clinician-directed geriatric case management; focused geriatric assessments to identify clinical and nonclinical factors that may impact care planning and future health care utilization; ED initiation of care and disposition planning; interprofessional and multidisciplinary work practices between the ED providers, hospital, primary care, and community health care providers; follow-up after discharge to maintain and facilitate care plans; and evaluation and monitoring of outcome measures for continuous quality improvement. (Sinha et al., 2011, pp. 678–680)

Furthermore, capacity building through the training of existing providers in geriatric competencies can also rapidly transform and enhance emergency care for older adults. This evidence base provides a framework to redesign emergency care for the older adult.

Models of Care for Vulnerable and High-Risk Populations

Historically, optimal and successful geriatric care programs have relied on multidisciplinary and collaborative practice to improve patient care and outcomes (Atwal & Caldwell, 2005). Interdisciplinary team members with varying roles and responsibilities help meet care needs of this vulnerable patient population and play an important role in effective care coordination, safe transitions, and optimal patient outcomes.

Several models of care have been studied in addressing the complicated care needs of older adults in acute care settings. Acute Care Units for the Elderly (ACE), Mobile Acute Care for the Elderly (MACE), and the Geriatric Evaluation and Management

Unit are models developed to improve care and health outcomes for older hospitalized adults (Steele, 2010). These models all include multiple variables and call for the interprofessional team not only to consider the acute treatment of the disease process but also to recognize the hazards of hospitalization, high-risk medications and polypharmacy, common geriatric syndromes, cognitive and functional decline, and the need for safe transition planning. Other models integrate geriatric principles to improve care for hospitalized geriatric patients, such as Nurses Improving Care for Health System Elders, an educational resource for nurses to improve geriatric care; and the Hospital Elder Life Program, an interdisciplinary team of volunteers and professionals focused on the prevention of delirium. Collectively all of these models studied have offered different mechanisms toward optimizing care for older adults in an acute care setting.

Developing an ACE model for the ED that incorporates the roles of interprofessional team members in the ED setting can help improve the care and management of older adults. Through changes in work flow, informatics, electronic medical records, and education, the leaders in geriatric emergency medicine have been able to describe a new model of care for geriatric patients in the ED setting. Culture change and workforce education must be at the forefront of implementing change.

Traditional ED models often rely on multidisciplinary teams, in which teams members function and work independently to complete tasks successfully. However, recognizing the unique challenges of caring for older adults in the acute care setting, a more effective strategy may be to incorporate an interdisciplinary team model, which is characterized by individuals working simultaneously with an appreciation for the contribution of the other team members. Enlisting interprofessional team members allows individuals with various talents and expertise to work together and introduce a dialogue that produces optimal outcomes for the geriatric patient population.

In the emergency care setting, there are a number of competing factors that need to be addressed concurrently. In addition to treating and stabilizing the acute trauma, illness, or complications that led to presentation to ED setting, there is also the responsibility to incorporate patient and caregiver needs, recognize the potential for geriatric syndromes in this vulnerable population, and pay particular attention to care transitions.

Education: Geriatric Competencies and Interprofessional Education

As the population ages and new care models are prepared to face these changes, it is necessary for team members to have special competencies related to geriatrics and IPE. There are many challenges related to enhancing geriatric care and workflow, especially when working with older, complex patients who often require a lot of time in a fast-paced ED environment. Effective communication and collaboration are essential competencies to facilitate optimal care management for complex geriatric patients in the ED.

All members of the health care workforce need to be prepared to work with an aging population. Hogan and colleagues recommended that "the geriatric competence of virtually all members of the healthcare workforce needs to be improved through significant enhancements in educational curricula and training programs, and then assessed through career-long demonstrations of this competence" (Hogan et al., 2010, p. 317). As a result, geriatrics-specific, competency-based consensus performance standards were created for medical students and residency training programs in internal medicine, family medicine, and emergency medicine. Furthermore, geriatric-based certification from professional societies exists in multiple disciplines, including nursing, social work, pharmacy, physical therapy, and physician assistant programs (Goldberg, Koontz, Rogers, & Brickell, 2012). Patient care is a complex activity that demands that health and social care professionals work together in an effective manner (Reeves et al., 2008). Although individual team members can contribute tremendously, learning to share expertise and experience is invaluable to optimizing patient care. It is imperative that there is good interprofessional communication and collaboration to help coordinate patient care in an effective manner (Reeves et al., 2008). Literature supports the use of IPE as a way to improve collaboration and patient care. In the ED setting, conceptually recognizing the difference between a multidisciplinary and an interdisciplinary team is the first step in accepting change. Health and social care professionals, such as doctors, nurses, pharmacists, physiotherapists, and social workers, need to work together effectively to take care of patients effectively. Training and educational programs have been developed as a possible way to improve how professionals work together to take care of patients (Goldberg et al., 2012).

Although there are very few randomized control trials designed to describe the effectiveness of IPP in the clinical care setting, a Cochrane review by Reeves et al. (2008) included six studies that evaluated the effects of IPE. Four of these studies found that IPE improved how professionals worked together and the care they provided in some way. IPE improved the working culture in an ED as well as patient satisfaction, decreased errors in the ED, improved the management of the care delivered to domestic violence victims, and improved the knowledge and skills of professionals providing care to mental health patients (Reeves et al., 2008). Therefore, IPE may be an effective strategy to improve attitudes and knowledge of interprofessional team members (that is, nurses and physicians), which ultimately have an impact on patient care (Campbell et al., 2001).

Workforce training must be included at the center of implementing this new model of interprofessional and interdisciplinary care in the ED setting. To successfully implement this new model of care, geriatric-focused, discipline-appropriate educational programs need to be identified and modified for ED physicians, physician assistants, nurse, nursing techs, social workers, pharmacists, and ancillary, clerical, and support staff. Educational topics should be designed to introduce staff, providers, clinicians, and administrators to vulnerabilities of geriatric patients and offer alternatives in their approach and interactions with older adults. Some of the fundamental topics address ageism, communication with older adults, detection of common geriatric syndromes, such as delirium, and recognition of dementia, as well as training on new clinical roles, available resources, screening tools and newly developed work algorithms and clinical protocols to address identified risks and issues commonly anticipated with this patient population. Ideally, the emergency care system of the future will integrate fundamental, specific geriatric principles with interprofessional skill sets to improve the care of older patients.

INTERPROFESSIONAL PRACTICE IN THE EMERGENCY SETTING

Interprofessional team-based models of care are an important way to meet the complex medical and psychosocial needs of the older adults who present in the ED setting. This innovative model of care in the ED setting has been the hallmark of exceptional geriatric clinical care for decades. Similar models have been replicated in outpatient, inpatient (ACE, MACE models), and home-based primary care; in programs for all-inclusive care for the elderly (often referred to as PACE); and, more recently, in dedicated Geriatric EDs (Reckrey et al., 2015).

In 2013, the Geriatric Emergency Department Guidelines were created as a consensus-based resource for optimal geriatric care in the emergency care setting. This includes an interdisciplinary team of care providers focused on the varying needs of the geriatric population and on training staff to recognize the unique care needs of this population and common geriatric syndromes. The overarching goal is to improve care outcomes for older adults by optimizing ED visits and effectively delivering and coordinating care that is most appropriate for the patient (American College of Emergency Physicians, n.d.).

Common Members of the Team: Geriatric ED Team

In a geriatric ED model, the interprofessional team includes an emergency physician, ED nurses, mid-level providers or physician extenders, a social worker, pharmacist, physical therapist, geriatric nurse or nurse practitioner, case manager and transitional care coordinator, a consulting geriatrician, and palliative care consultant. This team should have the opportunity to meet daily (if not multiple times a day) to collaborate and discuss acute cases, troubleshoot complex clinical and psychosocial issues, and make use of interprofessional team members' unique skill sets with the goal of improving health care outcomes, identifying high-risk patients, intervening with community resources, and preventing avoidable admissions. The purpose of these meetings allows for all team members to gather together to discuss cases, learn from each other, and develop a safe disposition plan.

Roles of Team Members

Emergency Physician and Physician Assistants

The emergency physician (EP) is often seen as the team leader to guide clinical decision making and management. The core skills of the emergency physician are to expertly and quickly gather relevant historical and clinical data, correlate with symptom presentation, stabilize and triage patient, formulate a diagnostic plan with therapeutic decision, and relate with patient, family, and PCP (Adams & Gerson, 2003). Once the patient is stabilized, the EP makes the critical decision to admit or discharge. The EP, with input from the interprofessional team, can assess the clinical, cognitive, functional, and psychosocial status of the patient to make an informed disposition decision and know when to call on additional members of the care team to improve the health outcomes for the patient.

ED Nurses

Emergency nurses are essential members of the team and are often challenged to multitask in a high-pressured environment. They are the first called to triage patients based on injuries or medical need; communicate effectively with patients, families, and care teams; and provide comfort and reassurance to patients and families at critical times. They specialize in assessing, intervening, and stabilizing a variety of traumas and illnesses and a wide range of medical conditions that may require urgent treatment and care. They must have the ability to quickly and accurately assess patients' physical, mental, and psychosocial conditions. They are often the first to recognize and attest to the patient's cognitive and functional status or limitations.

Geriatric Nurse and Geriatric Nurse Practitioner

The geriatric emergency medicine nurse and nurse practitioner (NP) perform focused assessments (including cognitive and functional screens) and use screening tools to assist in the evaluation of the complex, older adult presenting with change in mental status, falls, functional decline, or delirium in the setting of the acute illness. They are equipped to make recommendations and focus on further workup in the ED, safe transition of care, evaluations during hospitalization if admitted, and referral to appropriate outpatient services subsequent to discharge. The geriatric NP helps to improve communication and care coordination across practice sites, reduces unnecessary utilization, and assists with patient care, safe discharge, and transition planning.

Social Workers and Case Managers

Geriatric social workers and case managers have a versatile role in the emergency setting. They serve also a multitude of complex psychosocial needs of the aging population. The social worker can help older adults with psychosocial, medical, and financial challenges they may experience. As part of the care team, social workers are available to assist with assessments and offer counseling services, which often deal with end-of-life issues, bereavement, elder abuse, and other concerns common in older adults. They are helpful in identifying community resources for home care, visiting nurse services, meals, transportation, and applying for medical benefits and other resources available to older adults. They can help guide families through difficult care transitions from the home environment to long-term care, assist with filing necessary paperwork, and help with access to end-of-life care planning (advance directives, do-not-resuscitate orders). Case managers work closely with patients, social workers, and clinical staff to improve discharge planning, coordination of follow-up care, and health care utilization. The social workers and case managers act as liaisons between the patient, family members, and health care providers.

Pharmacists

Geriatric pharmacists with expertise in geriatric medication management can review medications for inappropriate drugs and drug interactions for patients with five or more medications to minimize problems with polypharmacy, suggest optimal simplified regimens, and provide education to clinicians and patients. The pharmacist serves as a resource for clinical providers, patients, and their families and caregivers. The pharmacist consults with staff to provide medication adjustments and recommendations appropriate for the geriatric patient, using the modified Beers criteria (Fick et al., 2003). The pharmacist reviews and clarifies all medications; contacts the outpatient pharmacy, PCP, or residence facility, if needed; and compiles an updated medication list and medication administration schedule for discharge.

Physical Therapists

The physical therapist focuses on maintaining and improving function in the older adult after an acute illness or injury to enable patients to remain functional in their community or assist with safe transition planning. Physical therapy consults are obtained in the geriatric ED for patients who present with a fall or a musculoskeletal complaint (back pain, extremity pain, or injury) or those identified as a fall risk. Physical therapists assess muscle strength and gait stability to identify the need for assistive devices, conditioning exercises, or outpatient or home physical therapy referrals. They also perform the required assessment for direct subacute rehabilitation facility placement for patients unable to be discharged home who have a qualifying hospitalization within the past 30 days, allowing placement directly from the ED.

Geriatrician

Geriatricians identify geriatric care needs of vulnerable patients in an acute setting and make expert assessments and recommendations on the unique care needs of older adult patients. This is especially true in the ED where, despite the acute presentation of illness, it is often the comprehensive evaluation of an older adult that guides clinical decisions. Geriatric liaisons provide recommendations focused on geriatric concerns and issues related to complex care management of the multimorbid patient. They can assist the ED team in recognizing complex clinical needs and atypical presentation of illness, assess decisional capacity, and assist in the coordination of safe transitions from the ED (to the hospital or home). Geriatricians can assist with complicated goals of care discussions and transitions of care and guide safe discharge planning (d'Arcy, Stearns, Domino, Hanson, & Weinberger, 2013).

Palliative Care

Consultations with palliative care professionals improve the medical care and quality of life for patients and families suffering with serious acute illness, chronic disease, terminal disease, and those at the end of life. The palliative care consultant frequently reviews and establishes the goals of care and assists patients and families in understand-ing treatment options and alternatives to acute inpatient care. Palliative care teams address pain management, shortness of breath, fatigue, nausea and loss of appetite, sleep disorders, depression, and constipation so patients can tolerate symptoms as they undergo medical treatments. Palliative care consultations assist the interprofessional team by providing a comprehensive understanding of the patient's and family's goals of care and an individual care plan that optimizes the patient's quality of life.

Interprofessional Team Role in Post-ED Care Coordination and Transition Management

Perhaps the most important role that the interprofessional team members play is in the collaborative work and care coordination involved in safe transitions of care. Col-lectively, all members provide essential input to make an informed disposition decision. The interprofessional team communicates their assessment to community providers if the patient is discharged or to inpatient providers if admitted to ensure a safe care transition.

Care transitions define the movements patients make between health care prac-titioners and settings as their condition and care needs change during the course of chronic or acute illness. These include logistical arrangements, education of the patient and caregivers, and coordination among health care professionals. Quality care transi-tions require careful consideration of patient preferences and clinical status. As patients undergo multiple care transitions, the potential for mismanagement, medical error, and recidivism increases. Significant quantitative evidence shows that both quality and patient safety are jeopardized, particularly in geriatric patients undergoing care transi-tions. It is imperative that interdisciplinary team members are involved to ensure the safest and most comprehensive transitional plan. For those not requiring acute hospi-talization, intensive interdisciplinary transitional care management (shared among social work, a nurse practitioner or nurse liaison, a case manager, and physical therapist) is done to ensure the success of the ED-to-home transition or to arrange another suitable care setting, such as subacute rehabilitation, hospice, home hospice, or long-term care. Effective ED-based resources are available seven days per week to formulate an appro-priate discharge plan with community partners to make home care services (visiting nurse and home health aides) and admission to nonacute beds available seven days a week. Additionally, effective care transitions include a discharge follow-up phone call from ED-based staff 24–48 hours after discharge to check on medications, "red flag" symptoms, and primary care or specialty follow-up appointments.

For those who are admitted to the hospital, and whose care is transitioned to other providers, it is also imperative that proper handoff is shared with inpatient teams. Important information such as clinical decisions, psychosocial assessments, and medi-cation adjustments identified in the ED can ultimately affect patient outcomes and therefore should be communicated to the inpatient teams.

At the center of the team are patients and their families. For our frail, vulnerable geriatric patient, involving the patient's family and primary caregivers is essential to improve patient outcomes and successful care transitions. Clinical decision making and intensive psychosocial interventions cannot be executed without the support of patient preferences. For older adults, this is a complex decision that requires a comprehensive approach aligning evidence-based clinical practice with the patients' overall goals of care.

REQUIRED COMPETENCIES IN KNOWLEDGE, ATTITUDES, AND SKILL

The required competencies in knowledge, skills, and attitudes in working with an interprofessional team in geriatric emergency medicine must take into account several factors to meet the unique needs of this population in the acute care setting. In 2009, the Partnership for Health in Aging was developed in response to the 2008 Institute of Medicine report *Retooling for an Aging America: Building the Health Care Workforce*, to meet the needs of the rapidly growing older population. As a result, a work group of 10 health care disciplines was created, to identify the multidisciplinary competencies in the care of older adults. These disciplines included medicine, dentistry, nursing, social work, pharmacy, physical therapy, occupational therapy, physician assistants, nutrition, and psychology (Goldberg et al., 2012). This work group identified six domains in the multidisciplinary competencies in the care of older adults: Health Promotion and Safety; Evaluation and Assessment; Care Planning and Coordination across the Care Spectrum (including end of life); Interdisciplinary and Team Care; Caregiver Support; and Healthcare Systems and Benefits (Partnership for Health in Aging, 2010). The competencies are broad and may vary based on the various disciplines. In working with interprofessional teams in geriatric emergency medicine, these domains should address discipline-specific core content in geriatrics and core emergency medicine. All members of the geriatric emergency medicine IPP should have the knowledge, skills, and attitude to address these issues as it relates to their specialty.

These disciplines are at different stages of developing competencies and can adjust to specialty and clinical practice. As described by Hogan et al. (2010), a consensus document addressing the minimum competencies specific for geriatric emergency medicine trainees includes content on core geriatrics principles, core emergency medicine principles, and adapting the principles of geriatrics to the emergency patient. For emergency medicine residents, these domains (presented in Table 16.1) include atypical presentation of illness, trauma, medication management, cognitive affective and behavioral health, complex or chronic illness in older adults, understanding end-of-life care and goals of care, and transitions of care.

LOGISTICS

Emergency care for the older adult involves treating acute illnesses and injuries, as well as exacerbations of chronic disease. For older adults, this also includes recognizing the geriatric syndromes that affect their health and quality of life. The comprehensive care of older adults takes time, which is often not feasible in a busy, fast-paced emergency setting. For this reason, innovative approaches are necessary to deliver optimal care to

Table 16.1: Geriatric Emergency Medicine Competencies

Domains	Knowledge	Skills	Attitudes
Medication Management	Beers criteria Polypharmacy	Thorough review of medication lists; recognize ADE	Appreciate how elder presentation may be a result of ADE
Cognitive Health and Behavioral Health	Recognize common syndromes, including dementia and delirium, and how each affects presentation	Use validated assessment tools such as CAM and FAST to diagnose delirium and dementia	Recognize how iatrogenic and environmental factors can impact cognition and behaviors in ED
Complex/ Comorbid Illness	Recognize how comorbid conditions can impact treatment and management	Assess and document comorbid conditions; anticipate predictable complications	Appreciate how chronic comorbid medical issues can effect acute presentation
End of Life Care	Familiarize with previous ACP	Discuss GOC, code status, MOLST, living will, HCP	Align treatment plans to GOC
Transitions of Care	Recognize sites of care, where patients come from, or where they can be discharged to	Communicate care plans with PCP, SNF providers, and inpatient providers	Appreciate different care settings; align care with GOC

Notes: ADE = adverse drug events; CAM = Confusion Assessment Method; FAST = Functional Assessment Screening Tool; ED = emergency department; ACP = advance care plan; GOC = goals of care; MOLST = Medical Order for Life Sustaining Treatment; HCP = health care proxy; PCP = primary care provider; SNF = skilled nursing facility.

this population. The value of optimizing the roles of interprofessional teams resides in the recognition of red flags that unfold from an ED visit. There are numerous scenarios that can exist. For example, perhaps the pharmacist discovers after reviewing a patient's coverage plan that a recurrent CHF exacerbation is not due to medication noncompliance but is instead occurring because the patient's health insurance will not cover medications. Perhaps dietary restrictions cannot be followed because the patient's primary source of nutrition comes from canned goods that are easiest for him to prepare. Perhaps the physical therapist discovers that a patient's recurrent falls began because the patient is using her late husband's cane rather than the proper assistive device.

All team members involved in the complex care of older adults must believe their work is valued, rewarding, and feasible. Geriatrics has unique challenges to workflow efficiency that require flexibility on the part of the team (Chun, 2011). Geriatric emergency care is further affected by the nature of its rapid-paced environment and need for quick decision making. However, taking the time to review these challenging cases and collaborate with members of the interprofessional team allows for safer, coordinated clinical care decisions that ultimately improve patient outcomes and provide long-term benefits. Though quick decisions are often required in dynamic clinical environments like the ED, patient safety and quality of care are paramount. Many hospitals recognize the value of care coordination and have incorporated short-stay or observation units to also meet the need of this population.

CHALLENGES AND STRATEGIES TO IPP

This new model of care requires a transformation of the traditional method in which care is provided to meet the needs of the aging emergency medicine population. As a result, it is not surprising that this new model of care also introduces ethical, institutional, and professional challenges. Members from the various professional teams, including nurses, administrators, emergency physicians, geriatricians, social workers, pharmacists, and physical therapists, all need to be empowered to provide valuable input on how to integrate their roles to this new model of care. This will create a more geriatric-friendly emergency care environment and will optimize care for complex older adults.

Ethical

There are a number of ethical issues that become relevant in geriatric emergency medicine. Emergency physicians are often meeting older adults in critical times when clinical practice and ethical judgments intersect and immediate life-altering decisions need to be made. Some of the basic ethical principles of beneficence ("doing good"), nonmaleficence ("do no harm"), and respecting patient autonomy are often challenged when considering the vulnerable nature of the geriatric patient population. Patients with cognitive impairment may lack the decisional capacity to make some challenging medical decisions. This includes not only informed consent but the ability to refuse care (Larkin, Marco, & Abbott, 2001). The risks and benefits of medical interventions and procedures have to be weighed with the frail nature of the patients. Discussing advanced directives in critical moments, relying on surrogates to guide difficult clinical decision making, such as resuscitative measures at the end of life, experiencing medical futility, communicating bad news, and navigating the dying process are all recognized challenges in emergency care. It is often in these difficult case scenarios where the role of IPP can be helpful. Partnering with social workers, nurses, and extended team members, such as pastoral care, can provide additional support for patients and families.

It is important to recognize that for older adults living with multiple chronic diseases, the goals of care may be to simply preserve function and prevent the worsening of disease, rather than cure the disease entirely. At times, it is safer to avoid a hospital admission or proceed with an aggressive intervention. As much as clinicians like to rely on evidence-based guidelines, unfortunately, these guidelines have not been studied or validated in many geriatric patients.

Ethical Strategy

Determining a patient's decision-making capacity is often challenging. Partnering with interprofessional team members can facilitate the assessment of a patient's decision-making capacity. Even patients with cognitive impairment or dementia can communicate their goals of care. Therefore, it is important to consider an individualized patient-centered approach to assessing capacity and communicating treatment options in a meaningful manner (Ganzini, Volicer, Nelson, & Derse, 2003).

When decisions are difficult, it may be helpful to have input from another clinician, geriatrician, or psychiatrist. Team members such as social workers, case managers, and nurse practitioners can, at the same time, reach out to family and a PCP to collaborate on advanced directives and ascertain the patient's expressed wishes.

Institutional

Meeting competing demands of the hospital administration may make an interprofessional model of care difficult to sustain. Financially, hospitals are interested in cost savings, decreasing ED and hospital length of stay, preventing readmissions, increasing revenue, and optimizing throughput. Providing comprehensive interprofessional care requires, time, resources, and a constant attention to the complexity of a patient-centered care plan. A team approach may delay care plan development for complex patients. This may negatively affect hospital throughput and lead to further ED crowding and delays. However, this model, a comprehensive interprofessional approach to geriatric emergency care, can add value by improving other institutional benchmarks, such as improving patient-centered outcomes, delivering accurate diagnoses, providing customer service, and increasing patient safety and satisfaction. It is important to recognize that although care for these patients may require more comprehensive assessments, tapping into additional resources with an interprofessional team that addresses the complex care needs to improve health outcomes is essential for the patient and valuable to the health system.

Institutional Strategy

A geriatric emergency care model is essentially high-quality patient-centered care that incorporates fiscally responsible interventions. To measure the impact of this new model of care, it is important to highlight and monitor the institutional goals and benchmarks that the interprofessional team addresses. The interprofessional team can lead to better patient outcomes, including decreasing or preventing iatrogenic complications, such as catheter-associated urinary tract infections, pressure ulcers, falls, and delirium, by early identification in the ED. Additional benefits of comprehensive care include decreased length of stay, better care transitions, and fewer readmissions. Partnering and collaborating with primary care practices, skilled nursing facilities, senior community centers and certified home care, visiting nurse and hospice agencies with shared objectives will enable this model of care to remain sustainable.

Professional

Defining and integrating the evolving roles of interprofessional team members into a geriatric ED requires ongoing involvement and education of ED staff at all levels and a complete culture change to traditional practices. Although it is important for all interprofessional team members to have special competencies related to geriatrics, working with a largely geriatric patient population has unique challenges to clinical efficiency that require flexibility of team members. In a busy ED environment with competing demands for time and resources, emergency physicians, RNs, and social workers are often pressured to multitask and improve throughput. Because of the complexity of their cases, older adults frequently require more time and attention. Emergency physicians and nurses may feel that the additional assessments required for older adults are not aligned with or relevant to their scope of practice. They may resort back to the acquired habit of simply admitting older adults to the hospital to complete workup when faced with an older adult patient with complex chronic problems and a poor support system. They often feel like they have not received the proper training to meet the additional demands of this population.

This is a complete culture change for the emergency physician to engage the interprofessional team in the clinical decision-making process. IPP allows clinicians the opportunity to explore other resources to allow the patient to be discharged home or to find a suitable alternative to acute care hospitalization. These same demands exist for interprofessional team members. For pharmacists, social workers, and registered nurses, older adults offer different challenges to their workflow and efficiency in an often chaotic environment. They have more complex medication lists, more drug–drug interactions, and more dosing and drug limitations. The purview of social work interventions and assessments can be time-consuming for patients who have cognitive and functional limitations, questionable decisional capacity, and other common symptoms of aging. RNs, who often spend more time at the bedside than any other health professional, may be more likely to understand the patients' capabilities and effectively advocate on their behalf.

Despite the need for IPP, many studies indicate that communication and collaboration can be problematic, especially in a chaotic environment. There may be concern that collaboration can be undermined by boundaries and a lack of understanding of team member roles.

Professional Strategy

One potential strategy is empowering the leadership of the various interprofessional teams on board. This requires understanding of the clinical work environment, identifying focused geriatric assessments applicable to the acute care setting, and having the necessary resources easily accessible.

The clinical algorithms presented in Table 16.2 can be helpful to highlight the roles of the interprofessional staff (for example, transitional nurse practitioners, social workers, and pharmacists) and identify high-risk patients who would benefit from each of the various interventions. A knowledgeable and engaged clinical staff all have something to contribute to the care of the patient.

Emergency care will continue to evolve to meet the demographic changes of the 21st century. It is necessary to improve quality and decrease the costs of health care for older adults. Goals of geriatric emergency care remain the same as for all emergency patients: to provide appropriate, timely, and comprehensive emergency care for acute

Table 16.2: Domain Challenges and Strategies to Overcome These Challenges

Domain	Challenges	Strategy to Overcome
Ethical	Decisional capacity, medical futility, frailty	Care offered/provided, shared decision making, advance directive
Institutional	Financial implications, hospital throughput, sustainability	Length of stay, quality metrics, patient outcomes, readmissions
Professional	Training, time, boundaries	Ageism, culture change, incorporating geriatric education into emergency department providers training, boundaries

illnesses and injuries and exacerbations of chronic disease. Optimal care for complex older adults requires the collaboration and expertise of interdisciplinary teams.

REFERENCES

Adams, J. G., & Gerson, L. W. (2003). A new model for emergency care of geriatric patients. *Academic Emergency Medicine, 10*, 271–274.

American College of Emergency Physicians. (n.d.). *Geriatric emergency department guidelines*. Retrieved from http://www.acep.org/geriEDguidelines

Aminzadeh, F., & Dalziel, W. B. (2002). Older adults in the emergency department: A systematic review of patterns of use, adverse outcomes, and effectiveness of interventions. *Annals of Emergency Medicine, 39*, 238–247.

Atwal, A., & Caldwell, K. (2005). Do all health and social care professionals interact equally? A study of interactions in multidisciplinary teams in the United Kingdom. *Scandinavian Journal of Caring Sciences, 19*, 268–273.

Campbell, J. C., Coben, J. H., McLoughlin, E., Dearwater, S., Nah, G., Glass, N., et al. (2001). An evaluation of a system-change training model to improve emergency department response to battered women. *Academic Emergency Medicine, 8*, 131–138.

Chun, A. (Ed.). (2011). *Geriatric care by design: A clinician's handbook to meet the needs of older adults through environmental and practice redesign*. Chicago: American Medical Association.

d'Arcy, L. P., Stearns, S. C., Domino, M. E., Hanson, L. C., & Weinberger, M. (2013). Is geriatric care associated with less emergency department use? *Journal of the American Geriatrics Society, 61*, 4–11.

Fick, D. M., Cooper, J. W., Wade, W. E., Waller, J. L., Maclean, J. R., & Beers, M. H. (2003). Updating the Beers criteria for potentially inappropriate medication use in older adults: Results of a US consensus panel of experts. *Archives of Internal Medicine, 163*, 2716–2724.

Ganzini, L., Volicer, L., Nelson, W., & Derse, A. (2003). Pitfalls in assessment of decision-making capacity. *Psychosomatics, 44*, 237–243.

Goldberg, L. R., Koontz, J. S., Rogers, N., & Brickell, J. (2012). Considering accreditation in gerontology: The importance of interprofessional collaborative competencies to ensure quality health care for older adults. *Gerontology & Geriatrics Education, 33*, 95–110.

Hogan, T. M., Losman, E. D., Carpenter, C. R., Sauvigne, K., Irmiter, C., Emanuel, L., & Leipzig, R. M. (2010). Development of geriatric competencies for emergency medicine residents using an expert consensus process. *Academic Emergency Medicine, 17*, 316–324.

Hwang, U., & Morrison, R. S. (2007). The geriatric emergency department. *Journal of the American Geriatrics Society, 55*, 1873–1876.

Institute of Medicine. (2008). *Retooling for an aging America: Building the health care workforce.* Washington, DC: National Academies Press.

Larkin, G. L., Marco, C. A., & Abbott, J. T. (2001). Emergency determination of decision-making capacity: Balancing autonomy and beneficence in the emergency department. *Academic Emergency Medicine, 8*, 282–284.

Partnership for Health in Aging. (2010). *Multidisciplinary competences in the care of older adults at the completion of the entry-level health profession degree.* Retrieved from http://www.americangeriatrics.org/files/documents/health_care_pros/PHA_Multidisc_Competencies.pdf

Pines, J. M., Mullins, P. M., Cooper, J. K., Feng, L. B., & Roth, K. E. (2013). National trends in emergency department use, care patterns, and quality of care of older adults in the United States. *Journal of the American Geriatrics Society, 61*, 12–17.

Reckrey, J. M., Soriano, T. A., Hernandez, C. R., DeCherrie, L. V., Chavez, S., Zhang, M., & Ornstein, K. (2015). The team approach to home-based primary care: Restructuring care to meet individual, program, and system needs. *Journal of the American Geriatrics Society, 63*, 358–364.

Reeves, S., Zwarenstein, M., Goldman, J., Barr, H., Freeth, D., Hammick, M., & Koppel, I. (2008). Interprofessional education: Effects on professional practice and health care outcomes. *Cochrane Database of Systematic Reviews, 1*, CD002213. doi:10.1002/14651858.CD002213.pub2

Samaras, N., Chevalley, T., Samaras, D., & Gold, G. (2010). Older patients in the emergency department: A review. *Annals of Emergency Medicine, 56*, 261–269.

Sinha, S. K., Bessman, E. S., Flomenbaum, N., & Leff, B. (2011). A systematic review and qualitative analysis to inform the development of a new emergency department-based geriatric case management model. *Annals of Emergency Medicine, 57*, 672–682.

Steele, J. (2010). Current evidence regarding models of acute hospitalized geriatric patients. *Geriatric Nursing, 31*, 331–347.

Wilber, S. T., Gerson, L. W., Terrell, K. M., Carpenter, C. R., Shah, M. N., Heard, K., & Hwang, U. (2006). Geriatric emergency medicine and the 2006 Institute of Medicine reports from the Committee on the Future of Emergency Care in the U.S. health system. *Academic Emergency Medicine, 13*, 1345–1351.

CONCLUSION

Carmen Morano

The programs represented in this text are a sample of what is happening at colleges and universities throughout the United States. There is no doubt that the number of interprofessional education (IPE) programs starting up is growing. Access to a vast array of excellent curricular resources is readably available, and there is no indication of it slowing down. Access to education programs at the pre-certificate level as well as to post-certificate continuing education is greater now than ever before. Achieving better health, better health care, and smarter spending (or reducing the cost of care) requires a workforce that has the capacity to engage in and evaluate interprofessional practice (IPP). All indicators are that IPE and IPP are here to stay. But before we celebrate, it is important that we are prepared to face the potential challenges.

CHALLENGE OR OPPORTUNITY

A 2015 Institute of Medicine report concluded that the challenge for IPE is to provide a road map that can lead to sustainability. The report stated that to accomplish this, IPE should engage in "a purposeful and comprehensive system of engagement with education and health care delivery systems" (Institute of Medicine, 2015, p. 2). Without this integration, it will ultimately be impossible to evaluate the real impact of IPE. The report goes on to emphasize the need for educational and health care delivery systems to collaborate on designing more comprehensive conceptual models that provide a "consistent taxonomy and framework for strengthening the evidence linking education and health system outcomes practice" (p. 3).

PERSON-CENTERED CARE

The next challenge is adoption throughout all health and social care of person-centered/participant-directed (PC/PD) models of care. The current and future workforce must be able to integrate into their care the PC/PD framework that Medicare, Medicaid, and managed care providers are now mandated to provide. With historical roots in understanding and responding to oppression and the social and institutional misuse of power and privilege, social work is uniquely positioned to make a significant contribution to this discussion. Power, privilege, oppression, and cumulative advantage and disadvantage are not abstract concepts that can be ignored in person-centered care. Even the use of the word "interprofessional" might be perceived as a micro-aggression toward all those individuals and family members who are now expected to be members of the interprofessional team.

FACULTY DEVELOPMENT

Preparing the workforce of the future requires a cohort of educators, preceptors, and mentors who themselves have interprofessional knowledge, attitudes, values, and skills is another challenge to designing competency-based models of IPE. As the number of IPE programs continues to grow, the demand for faculty, already in short supply, will be even greater than it already is. Faculty development requires a consistent and long-term investment of resources that goes beyond just human capital. If IPE is here to stay, it requires financial support that is not contingent on short-term grant funding.

SUSTAINABILITY

The challenge of sustaining IPE in the academy can be achieved only through a systemic approach that removes some of the institutional boundaries that continue to restrict cross-department interactions. As was discussed throughout part 3, it takes time for faculty to become an interprofessional team of academics capable of developing and delivering true interprofessional learning. The coordination of student schedules, allocation of student tuition, and division of faculty workload must be clarified long before the first course is offered. These planning efforts must be sustained if the actual program is to be as well.

EVALUATION

There needs to be a more purposeful approach to developing a body of empirical evidence that supports both the intellectual benefits of interprofessional learning and the financial benefits of IPP (Institute of Medicine, 2015). Without convincing evidence, the sustainability of IPE will always be at risk. Evaluating the short-term gains of IPE has indicated some success, but there is limited evidence evaluating the enduring gains of IPE. Strategies to evaluate what a student knows are not sufficient. Evaluation needs to include what students do with their IPE. The use of case simulation, portfolios, observations, and 360-degree evaluations are some of the tools that are worthy of further exploration.

As the literature calling for the expansion of IPE is replaced by literature reporting evidence of the short- and long-term benefits of IPE, it is tempting to conclude that IPE is here to stay. But before celebrating, I would like to relate a recent experience of a colleague, who happens to be a professor of social work and who called me the night before I was submitting this text to the publisher. My colleague's mother, Mrs. R., is an 84-year-old widowed female who was in the emergency department (ED) for what appeared to be a small skin ulcer on her foot. After 20 hours of lying on a gurney in a hall of the ED, she was admitted to the hospital, where a rotation of physicians, nurses, lab technicians, and even a social worker had visited at times ranging from 5 a.m. to 9 p.m.. It was abundantly clear to Mrs. R. that there was little, if any, communication among the professionals, and the conflicting instructions that each had to offer were especially confusing. At 9 a.m. the next day, Mrs. R. was informed that she would be discharged with a prescription for some expensive antibiotics. My colleague was concerned about how it might react with her mother's eight other medications. At that point, the doctor informed my colleague that if she did not agree to the new medication, her mother could go to a nursing home, where she could continue with the infusion treatment.

There is no doubt that the professionals at this institution are committed individuals who are tasked with managing large, complex caseloads with shrinking or nonexisting resources. Everyone is doing the best they can. One hopes that stories like that of my colleague will be a thing of the past. It is reassuring to know that the programs highlighted in this text are a sample of the outstanding work that is going on in the United States and will make a contribution to what is an excellent body of international work. After hearing my colleague's story, it is probably best to close this text with the recognition that IPE is still evolving (Hall & Weaver, 2001). Though this evolution is occurring a little slower than some would like, this text is evidence that we are making progress.

REFERENCES

Hall, P., & Weaver, L. (2001). Interdisciplinary education and teamwork: A long and winding road. *Medical Education, 35*, 867–875.

Institute of Medicine. (2015). *Measuring the impact of interprofessional education on collaborative practice and patient outcomes.* Washington, DC: National Academies Press.

Appendix A
CORE COMPETENCIES

The following core competencies and subcompetencies are from the *Core Competencies for Interprofessional Collaborative Practice: 2016 Update* (Interprofessional Education Collaborative, 2016), reprinted by permission.

Values and Ethics (VE) Subcompetencies

Core competency: Work with individuals of other professions to maintain a climate of mutual respect and shared values.

VE1: Place interests of patients and populations at center of interprofessional health care delivery and population health programs and policies, with the goal of promoting health and health equity across the life span.

VE2: Respect the dignity and privacy of patients while maintaining confidentiality in the delivery of team-based care.

VE3: Embrace the cultural diversity and individual differences that characterize patients, populations, and the health team.

VE4: Respect the unique cultures, values, roles/responsibilities, and expertise of other health professions and the impact these factors can have on health outcomes.

VE5: Work in cooperation with those who receive care, those who provide care, and others who contribute to or support the delivery of prevention and health services and programs.

VE6: Develop a trusting relationship with patients, families, and other team members (Canadian Interprofessional Health Collaborative, 2010).

VE7: Demonstrate high standards of ethical conduct and quality of care in one's contributions to team-based care.

VE8: Manage ethical dilemmas specific to interprofessional patient/population centered care situations.

VE9: Act with honesty and integrity in relationships with patients, families, communities, and other team members.

VE10: Maintain competence in one's own profession appropriate to scope of practice.

Interprofessional Communication (CC) Subcompetencies

Core competency: Communicate with patients, families, communities, and professionals in health and other fields in a responsive and responsible manner that supports a team approach to the promotion and maintenance of health and the prevention and treatment of disease.

CC1: Choose effective communication tools and techniques, including information systems and communication technologies, to facilitate discussions and interactions that enhance team function.

CC2: Communicate information with patients, families, community members, and health team members in a form that is understandable, avoiding discipline-specific terminology when possible.

CC3: Express one's knowledge and opinions to team members involved in patient care and population health improvement with confidence, clarity, and respect, working to ensure common understanding of information, treatment, care decisions, and population health programs and policies.

CC4: Listen actively, and encourage ideas and opinions of other team members.

CC5: Give timely, sensitive, instructive feedback to others about their performance on the team, responding respectfully as a team member to feedback from others.

CC6: Use respectful language appropriate for a given difficult situation, crucial conversation, or interprofessional conflict.

CC7: Recognize how one's own uniqueness, including experience level, expertise, culture, power, and hierarchy within the health team, contributes to effective communication, conflict resolution, and positive interprofessional working relationships (University of Toronto, 2008).

CC8: Communicate the importance of teamwork in patient-centered care and population health programs and policies.

Roles and Responsibilities (RR) Subcompetencies

Core competency: Use the knowledge of one's own role and those of other professions to appropriately assess and address the health care needs of patients and to promote and advance the health of populations.

RR1: Communicate one's roles and responsibilities clearly to patients, families, community members, and other professionals.

RR2: Recognize one's limitations in skills, knowledge, and abilities.

RR3: Engage diverse professionals who complement one's own professional expertise, as well as associated resources, to develop strategies to meet specific health and healthcare needs of patients and populations.

RR4: Explain the roles and responsibilities of other providers and how the team works together to provide care, promote health, and prevent disease.

RR5: Use the full scope of knowledge, skills, and abilities of professionals from health and other fields to provide care that is safe, timely, efficient, effective, and equitable.

RR6: Communicate with team members to clarify each member's responsibility in executing components of a treatment plan or public health intervention.

RR7: Forge interdependent relationships with other professions within and outside of the health system to improve care and advance learning.

RR8: Engage in continuous professional and interprofessional development to enhance team performance and collaboration.

RR9: Use unique and complementary abilities of all members of the team to optimize health and patient care.

RR10: Describe how professionals in health and other fields can collaborate and integrate clinical care and public health interventions to optimize population health.

Team and Teamwork (TT) Subcompetencies

Core competency: Apply relationship-building values and the principles of team dynamics to perform effectively in different team roles to plan and deliver patient-/population-centered care that is safe, timely, efficient, effective, and equitable.

TT1: Describe the process of team development and the roles and practices of effective teams.

TT2: Develop consensus on the ethical principles to guide all aspects of team work.

TT3: Engage health and other professionals in shared patient-centered and population-focused problem-solving.

TT4: Integrate the knowledge and experience of health and other professions to inform health and care decisions, while respecting patient and community values and priorities/preferences for care.

TT5: Apply leadership practices that support collaborative practice and team effectiveness.

TT6: Engage self and others to constructively manage disagreements about values, roles, goals, and actions that arise among health and other professionals and with patients, families, and community members.

TT7: Share accountability with other professions, patients, and communities for outcomes relevant to prevention and health care.

TT8: Reflect on individual and team performance for individual, as well as team, performance improvement.

TT9: Use process improvement to increase effectiveness of interprofessional teamwork and team-based services, programs, and policies.

TT10: Use available evidence to inform effective teamwork and team-based practices.

TT11: Perform effectively on teams and in different team roles in a variety of settings.

REFERENCES

Canadian Interprofessional Health Collaborative. (2010, February). *A national interprofessional competency framework.* Retrieved from http://www.cihc.ca/resources/publications

Interprofessional Education Collaborative. (2016). *Core competencies for interprofessional collaborative practice: 2016 update.* Washington, DC: Author.

University of Toronto. (2008). *Advancing the interprofessional education curriculum 2009. Curriculum overview. Competency framework.* Toronto: University of Toronto, Office of Interprofessional Education.

Appendix B

OVERVIEW OF THE WEB MODULES

Carmen Morano

The case study of Mrs. Garcia is designed around the Interprofessional Education Collaborative Core Competencies for Interprofessional Collaboration and Practice (2011; see also updates, Interprofessional Education Collaborative, 2016). These are four modules that review the core concepts relating to communicating with patients, families, communities, and other health professionals in a responsive and responsible manner that supports a patient-centered, team-based approach to health maintenance and disease treatment. Each module uses exercises and an unfolding patient case presented in a series of video vignettes to illustrate the effects of teamwork and communication on care providers, patients, and their support networks. Through these illustrations, the user is able to reflect on how strategies for interprofessional collaboration and practice can be adapted to facilitate quality, patient-centered care.

Each module includes interactive, video-based case vignettes with supplementary reflection, discussion, and debriefing activities aimed at introducing students to core interprofessional education competencies early in their respective programs. The modules follow Mrs. Garcia from an acute emergency admission to discharge and follow-up rehabilitation in a community setting. As a result, there is a suggested sequencing of the modules, though introductory slides have been included to allow for single selections from the series.

As the case unfolds, students can experience through storytelling a patient's continuity of care from acute to community care settings. While exploring issues relating to values, roles, teamwork, and communication, students are also exposed to issues relating to health and wellness, patient advocacy, and care transitions.

The case utilizes storytelling in a realistic context, such that no single character is characterized as "exemplary" or "incompetent" as a provider. Each character will display strengths and weaknesses. The modules are designed as small, granular e-learning resources—or reusable learning objects—with suggestions for extension activities for implementation in various settings, including face-to-face and online learning environments. The links to the modules are at http://ipelab.commons.gc.cuny.edu/ipe-elearning-resources/. The links to individual modules are as follows:

M1: Values and Ethics (http://hunter.cuny.edu/shp/centers/ipe/values-ethics/story.html)

M2: Roles and Responsibilities (http://hunter.cuny.edu/shp/centers/ipe/roles-responsibilities/story.html)

M3: Team and Teamwork (http://hunter.cuny.edu/shp/centers/ipe/teams-teamwork/story.html)

M4: Communication (http://hunter.cuny.edu/shp/centers/ipe/communication/story.html)

For instructors wishing to use the modules in a classroom setting, there is an instructor's manual that is also available for debriefing and assignments, at http://www.hunter.cuny.edu/shp/centers/ipe/guide/. The ITEACH team encourages you to complete the instructor or student evaluation, which can be found at https://www.surveymonkey.com/s/ipemodules.

These Web modules were made possible in part from a grant by the Josiah Macy Jr. Foundation. Some rights are reserved. This work and all associated e-learning content are licensed under a Creative Commons Attribution-NonCommercial-ShareAlike 4.0 International License. For questions and comments, please contact Shawn McGinniss at smcginni@hunter.cuny.edu.

REFERENCES

Interprofessional Education Collaborative. (2016). *Core competencies for interprofessional collaborative practice: 2016 update.* Washington, DC: Author.

Interprofessional Education Collaborative Expert Panel. (2011). *Core competencies for interprofessional collaborative practice: Report of an expert panel.* Washington, DC: Interprofessional Education Collaborative.

INDEX